Reviewing Earth Science

With Sample Examinations

Revised Edition

Thomas McGuire
Teacher, Science
Briarcliff High School
Briarcliff Manor, New York

When ordering this book, please specify:
either **R 518 P** *or* REVIEWING EARTH SCIENCE

AMSCO SCHOOL PUBLICATIONS, INC.
315 Hudson Street / New York, N.Y. 10013

NOTE TO THE TEACHER:

The books of this series—*Reviewing Biology, Reviewing Chemistry, Reviewing Earth Science,* and *Reviewing Physics*—offer an innovative format that comprehensively reviews and supplements the study of science as it is usually taught at the high school level. Each book is readily correlated with the standard textbooks for this level. The series is specifically geared to the needs of students who want to refresh their memory and review the material in preparation for final exams.

Reviewing Earth Science contains a review of the one-year introductory earth science course for college-bound students. The material is divided into fourteen topics, each of which is divided into major subtopic sections. The book is abundantly illustrated with clearly labeled drawings and diagrams that illuminate and reinforce the subject matter. Important science terms are boldfaced and are defined in the text. Other terms that may be unfamiliar to students are italicized for emphasis. In addition, the large work-text format makes *Reviewing Earth Science* easy for students to read.

Within each topic are several sets of multiple-choice questions that test students' knowledge and reasoning while provoking thought. Questions are often accompanied by diagrams that aid in reviewing and testing the materials. The almost 900 questions found in the text can be used for topic review throughout the year, as well as for final exams and homework assignments.

Reviewing Earth Science contains a complete set of Reference Tables. There is also a full Glossary, where students can find concise definitions of significant scientific terms. The extensive Index should be used by students to locate fuller text discussions of earth science terms and concepts. Exams at the back of the book can be used for extra practice and review.

Newly added to this revised edition of *Reviewing Earth Science* are fourteen special end-of-book features that explore current controversial issues in earth science, technology, and society. Reading comprehension, free response, and research questions presented at the end of each feature encourage students to evaluate the issues, and to make their own decisions about the impact of science and technology on society, the environment, and their lives.

The author wishes to acknowledge the helpful contributions of the following consultants in the preparation of this book: Harold N. Alper, Assistant Principal, Physical Sciences, South Shore High School, New York City; Bert Beiderman, Teacher, Geosciences, Stuyvesant High School, New York City; Marshal S. Lederer, Teacher, Earth Science, Franklin Delano Roosevelt High School, New York City; and Paul Speranza, Teacher, Earth Science, Lafayette High School, New York City.

Cover Photos: (Background shot) Kachemak Bay—Pebbles, Comstock Inc., Boyd Norton; Lava flow from Kilauea, Superstock, Ron Dahlquist; Lightning, Superstock, Schuster; Waves, Superstock, Ron Dahlquist.

ISBN 0-87720-153-6

Contents

TOPIC 1 Observation and Measurement of the Environment

THE NATURE OF OBSERVATIONS

An **observation**, such as "the sky is blue," is made by using one of your senses—the sense of sight. This sense, as well as those of touch, smell, taste, and hearing enable you to gather information about your environment. Your senses have limitations, but these can be overcome in part by using various instruments. For example, you can use a telescope to observe objects too distant to be seen with the unaided eye. **Instruments** are devices that extend the ability of your senses and that help you to make better observations.

Inferences. An **inference** is an interpretation of objects or events that have been observed. For example, if you observe that the sky is filling with dark clouds, you might infer that it will rain very soon. Your inference (in this case, a prediction) may or may not be correct. However, additional observations can increase the probability that your inference is correct. For example, if you also observe that the air is becoming more humid and that lightning appears in the distance, you can be even more confident about your prediction that it will rain. Making inferences, conclusions, or predictions that follow logically from observations is an important process of thinking in science. It is important that you understand the difference between observations and inferences. Observations, made with your senses, are direct information from your environment. Inferences are conclusions or predictions based upon your observations.

Classification. Observations of the properties of objects and events in your environment often become more meaningful when you arrange them into groups. For example, you might sort a bucket of rocks by size, color, or texture. The organization of objects or information into groupings is called **classification**. Systems of classification help you to organize information, to understand relationships between and within various groups, and to plan investigations.

QUESTIONS

1. An interpretation based upon an observation is called (1) a fact (2) an inference (3) a classification (4) a measurement
2. In order to make observations, an observer must always use (1) experiments (2) the senses (3) proportions (4) mathematical calculations

3. Using a ruler to measure the length of a stick is an example of (1) extending the sense of sight by using an instrument (2) calculating the percent of error by using a proportion (3) measuring the rate of change of the stick by making inferences (4) predicting the length of the stick by guessing
4. A classification system enables a person to (1) organize observations in a meaningful way (2) alter the properties of objects being studied (3) make careful plans for determining the accuracy of an observation (4) make accurate measurements of the dimensions of an object
5. Which statement about a burning candle is most likely an inference? (1) Carbon dioxide and water vapor are produced by the burning. (2) The wick gets shorter as the candle burns. (3) The candle wax is melting. (4) The flame is yellow.
6. A number of objects are grouped on the basis of common properties. What is this process called? (1) observation (2) inference (3) classification (4) predicting
7. Which statement made by a student after examining a rock specimen is an inference? (1) The rock came from a volcano. (2) The rock has rounded edges. (3) The rock is light-colored. (4) The rock contains large crystals.
8. Which statement about a stream is an inference rather than an observation? (1) It is clear enough to see the bottom. (2) Its velocity is 38 cm/s. (3) The water temperature is 15°C. (4) The stream is not polluted.
9. Which descriptive term illustrates an inference? (1) transparent (2) bitter (3) younger (4) smooth

SCIENTIFIC MEASUREMENTS

Measurements are observations of quantities made with instruments, such as balances, meter sticks, and clocks. You use instruments and their units of measure to assign a numerical value to a physical quantity, such as the length of a line or the amount of time during which an event took place.

All measurements consist of a number (quantity) and a unit, such as a *10 meter* line. In the case of the 10 meter line, the *physical quantity* that was measured is *length* and the *unit of measure* is the *meter*.

You will use several **basic units** of measurement while studying earth science. Four basic units, the metric symbol for each, and the physical quantities they measure are shown in Table 1-1. You are probably most familiar with the first three: the meter (m), the kilogram (kg), and the second (s). They are used to measure the physical quantities length, mass, and time, respectively.

Table 1-1. Basic Units of Measure Used in Earth Science

Unit of Measure	Metric Unit Symbol	Physical Quantity
Meter	m	length
Kilogram	kg	mass
Second	s	time
Degree Kelvin	K	temperature

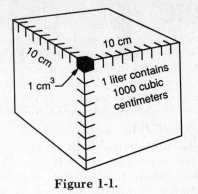

Figure 1-1.

Length is the distance between two points and is usually measured in meters, centimeters (1/100 meter), millimeters (1/1000 meter), or kilometers (1000 meters).

Mass is the quantity of matter in an object and is usually measured in kilograms or grams (1/1000 kilogram). The mass of an object is constant (remains the same) no matter where an object may be located. The weight of an object, however, may vary. Weight is a measure of the gravitational attraction between two objects, such as the earth and you. Weight depends on the masses of the objects and the distance between their centers. The mass of an object remains constant, while the weight of an object may vary. For example, if you traveled to the moon your mass would not change. When on the moon, however, your weight would be about one-sixth what it was on the earth. This is so because the gravitational attraction on the moon's surface is one-sixth that on the earth's surface.

Time may be defined as a measurable period during which an event or a process takes place. Time is often measured in seconds, minutes, or hours; but it may also be measured in days, months, years, seasons, decades, and eras.

Derived Units of Measure.
Measuring certain physical quantities requires the use of a combination of basic units. For example, velocity can be measured in meters per second (m/s). Density can be measured in kilograms per cubic meter (kg/m^3) or grams per cubic centimeter (g/cm^3). Units of measure that consist of combinations of basic units are called **derived units**.

Some units of measure that look like basic units are really derived units that have been given a special name. A common example is the liter, familiar to us from one-liter soda bottles. The liter (L) is used to measure the physical quantity **volume**, the amount of space matter occupies. A liter has been defined as the volume of a cube 10 centimeters (10 cm) on a side. See Figure 1-1. You can calculate the volume of this cube by simply applying the equation for the volume of a cube or of a rectangular object:

$$\textbf{Volume} = \textbf{length} \times \textbf{width} \times \textbf{height}$$

$$V = l \times w \times h$$

For the cube,

$$V = 10 \text{ cm} \times 10 \text{ cm} \times 10 \text{ cm}$$

$$V = 1000 \text{ cm}^3 = 1 \text{ L}$$

A closer look at the calculation reveals that while the liter is a unit of measure for volume, it is derived from a combination of the basic unit for length, the meter. Each dimension of the cube is 10 cm in length, or one-tenth of a meter (10 cm = 0.1 m).

If the cube in Figure 1-1 were to decrease in size so that it measures 1 cm on a side, what would its volume be? Its volume would be 1 cm³, or 1 mL (1/1000 liter).

PROCESS OF INQUIRY SKILL

Reading the Scale on a Standard Measuring Instrument. Being able to read a scale on a standard measuring instrument, such as a ruler, bal-

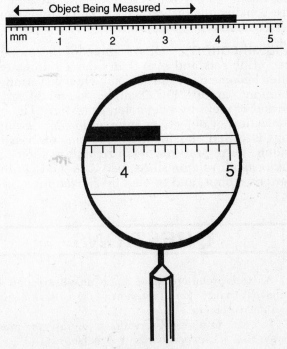

Figure 1-2.

ance, graduated cylinder, compass, protractor, or barometer, is an important skill in science. A scale is a series of lines or points that mark off known spaces, intervals, or distances on a measuring instrument. You should be able to read the scale on a standard measuring instrument to an accuracy of half the smallest scale calibration of the instrument.

Example: When the length of an object falls between two lines on a scale, the measurement can be estimated. In the enlarged scale of a metric rule, shown in Figure 1-2, approximately how long is the object in centimeters?

Answer: 4.35 cm

QUESTIONS

10. Which term is best defined as the amount of matter an object contains? (1) mass (2) volume (3) density (4) weight

11. The diagram below represents the scale of a triple beam balance. What mass is indicated by this scale?

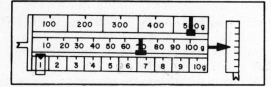

(1) 175 g (2) 715 g (3) 517 g (4) 571 g

12. Which term is best defined as a measure of the amount of space a substance occupies? (1) mass (2) volume (3) density (4) weight

13. Using the centimeter ruler provided in the *Earth Science Reference Tables*, determine the length of line segment *X-Y*.

X ————————————————— Y

(1) 5.8 cm. (2) 6.1 cm. (3) 6.4 cm. (4) 7.1 cm.

14. What is the air pressure indicated by the diagram of the mercury barometer?
(1) 1028.1 mb (2) 1028.5 mb
(3) 1029.5 mb (4) 1031.0 mb

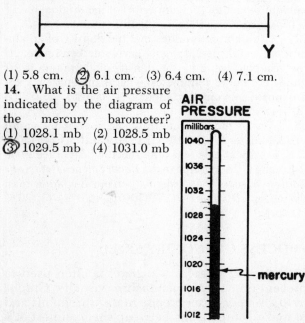

AIR PRESSURE

millibars

— mercury

PROCESS OF INQUIRY SKILL

Using Scientific Notation. Scientists often work with very large or very small numbers. These numbers are easier to read, write, and use in calculations if they are expressed in a mathematical shorthand known as **scientific notation**.

A number written in scientific notation is written in the form

$$M \times 10^n$$

where **M** is a number between 1 and 10 (but not 10), and 10^n is a power of 10.

The number 2500 written in scientific notation is 2.5×10^3. The first factor, 2.5, is a number between 1 and 10; and the second factor, 10^3, is a power of 10. So 2.5×10^3 really means 2.5×1000.

Sample Problems

1. Write 27,508 in scientific notation.
   Step 1: Determine **M** by moving the decimal point in the original number to the left or right so that only one nonzero digit is to the left of the decimal.

$$2.7508$$

   Step 2: Determine **n**, the exponent of 10, by counting the number of places the decimal point has been moved. If moved to the *left*, **n** is *positive*. If moved to the *right*, **n** is *negative*.

$$4\ 3\ 2\ 1$$
$$2'7'5'0'8$$

   ← 4 places to the left
   $27,508 = 2.7508 \times 10^4$

2. Write 0.00875 in scientific notation.
   Step 1:   0. 0 0 8.7 5

   Step 2:   1 2 3
              0. 0'0'8'75

   3 places to the right →
   $0.00875 = 8.75 \times 10^{-3}$

A negative power of 10 does not mean a negative number. $8.75 \times 10^{-3} = 0.00875$. Note that 10^{-3} indicates a number less than 1.

Metric Prefixes. The metric system has the advantage of using a single number base, ten, to which larger or smaller units are related. The size of the unit in the metric system is designated by prefixes. The most commonly used prefixes are shown in Table 1-2; their meanings, or values, are expressed in scientific notation.

Table 1-2. Common Prefixes of the Metric System

Prefix	Meaning	Scientific Notation	Example
Milli-	one thousandth $\left(\dfrac{1}{1000}\right)$	10^{-3}	millimeter (mm)
Centi-	one hundredth $\left(\dfrac{1}{100}\right)$	10^{-2}	centimeter (cm)
—	one (1)	10^{0}	meter (m)
Kilo-	one thousand (1000)	10^{3}	kilometer (km)

QUESTIONS

15. 3.5×10^{-3} equals (1) 0.0035 (2) 3.5 (3) 350 (4) 3500

16. Which of the following numbers is the largest? (1) 3×10^{8} (2) 8×10^{3} (3) 5×10^{5} (4) 5.069×10^{5}

17. 805,000 equals (1) 8×10^{5} (2) 8.05×10^{5} (3) 8×10^{6} (4) 8.05×10^{6}

18. The prefix centi- means the same as (1) 10^{-2} (2) 10^{-1} (3) 10^{2} (4) 10^{3}

19. According to the *Earth Science Reference Tables*, the earth's radius is approximately (1) 637 km (2) 6370 km (3) 63,700 km (4) 637,000 km

20. The circumference of the earth is about 4.0×10^{4} kilometers. This value is equal to (1) 400 km (2) 4000 km (3) 40,000 km (4) 400,000 km

21. A 10.0-milliliter sample of a substance has a mass of 20.0 grams. What would be the mass of a 200.-milliliter sample of the same substance? (1) 200. g (2) 400. g (3) 600. g (4) 800. g

22. How many millimeters are there in one centimeter? (1) 1 (2) 10 (3) 100 (4) 1000

23. The average distance from the earth to the sun is approximately 149,600,000 kilometers. This distance correctly expressed in scientific notation (powers of ten) would be (1) 1.496×10^{6} km (2) 1.496×10^{8} km (3) 1.496×10^{9} km (4) 1.496^{9} km

Error in Measurement.

Because of limitations of the senses or of instruments used, no measurement is completely free of error. Error in a scientific measurement is often expressed in terms of **percent error**, or percent deviation from accepted value.

PROCESS OF INQUIRY SKILL

Determining Percent Error. Percent error is a convenient way of comparing a measurement with the commonly accepted value for that measurement. To calculate percent error, divide the difference between the measured and accepted value by the accepted value, and then multiply by 100%. (Note: You always subtract the smaller value from the larger value.)

Percent Error

$$= \frac{\text{Difference From Accepted Value}}{\text{Accepted Value}} \times 100\%$$

Sample Problem

In measuring a table, a student found its length to be 1.9 meters. If the accepted value is 2.0 meters, what is the percent error of the student's measurement?
Solution:

Percent Error

$$= \frac{\text{Accepted Value} - \text{Measured Value}}{\text{Accepted Value}} \times 100\%$$

$$\text{Percent Error} = \frac{2.0 \text{ m} - 1.9 \text{ m}}{2.0 \text{ m}} \times 100\%$$

$$= \frac{0.1 \text{ m}}{2.0 \text{ m}} \times 100\% = 5\%$$

QUESTIONS

24. A student measures the length of a room to be 6.9 meters. If the actual length of the room is 7.5 meters, the student's percent deviation (percent error) is (1) 20% (2) 14% (3) 8% (4) 6%

25. A student determines the volume of a cubic crystal to be 8.6 cubic centimeters. What is her percent deviation if the correct volume of the crystal is 8.0 cubic centimeters? (1) 6.0% (2) 6.5% (3) 7.0% (4) 7.5%

26. A student measured the mass of a rock sample and recorded it as 51 grams. Later it is found that the accepted value of the rock's mass is 60. grams. According to the *Earth Science Reference Tables*, what was the percent deviation (percent error) of the original mass? (1) 7% (2) 9% (3) 15% (4) 18%

27. A student determines that the density of an aluminum sample is 2.9 grams per cubic centimeter. If the accepted value for the density of aluminum is 2.7 grams per cubic centimeter, what is the student's approximate percent deviation? (1) 0.70% (2) 0.20% (3) 7.4% (4) 20.%

28. What is the percent error of an error of one meter in a kilometer? (1) 0.1% (2) 1% (3) 10% (4) 100%

29. A student calculates the specific heat of ice to be 0.40 cal/g C°. According to the *Earth Science Reference Tables*, what is the student's percent deviation from the accepted value? (1) 2.5% (2) 2.0% (3) 20.% (4) 25.%

PROCESS OF INQUIRY SKILL

Interpreting Graphs. A graph is often used to present numerical relationships visually. Graphs help a reader to see trends in measurements and to make comparisons between them, almost at a glance. For this reason, earth scientists frequently find it useful to display data in a graph.

For example, the four simple line graphs shown in Figure 1-3 represent relationships between the two variables x and y. Values for x are found along the bottom of a graph (horizontal axis), starting from the origin (the point labeled "O"). Values for y are found along the side of a graph (vertical axis), also starting from the origin. One of the most important features of each graph is the way in which the line, or curve, runs uphill or downhill (slopes) as we move to the right.

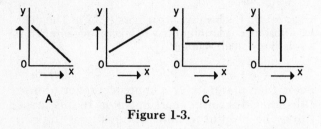

Figure 1-3.

Graph A clearly slopes downhill as we follow it to the right. In this case, the curve has a negative slope, because the value of y decreases as the value of x increases.

Graph B clearly slopes uphill as we follow it to the right. Graph B shows a positive slope, because the value of y increases as the value of x increases.

Graph C shows a zero slope. The value of y is the same regardless of the value of x.

Graph D shows an infinite slope. The value of x is the same regardless of the value of y.

QUESTIONS

30. Over the years, sources of petroleum have become scarcer. Which graph best represents this relationship?

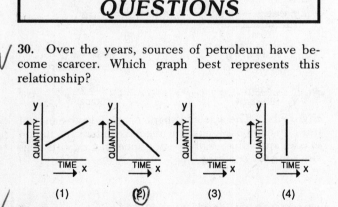

(1)   (2)   (3)   (4)

31. The graph below shows the relationship between mass and volume for a certain material. The slope of the line is
(1) positive   (2) negative   (3) zero   (4) infinite

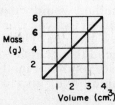

DENSITY

When you determine the mass (**M**) of a sample of the metal aluminum at a given temperature, you discover that its volume (**V**) is definite. For example, by doubling the mass of aluminum, you double its volume. See Table 1-3. You can state your observation in mathematical terms that express the following relationship:

Mass is directly proportional to volume.

$$M \propto V$$

Table 1-3. Mass of Aluminum vs Volume of Aluminum

Mass (g)	Volume (mL)
27	10
54	20
81	30
108	40

Likewise, if you plot the masses of various samples of aluminum against their volumes, you will observe that the points fall on a straight line that passes through the origin (zero mass has zero volume). See Figure 1-4. The graph is characteristic of two variables that are directly proportional to each other—in this case, mass and volume.

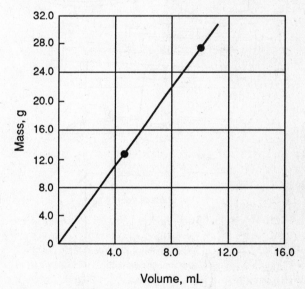

Mass of aluminum
vs volume of aluminum
Figure 1-4.

The relationship pictured in the graph can also be expressed as

$$M = DV$$

where **M** is mass, **V** is volume, and **D** is the slope, or inclination, of the straight line. By solving for **D** (density), you will arrive at the equation

$$\text{density} = \frac{\text{mass}}{\text{volume}}$$

$$D = \frac{M}{V}$$

Thus, the slope of the line (density) is equal to the ratio of mass to volume. When mass is expressed in grams (g) and volume in cubic centimeters (cm³), the unit of measure for the physical quantity density becomes g/cm³ or g/mL. Therefore, **density** is the mass per unit volume of a substance.

There is less mass (quantity of matter) in 1 cm³ of aluminum than in 1 cm³ of lead. That is to say, 1 gram of aluminum has a larger volume than an equal mass of lead. See Figure 1-5. Likewise, each of the volumes shown in Figure 1-6 contains the same mass of substance; it is apparent, how-

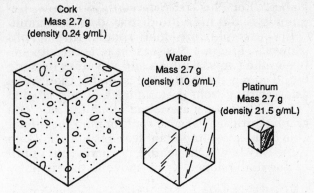

Cork
Mass 2.7 g
(density 0.24 g/mL)

Water
Mass 2.7 g
(density 1.0 g/mL)

Platinum
Mass 2.7 g
(density 21.5 g/mL)

Figure 1-6. Each substance's mass is 2.7 g. The densest substance (platinum) has its mass concentrated in a relatively small volume.

ever, that platinum is a more compact (dense) substance than either cork or water. In this sense, it may be helpful to think of density as the concentration of matter. Dense substances have their mass concentrated into a relatively small volume.

At the same temperature and pressure, objects of the same substance have the same density, no matter how large or small they are. See Figure 1-7. Density serves as an identifying property. Every pure substance has a unique density.

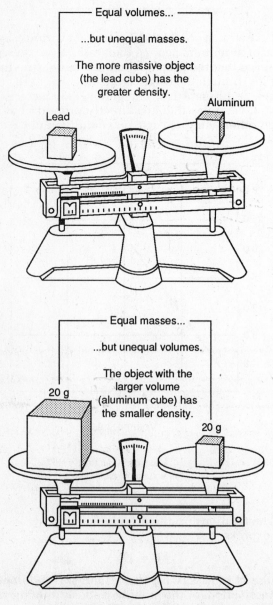

Equal volumes...

...but unequal masses.

The more massive object (the lead cube) has the greater density.

Lead

Aluminum

Equal masses...

...but unequal volumes.

The object with the larger volume (aluminum cube) has the smaller density.

20 g

20 g

Figure 1-5.

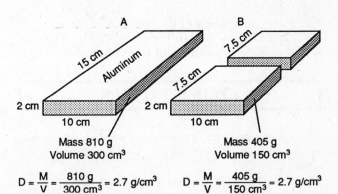

A

15 cm

Aluminum

2 cm

10 cm

Mass 810 g
Volume 300 cm³

$$D = \frac{M}{V} = \frac{810 \text{ g}}{300 \text{ cm}^3} = 2.7 \text{ g/cm}^3$$

B

7.5 cm

7.5 cm

2 cm

10 cm

Mass 405 g
Volume 150 cm³

$$D = \frac{M}{V} = \frac{405 \text{ g}}{150 \text{ cm}^3} = 2.7 \text{ g/cm}^3$$

Figure 1-7. The size and shape of a solid substance of uniform composition do not affect its density. Although masses and volumes of the substance may vary, its density remains constant.

PROCESS OF INQUIRY SKILL

Finding the Density of a Substance. If you are asked to identify a certain piece of metal (irregular in shape) in the laboratory, one of the properties that might help you do so is the metal's density. What method would you use to measure the metal's density? First, you would measure the metal's mass on a balance. Then, by measuring the water displaced in a graduated cylinder, you would measure its volume. Finally, dividing the mass by the volume will give you the metal's density.

Sample Problems

1. A sample of metal with a mass of 50.0 grams is placed in a graduated cylinder containing 40.0 milliliters of water. The new water level is shown in Figure 1-8. What is the density of the metal? What is the metal? (Use Table 1-4 to identify the metal.)

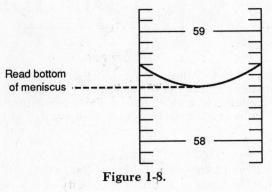

Read bottom of meniscus

Figure 1-8.

Table 1-4. Density of Solids

Solid	Density (g/mL)
Aluminum	2.70
Iron	7.87
Copper	8.96
Silver	10.50
Lead	11.35
Gold	19.32

Solution:

$$D = \frac{M}{V}$$

M (mass) = 50.0 g

V (volume) = Final volume − Initial volume

= 58.5 mL − 40.0 mL

= 18.5 mL

$$D = \frac{M}{V}$$

$$D = \frac{50.0 \text{ g}}{18.5 \text{ mL}}$$

$$D = 2.70 \text{ g/mL}$$

The metal must be aluminum.

If you want to find the density of a rectangular object (regular in shape), you would still measure the mass of the object on a balance. Its volume can be found by using the equation **V = lwh**. Dividing the mass by the calculated volume will give you the object's density.

2. Figure 1-9 represents a rectangular object with a mass of 450 grams. What is the density of the object?

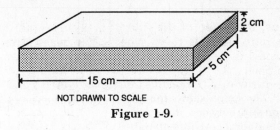

NOT DRAWN TO SCALE

Figure 1-9.

Solution:

$$D = \frac{M}{V}$$

M (mass) = 450 g

V (volume) = lwh

= 15 cm × 5 cm × 2 cm

= 150 cm³

$$D = \frac{M}{V}$$

$$D = \frac{450 \text{ g}}{150 \text{ cm}^3}$$

$$D = 3 \text{ g/cm}^3$$

3. What is the density of a rock that has a mass of 35 grams and a volume of 7.0 cubic centimeters?

Solution:

$$D = \frac{M}{V}$$

$$D = \frac{35 \text{ g}}{7.0 \text{ cm}^3}$$

$$D = 5.0 \text{ g/cm}^3$$

QUESTIONS

32. A student calculates the densities of five different pieces of aluminum, each having a different volume. Which graph best represents this relationship?

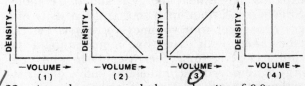

33. An unknown sample has a density of 6.0 grams per cubic centimeter. If the sample were cut in half, each half would have a density of (1) 12.0 g/cm³ (2) 9.0 g/cm³ (3) 3.0 g/cm³ (4) 6.0 g/cm³

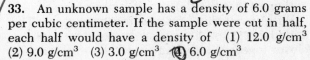

34. The diagram below represents a solid object with a mass of 60 grams. What is the density of the object?

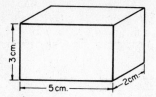

(1) .16 g/cm³ (2) 2 g/cm³ (3) .5 g/cm³ (4) 6 g/cm³

35. The graph shows the relationship between mass and volume for a certain material. The density of this material is
(1) 0.5 g/cm³ (2) 2.0 g/cm³
(3) 5.0 g/cm³ (4) 8.0 g/cm³

36. What is the density of a rock which has a mass of 35 grams and a volume of 7.0 cubic centimeters? (1) 5.0 g/cm³ (2) 0.20 g/cm³ (3) 28 g/cm³ (4) 42 g/cm³

Flotation.

A convenient way to estimate the relative densities of different objects that are similarly shaped is to place them simultaneously in a liquid of known density to see how they float or whether they sink. For example, objects with a density greater than water (1 g/cm³) will sink; and objects with a density less than 1 g/cm³ will float in water. The faster an object sinks, the more dense it must be; the higher an object floats, the less dense it must be. That is why a block of balsa wood floats higher—more of its surface is above the water—than a block of oak. In addition, if an object and a liquid have exactly the same density, the object will remain suspended in the liquid.

Factors That Affect Density.

Most matter can exist in three physical states, or **phases**—**solid, liquid,** and **gas.** Most substances are densest in their solid phase. For example, a solid piece of iron will sink when dropped into its liquid—hot, molten iron. But water is an exception. Since solid water (ice) floats on liquid water, you infer that solid ice must be less dense than liquid water. Unlike other substances, water reaches maximum density in the liquid phase at a temperature of about 4°C. When cooled from 4°C to 0°C, water expands (its volume increases) and becomes less dense. See Figure 1-10 A and B.

The density of a gas varies with temperature and pressure. With increasing temperature, a gas expands. When heat energy is added, gas molecules move farther apart so that the density of a gas (mass per unit volume) decreases. On the other hand, with decreasing temperature, a gas contracts (its volume decreases). When heat energy is removed, gas molecules move closer together so that the density of a gas increases.

With increasing pressure, a gas contracts. The added pressure forces gas molecules to move closer together into a smaller volume. Thus, the

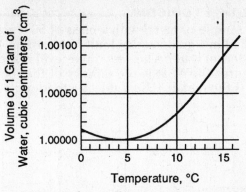

Figure 1-10A. Volume of 1 gram of water at different temperatures. The density of water is greatest at about 4°C. At this temperature, the volume of 1 gram of water is 1 cubic centimeter. Its density then equals 1 g/cm³.

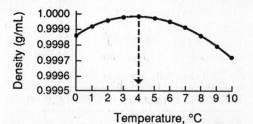

Figure 1-10B. The density-temperature plot for water. As the temperature increases from 0°C to 4°C, the density of water increases. The density of water is greatest at about 4°C. As the temperature increases from 4°C, the density of water tends to decrease.

density of a gas increases. With decreasing pressure, a gas expands. When pressure is lowered, gas molecules move more freely about in a larger volume. Thus, the density of a gas decreases.

The densities of most solids and liquids are affected by changes in temperature and pressure. But these effects are slight when compared with the effects that changes in temperature and pressure have on the densities of gases.

QUESTIONS

37. As a sample of water is removed from a lake and the temperature and pressure of the water remain constant, the density of the water in the sample will (1) decrease (2) increase (3) remain the same

38. If a wooden block were cut into eight identical pieces, the density of each piece compared to the density of the original block would be (1) less (2) greater (3) the same

39. As water cools from 4°C to 0°C, its density (1) decreases (2) increases (3) remains the same

40. As a volume of air expands due to heating, the density of this air will (1) decrease (2) increase (3) remain the same

41. In which phase (state) do most earth materials have their greatest density? (1) solid (2) liquid (3) gaseous

42. Compared to the density of water, the density of ice is (1) less (2) greater (3) the same

43. The diagram below represents two beakers, each containing an ice cube and clear liquid. In beaker *A* the ice cube floats, and in beaker *B* the ice cube rests on the bottom.

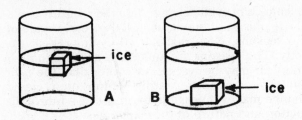

What is the most probable cause for the difference in behavior of the ice cubes in the two beakers? (1) The ice cube in beaker *B* is heavier than the ice cube in beaker *A*. (2) The ice cube in beaker *B* is less dense than the ice cube in beaker *A*. (3) The liquid in beaker *B* is less dense than the liquid in beaker *A*. (4) The liquid in beaker *B* is more dense than the liquid in beaker *A*.

44. The diagram at the right represents a cylinder that contains four different liquids, *W*, *X*, *Y*, and *Z*, each with a different density (*D*) as indicated. A piece of solid quartz having a density of 2.7 g/cm^3 is placed on the surface of liquid *W*.

When the quartz is released, it will pass through (1) *W*, but not *X*, *Y*, or *Z* (2) *W* and *X*, but not *Y* or *Z* (3) *W*, *X*, and *Y*, but not *Z* (4) *W*, *X*, *Y*, and *Z*

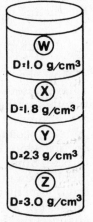

Directions (45–49): Base your answers to questions 45 through 49 on your knowledge of earth science, the *Earth Science Reference Tables*, and the graph below. The graph shows the mass and volume for five different samples of the mineral pyrite.

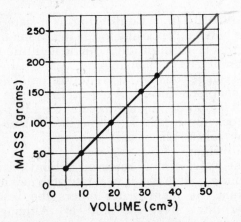

45. According to the graph, the density of pyrite is about (1) 0.5 g/cm^3 (2) 2.5 g/cm^3 (3) 5.0 g/cm^3 (4) 7.5 g/cm^3

46. If a sample of pyrite has a volume of 50 cm^3, its mass would be (1) 15 g (2) 150 g (3) 250 g (4) 350 g

47. The density of pyrite and the density of water were plotted on the same graph. Which diagram below best represents how the graph should appear?

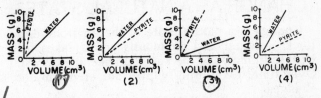

48. If one of the original samples of pyrite were cut in half, the density of each half would be (1) less than the original sample (2) greater than the original sample (3) the same as the original sample

49. A mineral expands when heated. Which graph best represents the relationship between change in density and change in temperature when that mineral is heated?

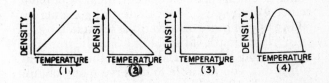

Directions (50–54): Base your answers to questions 50 through 54 on your knowledge of earth science and on the diagram below which represents five different materials several minutes after they have been placed in a container of water at constant 20°C temperature. The distances between the marks on the various materials are equal.

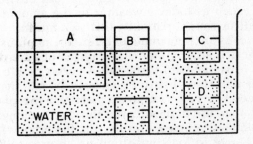

50. Which material has the greatest density? (1) A (2) E (3) C (4) D

51. Which materials have the same density? (1) A and B (2) A and C (3) B and C (4) C and D

52. The original block of material *A* is cut into several pieces. When compared with the density of the original block, the density of each piece will be (1) less (2) greater (3) the same

53. Material *D* is removed from the container and compressed to half its size. If it is then returned to the container, it will (1) float at the surface (2) float beneath the surface (3) sink to the bottom

54. The water is cooled from 20°C to 4°C. If the temperature and volume of material *A* remain the same, it would (1) float lower in the water (2) float higher in the water (3) float at the same level

TOPIC 2 How Changeable Is Our Environment?

CHANGE AS A NATURAL STATE

Change is a natural state of the environment. Rocks weather and mountains erode; lakes fill with sediment, and the new land becomes forest. Over time, everything within our environment changes.

In earth science, a change or a series of changes in the earth's environment is called an **event**. An event occurs in the earth's environment only if properties of matter or properties of a system are altered. An event can be described with respect to time and space (location) and in terms of the rate at which it occurs.

Time is a frame of reference used to describe events, or changes, that are occurring now or have occurred in the past. You can describe events by making two or more observations separated by an appropriate length of time. For example, from the moment you light a candle until the time you snuff it out, you are able to observe many chemical and physical changes that take place in the chemical and physical properties of the candle. In such a case, the changes you observed occurred in the course of time. The candle may have decreased in height by 2.5 centimeters (1 inch) after burning for 10 minutes. Time became the frame of reference for describing the changes in the candle. Similarly, you can observe changes that occur in the course of time in our environment, such as today's weather or the amount of rainfall in your community this past month.

Space is another frame of reference often used to describe environmental changes. For example, a city dweller who visits the Amazon jungle in Brazil will most likely be amazed by the many changes she or he observes between the plant and animal life of the city and those of the jungle. The dramatic changes result from the city dweller's change in location—from urban area to the jungle—and not from any changes that had taken place in the jungle while the city dweller was traveling to Brazil. In such a case, the changes observed by the city dweller resulted from a change of location. The frame of reference to describe the event is space and not time.

A change in our environment can also be described in terms of the rate at which it occurs. Some events, such as a bolt of lightning, are very rapid. Others, like the movement of continents over the surface of the earth, are so slow that they are very difficult to measure.

Cyclic and Noncyclic Changes.
Many environmental changes are **cyclic** in nature—that is, they are continually repeated in the same way.

Examples of cyclic changes are the monthly cycle of the phases of the moon and the yearly cycle of the seasons. Note that not all cycles repeat exactly. The seasons are an annual cycle, although one year may be warmer or cooler than the previous year. The repeating action of a cyclic change makes it possible to predict the future direction and nature of these changes.

Some changes are *noncyclic*—that is, they are *not* continually repeated in the same way. Over the course of time, noncyclic changes may follow a pattern or trend that could help in making predictions about future changes. For example, the human population has increased at an accelerating rate for thousands of years. The trend of an ever-increasing population is likely to continue in the future. Certain chemical changes, such as the rusting of iron, are also noncyclic.

ENERGY AND CHANGE

Most changes happen at **interfaces**, boundaries where different kinds of matter or systems come together in the environment. For example, waves are formed at the interface between the hydrosphere (ocean) and the atmosphere (air). Change occurs when energy is exchanged across an interface. Simultaneously, one part of the environment loses energy, while the other part of the environment gains energy. The parts of the environment on both sides of the interface are changed by the flow of energy. In the above example, energy flows from the atmosphere to the hydrosphere. In other words, the properties of the different kinds of matter or systems along the interface are constantly being altered by the flow of energy.

Equilibrium. **Equilibrium** is a state of balance between opposing forces in a system. A system that is in equilibrium can be identified by an apparent lack of change. A rock lying halfway up a hill can be considered in equilibrium. The gravitational force pulling it toward the center of the earth is opposed by the force of the hill pushing the rock upward. Such systems in which no movement takes place are said to be in **static equilibrium**.

The water in a full reservoir behind a dam represents a system that is in a state of **dynamic equilibrium**. As more water enters the reservoir, water flows over the spillway. Although the amount of water in the full reservoir remains the same, water is constantly being added and removed. Dynamic equilibrium can only occur if there is constant movement of the parts of the system.

Modification of the Environment.
Many systems in the natural environment are in a state of dynamic equilibrium. In a forest, for example, trees may be struck by lightning or shrubs may be killed by insects, but the forest itself is not disturbed. New plants eventually replace the dead plants, and although changes take place on a small scale, the overall system remains in balance.

Major natural events, such as forest fires and volcanic eruptions, destroy the natural balance, or equilibrium, of nearby environmental systems. Human activities can also destroy the natural balance of an environment. Cutting down forests, building on flood plains, and diverting water from rivers are examples of human activities that can upset the state of equilibrium in an environmental system.

ENVIRONMENTAL POLLUTION

Pollution occurs when the concentration of any form of energy or matter that is added to the environment becomes harmful to living things or interferes with the intended use of that portion of the environment. As a result of human activities, many kinds of pollutants have been added to all parts of the environment. Pollutants include solid materials, liquid wastes, gases, organisms, and various forms of energy, such as heat, sound, and nuclear radiation.

Pollutants are added to the environment by natural processes as well as by human activities. Examples of natural pollutants are animal wastes, pollen, and volcanic ash. Mechanisms in nature normally clear the environment of these pollutants. Human activities, however, often add such large quantities of pollutants to the environment that natural cleansing mechanisms cannot take care of them. In addition, some pollutants, such as plastics, are not broken down easily by natural processes.

An increase in the concentration of carbon dioxide in the atmosphere since the beginning of the industrial revolution exemplifies the effect of human activities on the environment. Photosynthetic organisms in the oceans and on land take in carbon dioxide from the air and give off oxygen. Animals breathe in oxygen and give off carbon dioxide. For millions of years, the concentration of carbon dioxide in the atmosphere remained relatively constant because these activities were in balance. However, in recent decades, human activities have upset this natural balance. As human energy needs have increased, more and more fossil fuels have been burned, causing an increase in the concentration of carbon dioxide in the atmosphere. In addition, as more forests have been cleared and as more land has been used for other purposes, fewer plants are now available to use up the excess carbon dioxide. As a result, the carbon dioxide content of the atmosphere has increased over the past several decades.

Carbon dioxide in the air retains the heat of the earth much as the glass of a greenhouse keeps in the heat. Many scientists are afraid that, if we allow concentrations of carbon dioxide in the atmosphere to continue to rise, this "greenhouse effect" will bring about dramatic climatic changes. Some scientists (climatologists), citing the recent drought, believe we already are experiencing a greenhouse effect. Many expect this effect to bring us continuing hot and dry summers.

QUESTIONS

1. An interface can best be described as (1) a zone of contact between different substances across which energy is exchanged (2) a region in the environment with unchanging properties (3) a process that results in changes in the environment (4) a region beneath the surface of the earth where change is not occurring

2. Which is a cyclic change? (1) the decay of a radioactive substance (2) the extinction of a species (3) the movement of the earth's crust during an earthquake (4) the earth's daily rotation

3. The rising and the setting of the sun are examples of (1) noncyclic events (2) predictable changes (3) random motion (4) unrelated events

4. Which event would be the most predictable one year in advance of the event? (1) a hurricane in Florida (2) an earthquake in California (3) a volcanic eruption in Japan (4) an eclipse of the sun

5. The climates of densely populated industrial areas tend to be warmer than similarly located sparsely populated rural areas. From this observation, what can be inferred about the human influence on local climate? (1) Local climates are not affected by increases in population density. (2) The local climate in densely populated areas can be changed by human activities. (3) In densely populated areas, human activities increase the amount of natural pollutants. (4) In sparsely populated areas, human activities have stabilized the rate of energy absorption.

6. Which of the sources of energy listed below is most nearly pollution free? (1) nuclear (2) solar (3) coal (4) natural gas

7. Which pollutant is *not* usually produced or added to the environment by human activities? (1) sound (2) pollen (3) radiation (4) smoke

8. Which is the *least* probable source of atmospheric pollution in heavily populated cities? (1) human activities (2) industrial plants (3) natural processes (4) automobile traffic

9. Future changes in the environment can best be predicted from data that are (1) highly variable and collected over short periods of time (2) highly variable and collected over long periods of time (3) cyclic

and collected over short periods of time   (4) cyclic and collected over long periods of time

10. How will the quality of the environment most likely be affected by the continued dumping of large amounts of industrial waste into a river?   (1) The environment will be unaffected.   (2) Minor, temporary disruptions will occur only near the industrial plant.   (3) Major damage could occur downstream from the industrial plant.   (4) The environment will always adjust favorably to any changes caused by industrial waste.

Directions (11–15): Base your answers to questions 11 through 15 on the diagram below, which shows air, water, and noise pollution in a densely populated industrial area, and on your knowledge of earth science. Write the *number* of the word or expression that best completes *each* statement or answers *each* question.

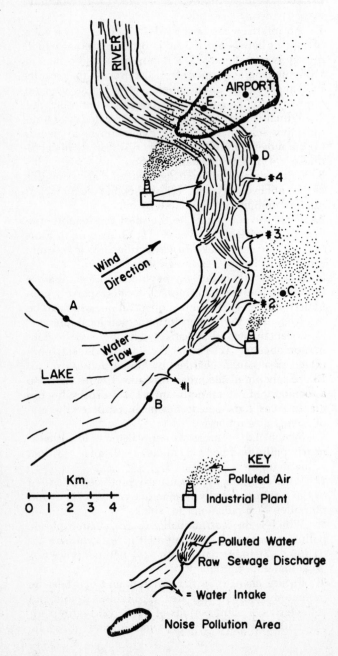

11. Air pollution would probably be greatest at which location?   (1) *A*   (2) *B*   (3) *C*   (4) *D*
12. Water pollution would probably be greatest at which location?   (1) *A*   (2) *B*   (3) *C*   (4) *D*
13. Noise pollution would be greatest at which location?   (1) *B*   (2) *C*   (3) *D*   (4) *E*
14. Which location is subjected to the greatest number of pollution factors?   (1) *A*   (2) *B*   (3) *D*   (4) *E*
15. If the water intakes supplied drinking water to the area, which intake would most likely require the most extensive purification procedures?   (1) #1 (2) #2   (3) #3   (4) #4

PROCESS OF INQUIRY SKILL

Types of Graphs.   A graph is a visual way to organize and present data. Instead of reading paragraphs of information or studying columns of figures, you can see the data in a graph and make comparisons between variables almost at a glance. Unlike a data table, a graph helps you to visualize changes in data, to understand relationships between variables within the data, and to picture trends or patterns in data.

Line Graph.   A line graph, such as the one in Figure 2-1, shows how a measured quantity changes with respect to time, distance, or some other variable.

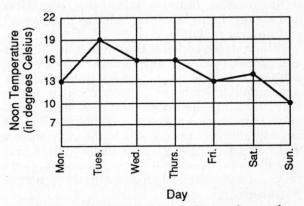

Figure 2-1. Noon temperature during the week.

Line graphs are constructed by plotting data on a **coordinate system** that is set up on vertical and horizontal axes. The horizontal (**x**) axis is usually used for the independent variable. It usually indicates a uniform change, such as hours, years, or centimeters. The vertical (**y**) axis is used for the dependent variable. It usually indicates the amount of the measured quantity being studied, such as temperature, height, or population. Normally, you know in advance the regular change expected in the independent variable. The values of the dependent variable are what you are trying to find or know more about. You draw the graph in order to see how the dependent variable changes with respect to the independent variable.

The rise or fall of the line in Figure 2-1 shows the increase or decrease in noon temperature during the week. When the line graph moves upward to the right, it represents a continuous increase. When the line graph moves downward to the right, it indicates a continuous decrease. No change is represented by a horizontal line. The steeper the line segment rises to the right, the greater the slope of the segment and the greater the increase in temperature. Likewise, the steeper the line segment falls to the right, the greater the decrease in temperature.

Not all line graphs are straight lines. Some line graphs are curved. You can still determine the general slope of a curved line by observing the way it runs on the graph.

Pie and Bar Graphs.   Sometimes a line graph is not the best kind of graph to use when organizing and presenting data. In earth science, you will sometimes see the bar graph and the pie graph used. The bar graph is useful in comparing data about one thing at different times. For example, the bar graph in Figure 2-2 compares monthly rainfall, or precipitation (PPT.), over a period of a year.

Average Monthly Precipitation for Lake Placid, N.Y.

Month	PPT. (mm)	Month	PPT. (mm)
J	81	J	107
F	71	A	84
M	86	S	86
A	71	O	74
M	81	N	86
J	94	D	86

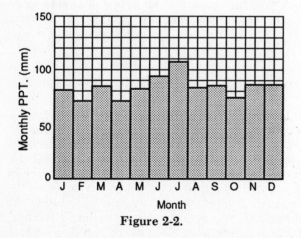

Figure 2-2.

The pie graph is used to show how a certain quantity has been divided into several parts as well as to show the comparison between these parts. The pie graph in Figure 2-3 shows the most abundant chemical elements in rocks of the earth's crust.

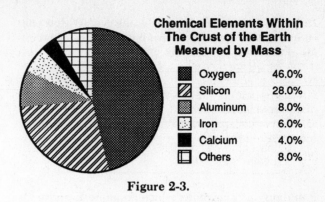

Chemical Elements Within The Crust of the Earth Measured by Mass

Oxygen	46.0%
Silicon	28.0%
Aluminum	8.0%
Iron	6.0%
Calcium	4.0%
Others	8.0%

Figure 2-3.

QUESTIONS

16.   Which graph represents the greatest rate of temperature change?

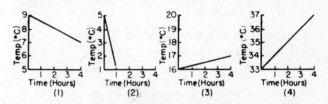

17.   The graph below represents the relationships between temperature and time as heat is added at a constant rate to equal masses of four substances labeled A, B, C, and D. The temperature of which substance increased most rapidly?

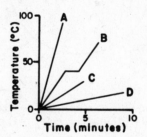

(1) A (2) B (3) C (4) D

18.   A student measures the distance from a bridge to a rock every day for a week. What is indicated by the graph of these measurements as shown below?

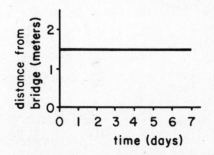

(1) No change in time or distance took place.   (2) As distance decreased, time increased.   (3) As distance increased, time decreased.   (4) As time increased, distance remained the same.

How Changeable Is Our Environment?

19. The data table below shows the average dust concentrations in the air over many years for selected cities of different populations.

Population in Millions	Dust Particles/ Meter^3
less than 0.7	110
between 0.7 and 1.0	150
greater than 1.0	190

Based on this data table, which graph best represents the general relationship between population and concentration of dust particles?

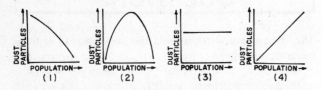

20. The circle graph below shows the sources of the electrical energy used in New York State in 1982.

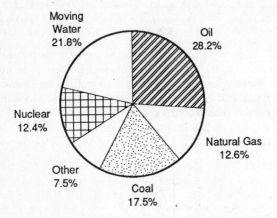

The largest amount of electrical energy came from
(1) coal   (2) oil   (3) moving water   (4) natural gas

Directions (21–22): Base your answers to questions 21 and 22 on the graph below and on your knowledge of earth science. Write the *number* of the word or expression that best completes *each* statement or answers *each* question.

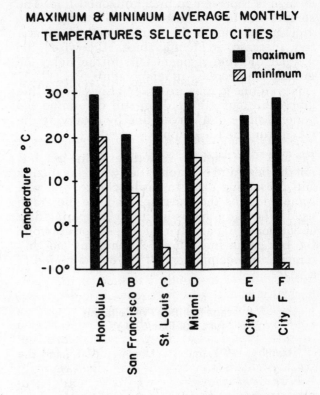

MAXIMUM & MINIMUM AVERAGE MONTHLY TEMPERATURES SELECTED CITIES

The graph above represents data collected from six cities, showing the average maximum and the average minimum temperatures for a 12-month period.

21. Which location has the highest average maximum monthly temperature?   (1) *A*   (2) *B*   (3) *C*   (4) *D*

22. Which location has the largest difference in average monthly temperatures?   (1) *A*   (2) *B*   (3) *E* (4) *F*

TOPIC **3** What Is Our Model of the Earth?

MODELS

A **model** is a representation of an object or a natural event. For example, a geographical globe is a model of the earth as a small sphere. A graph is a model of the relationship between two variables. Maps, equations, and diagrams are also models. Several types of models are used in earth science to describe the earth's characteristics, to explain events in the earth's environment, and to describe the earth's interactions with other bodies in the universe.

The Shape of the Earth.
Many models of the earth, such as a globe, show the earth shaped round like a ball or a sphere. For most purposes, these models are good representations of the shape of the earth, because the earth is *nearly a perfect sphere*. The earth is actually an **oblate spheroid**, slightly flattened at the poles and bulging a little at the equator. The following evidence shows that the earth is not a perfect sphere—that it is slightly oblate. However, you must be careful not to exaggerate the earth's "out of roundness" based on this evidence, for the same evidence supports the view that the earth is *nearly a perfect sphere* and that it can be modeled as a round object.

Diameter and Circumference Measurements.
Earth measurements, taken either on the earth's surface or from orbiting satellites in space, have uncovered the following facts:

	Diameter	Circumference
Polar	12,714 km	40,008 km
Equatorial	12,757 km	40,076 km

To be defined as a perfect **sphere**, the earth must be a round object on whose surface all points are equidistant from its center. However, both sets of measurements show a slight bulge at the earth's equator and a flattening at its poles. The earth is not perfectly round. Therefore, the true shape of the earth should be described as an oblate spheroid. See Figure 3-1. Note, however, how the differences in each set of measurements show only slight variations from a spherical shape. These differences are so slight that they would not be detected by a person looking at a small (scaled down) model of the earth, such as a globe.

Gravity Measurements.
Gravity provides further evidence that the earth is an oblate spheroid.

Recall that gravitational force is inversely proportional to the distance between two objects. The shorter the distance, the greater the gravitational force. Objects closer to the center of the earth should weigh more than objects farther away. Also, recall that a sphere is an object on whose surface all points are equidistant from its center. If gravity measurements (the weight of an object) were equal all over the earth, then all points on the earth would be equidistant from the center of the earth, and the earth would be defined as a perfect sphere. However, this is not the case. Careful measurements show that the weight of an object is not exactly the same all over the earth. For example, an object showing a weight of 180 newtons on a spring balance at the earth's North Pole or South Pole loses weight as it approaches the equator, where it weighs only 179 newtons. In other words, the object must be nearer the earth's center at the poles than at the equator. Hence, the earth by this evidence cannot be a perfect sphere.

Photographs From Space.
Photographs taken by satellite at great distances in space show the earth slightly bulging at its equator and flattening out at its geographic poles. They also provide evidence that the earth is not a perfect sphere.

Observations From Astronomy.
The North Star, Polaris, is positioned almost directly over the earth's axis of rotation at the North Pole. Based on the geometry of a sphere, the altitude of Polaris should change as an observer moves north or south in the Northern Hemisphere. See Figure 3-2, a spherical model of the earth.

Altitude is the height, measured in degrees, of a heavenly body above the horizon of the observer. If the earth were a perfect sphere, then

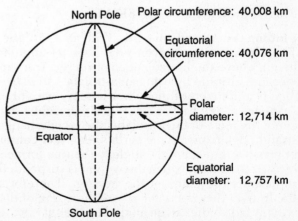

Figure 3-1. Dimensions of the earth.

15

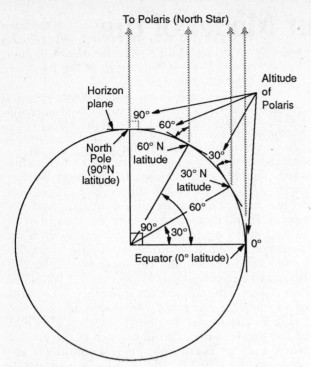

Figure 3-2. The angular altitude of Polaris if the earth were a perfect sphere.

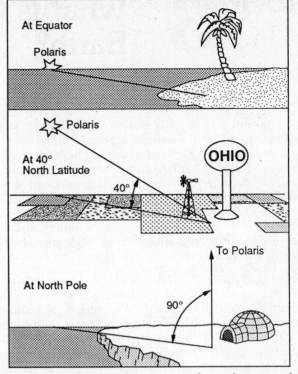

Figure 3-3. If the earth were a perfect sphere, an observer's latitude would equal the angular altitude of Polaris.

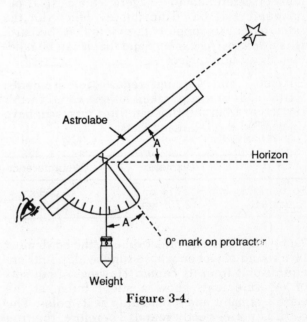

Figure 3-4.

according to Figure 3-2, at latitude 90°, or the North Pole, the altitude of Polaris would be 90°. At latitude 0°, or the equator, the altitude of Polaris would be 0°. (Polaris would be on the horizon.) Thus, the angular altitude of Polaris would be equal to the degree of latitude of the observer if the earth were a perfect sphere. See Figure 3-3. However, modern evidence shows that the altitude of Polaris does not vary exactly with the latitude of an observer. A very slight correction must always be made when an observer compares his or her true latitude with the measured altitude of Polaris. (However, for this topic and in general, we will use the altitude of Polaris to determine one's latitudinal position in the Northern Hemisphere *without* making any correction.) Once again, this evidence supports the view that the earth is not a perfect sphere but is very nearly so.

PROCESS OF INQUIRY SKILL

Finding the Altitude of a Star With an Astrolabe. The altitude of a heavenly body is its angular height above the horizon of an observer. You can measure altitude by using an astrolabe. An *astrolabe* is a protractor from which a heavy weight is suspended. See Figure 3-4. When you sight a star along the edge of the astrolabe, the weight hangs straight down toward the earth's center, or center of mass. A line at a right angle to the line formed by the string from which the weight is suspended represents the plane of the horizon. Therefore, the line on the protractor where the string of the weight falls indicates an angle that is equal to the altitude of the star above the horizon.

QUESTIONS

1. Polaris is used as a celestial reference point for the earth's latitude system, because Polaris (1) always rises at sunset and sets at sunrise (2) is located over the earth's axis of rotation (3) can be seen from any place on earth (4) is a very bright star

2. What is the latitude of the observer shown below?

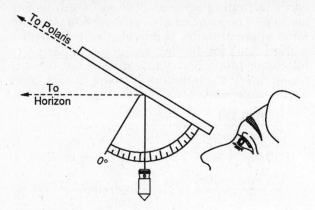

(1) 35° N.   (2) 55° N.   (3) 90° N.   (4) 125° N.

3. The diagram below indicates the altitude of Polaris as measured at three locations in the earth's Northern Hemisphere.

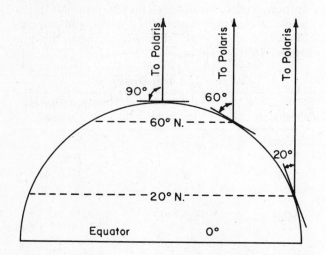

These observations could lead to the inference that the earth   (1) has a curved surface   (2) has an elliptical orbit   (3) rotates 15° per hour   (4) revolves around the sun

4. What is the latitude of point *A* in the diagram below?

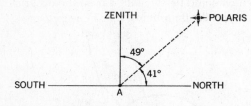

(1) 8° N.   (2) 41° N.   (3) 49° N.   (4) 59° N.

5. According to the data below, what is the exact shape of the earth?

<u>Actual Dimensions of the Earth</u>

Equatorial Radius	6,378 km
Polar Radius	6,357 km
Equatorial Circumference	40,076 km
Polar Circumference	40,008 km

(1) slightly flattened at both the equator and the poles
(2) slightly bulging at both the equator and the poles
(3) slightly flattened at the equator and slightly bulging at the poles   (4) slightly flattened at the poles and slightly bulging at the equator

6. The best evidence of the earth's nearly spherical shape is obtained through   (1) telescopic observations of other planets   (2) photographs of the earth from an orbiting satellite   (3) observations of the sun's altitude made during the day   (4) observations of the moon made during lunar eclipses

7. At sea level, which location would be closest to the center of the earth?   (1) 45° South latitude   (2) the equator   (3) 23½° North latitude   (4) the North Pole

8. Observations show that one degree of latitude at the equator equals a distance of 110.569 kilometers. This distance steadily increases until, at the poles, one degree of latitude equals 111.700 kilometers. Which inference is best supported by these observations?   (1) Polar drift continues to occur at the present time.   (2) As the earth moves around the sun, its orbital velocity varies.   (3) The earth is not a perfect sphere.   (4) Polaris' altitude increases with an increase in latitude.

9. Which set of photographs taken over a period of one year would supply the best evidence of the earth's shape?   (1) photographs of the sun from the earth   (2) photographs of the earth from the moon   (3) photographs of the earth's shadow on the moon   (4) photographs of the star paths from the North Pole

10. Which diagram best shows the shape of the earth drawn to scale?

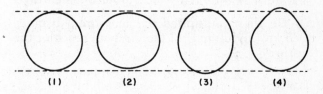

11. At what latitude would an observer on the earth find the altitude of Polaris to be 37°?   (1) 37° South   (2) 53° North   (3) 37° North   (4) 90° North

12. A navigator aboard ship measures the altitude of Polaris as shown in the diagram. What is the latitude of the ship's position at the time the measurement was taken?

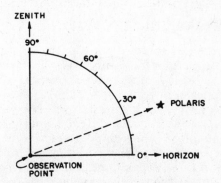

(1) 10° North   (2) 20° North   (3) 40° North   (4) 70° North

13. At which latitude will Polaris be overhead? (1) 0°   (2) 23½° N.   (3) 90° S.   (4) 90° N.

PROCESS OF INQUIRY SKILL

Determining the Circumference of the Earth.
The circumference of the earth was determined approximately 2,000 years ago by the Greek mathematician Eratosthenes, who was living in Egypt. His method, based on the geometry of a sphere, is still valid today. Eratosthenes measured the altitude of the sun at two points that were a substantial distance apart on the earth, with one directly north of the other. Using Eratosthenes' example, as you examine the two points A (Alexandria) and S (Syene) in Figure 3-5, you will notice that the line joining these points is part of the circle (**circumference**) that goes around the earth through the North Pole and the South Pole. The circumference of the earth was found as follows:

(1) The distance between the two points A and S was measured to be 925 kilometers.
(2) Eratosthenes then found out what part of the whole circle that measured distance from A to S is by using simple geometry. (The alternate interior angles made by parallel lines of the sun's rays are equal.) He knew that the sun was directly overhead in Syene but was 7.2° less than overhead in Alexandria. Therefore, the arc AS is also 7.2°, which is one-fiftieth of the whole distance (360°) around the earth.

$$\frac{7.2° \text{ (arc)}}{360° \text{ (circumference)}} = \frac{1}{50} \quad \begin{array}{l}\text{the whole distance} \\ \text{around the earth}\end{array}$$

(3) He then multiplied the measured distance (925 km) by 50 to find the circumference of the earth.

$$925 \text{ km} \times 50 = 46,250 \text{ km}$$

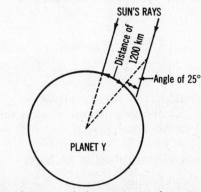

Figure 3-5. Since 7.2° is 1/50 of a circle, the distance from Syene to Alexandria must, therefore, be 1/50 of the circumference of the earth.

You can also calculate the circumference of the earth by setting up a proportion based on Eratosthenes' measurements. A proportion is a statement of equal ratios. It provides a useful mathematical tool for finding unknown values. The following proportion states that in the two different ratios, the numbers compare to each other in the same way.

$$\frac{925 \text{ km}}{\text{Circumference}} = \frac{7.2°}{360°}$$

$$925 \text{ km} \times 360° = \text{Circumference} \times 7.2°$$

$$\frac{925 \text{ km} \times 360°}{7.2°} = \text{Circumference}$$

$$46,250 \text{ km} = \text{Circumference}$$

The accepted value for the earth's polar circumference is 40,008 kilometers. Eratosthenes' calculations were remarkably accurate when compared with our modern measurements. If you know the circumference of the earth, you can calculate the other earth dimensions from the formulas listed in Table 3-1.

Table 3-1. Earth Dimensions

Dimension	Formula	Approximate Value
Diameter	$d = C/\pi$	12,800 km 8,000 mi
Radius	$r = \dfrac{d}{2}$ or $\dfrac{C}{2\pi}$	6,400 km 4,000 mi
Volume	$V = 4/3\pi r^3$	1.08×10^{12} km³ 2.7×10^{11} mi³
Surface area	$A = 4\pi r^2$	5.14×10^8 km² 8.04×10^5 mi²

QUESTIONS

14. Which could be calculated from the observations shown in the diagram below?

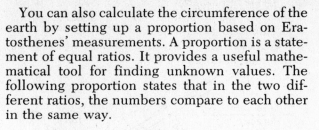

(1) circumference of planet Y (2) density of planet Y (3) distance to the sun from planet Y (4) diameter of the sun

15. The diagram below shows stations A and B, which are located on a north-south line. At noon, the altitude of the sun is 90° at station B and 30° at station A. What is the distance between stations A and B? [earth's circumference is 40,000 km.]

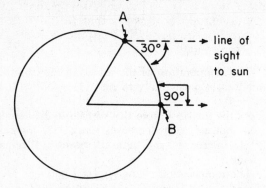

(1) 30 km   (2) 2,222 km   (3) 6,666 km   (4) 10,000 km

16. The diagrams below represent true scale models for the solid earth. Which diagram would best show the ocean depth also drawn to the same scale?

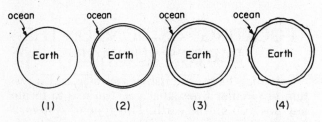

17. If the deepest parts of the ocean are about 10 kilometers and the radius of the earth is about 6,400 kilometers, the depth of the ocean would represent what percent of the earth's radius?   (1) less than 1% (2) about 5%   (3) about 25%   (4) more than 75%

18. Based on the diagram below, what is the circumference of planet X?

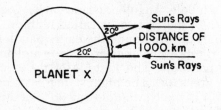

(1) 9,000 km   (2) 18,000 km   (3) 24,000 km (4) 36,000 km

STRUCTURE OF THE EARTH

The outer portion of the earth is generally classified into three major parts: lithosphere (solid), hydrosphere (liquid), and atmosphere (gas). See Figure 3-6. The **lithosphere** is the dense, solid shell of the earth composed of rock and soil that surrounds the more fluid inner layers. It varies in thickness from 72 to 153 kilometers. Oxygen and silicon are the two most common elements that compose the lithosphere. It also contains many other elements, including aluminum, iron, and calcium.

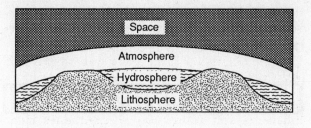

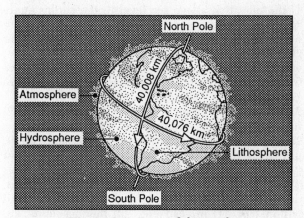

Figure 3-6. Parts of the earth.

The **hydrosphere** consists of the waters of the earth—the oceans, lakes, rivers, and water in the ground. The oceans extend to an average depth of 3.5 kilometers and cover about 70% of the earth's surface. Water is a chemical compound composed of oxygen and hydrogen with various other elements and compounds present in solution.

The **atmosphere** is the shell of gases that surrounds the earth. It extends out several hundred kilometers into space and is stratified, or layered, into zones.

The principal layers of the atmosphere, listed in order of increasing altitude, are the *troposphere*, the *stratosphere*, the *mesosphere*, and the *thermosphere*. Each layer is characterized by the pattern of vertical temperature trends shown in the *Earth Science Reference Tables* (page 170).

The lowest layer, the **troposphere**, is the most important to life on earth since it contains elements necessary to support life. Although it is relatively thin, it contains most of the mass of the atmosphere. The composition of the troposphere is generally 78% nitrogen and 21% oxygen, with water vapor, carbon dioxide, argon, neon, and other gases making up the remainder. Strong winds, storms, and turbulence occur in this layer of the atmosphere. Most of the water vapor in the atmosphere is in the troposphere and, hence, most of the clouds. Temperature in the troposphere generally decreases with increasing altitude.

The *tropopause* is the layer of the atmosphere separating the troposphere from the stratosphere. Likewise, the *stratopause* is the boundary layer between the stratosphere and the next layer of the atmosphere, the mesosphere. And the *mesopause* is the boundary layer between the mesosphere and the thermosphere.

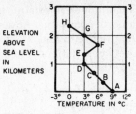

QUESTIONS

19. According to the *Earth Science Reference Tables*, as the elevation above sea level in the earth's atmosphere increases, the measured atmospheric pressure will (1) decrease (2) increase (3) remain the same

20. According to the *Earth Science Reference Tables*, which part of the atmosphere has the *smallest* distance from the bottom to the top of its zone? (1) troposphere (2) stratosphere (3) mesosphere (4) thermosphere

21. The hydrosphere is mostly (1) solid rock (2) liquid water (3) gaseous air

22. According to the *Earth Science Reference Tables*, nitrogen is the most abundant element in the (1) crust (2) hydrosphere (3) troposphere (4) mantle

23. According to the *Earth Science Reference Tables*, nearly all the water vapor in the atmosphere is found within the (1) mesosphere (2) thermosphere (3) troposphere (4) stratosphere

24. In which sequence are the earth layers arranged in order of increasing average density? (1) atmosphere, hydrosphere, lithosphere (2) hydrosphere, lithosphere, atmosphere (3) lithosphere, atmosphere, hydrosphere (4) atmosphere, lithosphere, hydrosphere

25. Which model best represents the volume of each gas in the troposphere? [Refer to the *Earth Science Reference Tables*.]

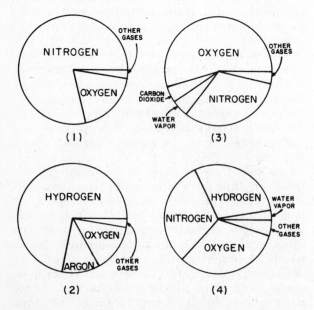

Directions (26–29): Base your answers to questions 26 through 29 on the graph below, which represents the temperature of a parcel of air as it is lifted through the atmosphere. Write the *number* of the word or expression that best completes the statement or answers the question.

26. The temperature of the air at an elevation of 2 kilometers is most likely to be (1) −2.5° (2) 2.5° (3) 3° (4) 0°

27. As the air rises from the surface to 1 kilometer, its temperature (1) decreases, only (2) increases, only (3) increases, and then decreases (4) remains the same

28. The temperature change is *least* between letters (1) *B* and *C* (2) *D* and *E* (3) *E* and *F* (4) *G* and *H*

29. Between which two points does the temperature increase with an increase in elevation (a temperature inversion)? (1) *A* to *D* (2) *D* to *E* (3) *E* to *F* (4) *F* to *H*

LOCATING POSITIONS ON THE EARTH'S SURFACE

Scientists have established a surface grid, a system of circular lines, that you can use to locate any position on the earth. This type of system, a **coordinate system**, assigns to every position on the earth a pair of coordinates (two numbers) called *latitude* and *longitude*. Like any other coordinate system, the latitude-longitude system's grid has two main reference lines—the equator and the prime meridian.

The **equator** is an imaginary line that circles the earth halfway between the North Pole and the South Pole. Angular distance in degrees north or south of the equator is called **latitude**. Imaginary lines drawn around the earth, parallel to the equator, represent lines of latitude and are often called **parallels**. The latitude of the equator is zero degrees (0°). The highest degrees of latitude are 90° N at the North Pole and 90° S at the South Pole. See Figure 3-7.

The *prime meridian* is an imaginary line (semicircle) that runs through Greenwich, England, from the North Pole to the South Pole. Angular distance in degrees east or west of the prime meridian is called **longitude**. Imaginary semicircles (**meridians**) drawn around the earth from the North Pole to the South Pole represent lines of longitude. The longitude of the prime meridian is zero degrees (0°). See Figure 3-8. If you move east and west away from the prime meridian, the farthest you can get from it is 180°. The 180th meridian is half the distance around the earth. The half of the world that is west of the prime meridian has west longitude. The half of the world that is east of the prime meridian has east longitude. See Figure 3-9.

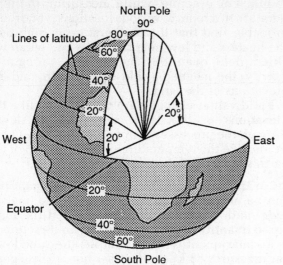

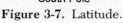

Figure 3-7. Latitude.

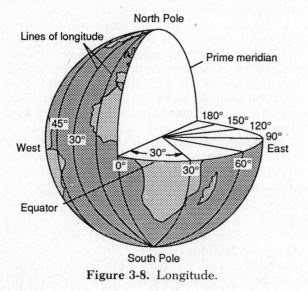

Figure 3-8. Longitude.

Navigation.

Navigation is the science of locating your position on the earth. Any location can be expressed as the measure of your angle north or south of the equator (latitude) and as the measure of your angle east or west of the prime meridian (longitude). In other words, each place on the earth has its own unique coordinates of latitude and longitude. Any location north of the equator has a latitude that is equal to the angle of Polaris (the North Star's altitude) above the horizon. For example, New York City's latitude is 40° N, the angle of Polaris above the horizon at New York City. Residents of the Northern Hemisphere are fortunate to have a bright star located almost exactly above the earth's North Pole. Residents of the Southern Hemisphere, however, must use certain other stars when locating the South Pole.

Approximate longitude can be calculated if you know the present clock time along the prime meridian at Greenwich (**Greenwich Mean Time**) and if you know the local clock time. To find longitude, you must first find the time difference, in hours, between local clock time and Greenwich time. Your longitude will then be this time difference multiplied by 15° per hour. (The rate at which the sun appears to move from east to west is 15° per hour.) If local time is earlier than Greenwich time, your position is west of the prime meridian or west longitude. If local time is later than Greenwich time, your position is east of the prime meridian or east longitude.

For example, there is a time difference of 5 hours between London, which is located at the prime meridian (0° longitude), and New York City. Multiplying 15° by 5 (hours), you find a difference of 75°. The fact that New York time is 5 hours earlier than London time indicates that New York is west of London. Therefore, the longitude of New York is 75° W. See Figure 3-10.

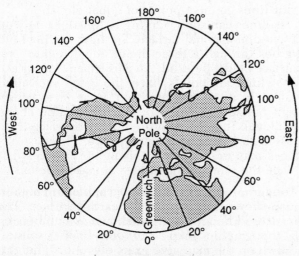

Meridians of longitude

Figure 3-9.

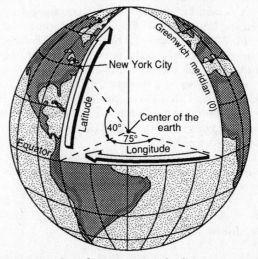

Figure 3-10. Coordinate system for locating positions on earth. The parallels of latitude and the meridians of longitude enable us to locate positions such as that of New York City (latitude 40°N, longitude 75°W).

30. Upon what measurement is the earth's latitude and longitude system based? (1) star angles (2) gravity intensity (3) magnetism direction (4) apparent solar diameter

31. The diagram below represents a portion of a map of the earth's grid system. What is the approximate latitude and longitude of point A?

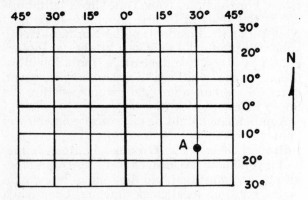

(1) 15° N. 30° W. (2) 15° S. 30° W. (3) 15° N. 30° E. (4) 15° S. 30° E.

32. As an observer travels eastward along the 40° N parallel of latitude, the altitude of the North Star will (1) decrease (2) increase (3) remain the same

33. Ship *X* and ship *Y* are sailing along the equator. The difference in local solar time between them is 2 hours. What is their difference in longitude? (1) 0° (2) 15° (3) 30° (4) 45°

34. As a ship crosses the prime meridian, the altitude of Polaris is 65°. What is the ship's location? (1) 0° longitude, 65° South latitude (2) 0° longitude, 65° North latitude (3) 0° latitude, 65° West longitude (4) 0° latitude, 65° East longitude

35. Cities located on the same meridian (longitude) must have the same (1) altitude (2) latitude (3) length of daylight (4) solar time

36. A person knows the solar time on the prime meridian and the local solar time. What determination can be made? (1) the date (2) the altitude of Polaris (3) the longitude at which the person is located (4) the latitude at which the person is located

37. An observer on a moving ship notices that the altitude of Polaris increases each night. Local solar noon occurs at the same time each day. In what direction is the ship moving? (1) due east (2) due south (3) due west (4) due north

38. Based on the Generalized Bedrock Geology Map of New York State in the *Earth Science Reference Tables,* what could be the approximate location of an observer if he measured the altitude of Polaris to be 41 degrees above the horizon? (1) Watertown (2) Massena (3) Buffalo (4) New York City

FIELDS

A **field** is a region of space in which a similar quantity can be measured at every point or lo-cation. For example, while measuring the temperature of a room at various locations, you would probably find that the temperature is high near the heaters and low near the walls and windows. Other field quantities include the strength of gravity, the magnetic field of the earth, and the elevations of the land.

Field values change with time. Some, like the elevations of the land, change very slowly through the processes of uplift and erosion. Other fields, like the temperature or illumination of the earth's surface, change rapidly.

Scalars and Vectors.
Physical quantities can be measured and described by size (magnitude) and, sometimes, by direction. If the measured quantity has magnitude but no direction, it is a **scalar** quantity. For example, the speed of a car measures 88 kilometers per hour. This speed measurement has no direction associated with it; therefore, speed is a scalar quantity. Examples of scalar earth fields are temperature, relative humidity, and atmospheric pressure.

If the measured quantity has both magnitude (size) and direction, it is a **vector** quantity. For example, you cannot simply drive 88 km/hr when you are traveling from New York to Los Angeles. You must also drive in *the proper direction.* Your velocity, then, is 88 km/hr (55 mph) west. This velocity measurement, unlike speed, has both magnitude (speed) and direction associated with it; therefore, velocity is a vector quantity. Examples of vector earth fields are magnetism, gravity, and wind velocity.

Mapping Earth Fields.
Field maps are models on which scalar or vector quantities are plotted. To show varying values of either scalar or vector quantities within a field, isolines may be drawn. **Isolines** connect points of equal value on a field map. See Figure 3-11. Types of isolines include isotherms, isobars, and contour lines. **Isotherms** connect points of equal temperature. **Isobars** connect points of equal air pressure. **Contour lines** connect points of equal elevation.

Isolines can show varying field values only on a two-dimensional surface. To show varying field values through a three-dimensional region, isosurfaces must be used. An **isosurface** is a surface on which all points have the same measured value. In a topographic field, isosurfaces represent horizontal planes of equal elevation above sea level. In a temperature field, isosurfaces represent zones of equal temperature. These isosurfaces may be warped by rising air currents that place the same temperatures at various levels.

Topographic Maps. A **topographic**, or **contour**, **map** shows the shape of the earth's surface. The measured heights may be shown as numbers on a topographic map. *Contour lines* (isolines) drawn on the map give exact elevations (heights above sea level) for a region and show the shape of the land. See Figure 3-12. Each contour line

A.

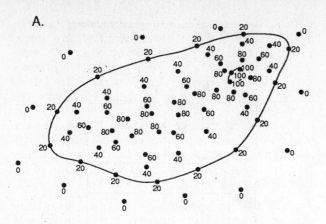

B.

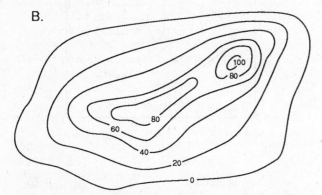

Figure 3-11. Elevation above sea level is being measured in this topographic field. Many points in a region have been measured and plotted on a map, and isolines (contour lines) have begun to be drawn in. Isolines are drawn in and connect points of equal value in a region.

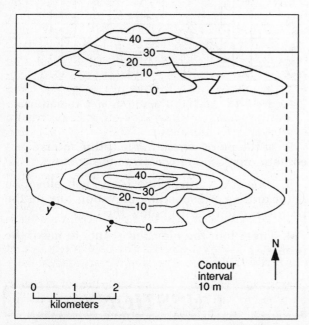

Figure 3-12. A topographic map of an island. The contour interval is 10 meters. However, the distance from point *X* to *Y* is approximately 1.5 kilometers based on the scale.

What Is Our Model of the Earth?

is separated from the next by a uniform difference in elevation known as the **contour interval**. In other words, the contour interval is the difference in height between two adjacent contour lines. Where the contour lines are close, the slope of the ground is steep. Where the contour lines are far apart, the slope of the ground is gentle. *NOTE:* Do not confuse a contour interval, which shows a difference in height, with distance along the ground. You measure the horizontal distance between two points on consecutive contour lines by using the map scale.

From the shape of a set of contours you can recognize landscapes, such as hills, valleys, depressions, cliffs, etc. See Figure 3-13. A topographic map may also use other symbols or colors to represent bodies of water, vegetation, and structures, such as buildings and roads. A key or legend describing the symbols is always provided.

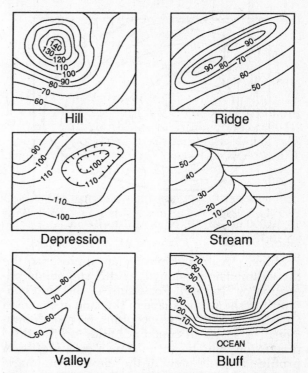

Figure 3-13. The closer the contours, the steeper the slopes. Special marks on the depression contours are called *hachures*. Where a river has cut a valley through land, contour lines plainly show the valley. Contours bend in the direction of the high land from which the river is running. They make "V's" at small streams, where the "V" points upstream. The direction in which a river flows can be determined by the elevations of marked contour lines. A river flows from higher to lower elevations.

QUESTIONS

39. A vector quantity must include both magnitude and direction. Which is a vector quantity? (1) precipitation (2) temperature (3) humidity (4) wind

40. The diagram below is a contour map. Between which two points is the slope of the hill steepest?

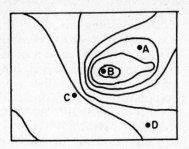

(1) *A* and *B* (2) *B* and *C* (3) *C* and *D* (4) *A* and *D*

41. Which is true of isolines on a weather map? (1) They are of equal length. (2) They are evenly spaced. (3) They connect points with equal readings. (4) They are constant for 24 hours.

42. What is the elevation of the highest contour line shown on the map below?

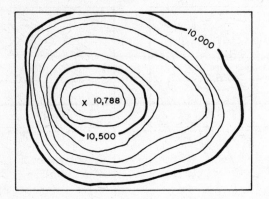

(1) 10,000 m (2) 10,688 m (3) 10,700 m
(4) 10,788 m

Profiles. A topographic map represents the three dimensions—length, width, and height (elevation or altitude). For example, the zero contour line shows the shape of the land at sea level (coastline). The single contour is two dimensional. A series of contours builds up the third dimension, which can be shown on a profile. A **profile** is a side view of the elevations along a particular line, the baseline, that crosses contour lines on a topographic map. The profile in Figure 3-14 shows how the land would appear if a slice were made along the baseline HI.

PROCESS OF INQUIRY SKILL

Making Profiles From Contour Maps. A profile shows the ups and downs of a baseline across the contour lines of a topographic map. Wherever the baseline meets a contour line, the exact height above sea level can be plotted on a vertical scale. See Figure 3-15.

It is easy to make a profile by following these simple steps illustrated in Figure 3-15:

1. Draw a baseline across the contours on the topographic map (baseline MN).

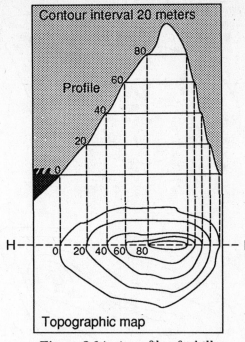

Figure 3-14. A profile of a hill.

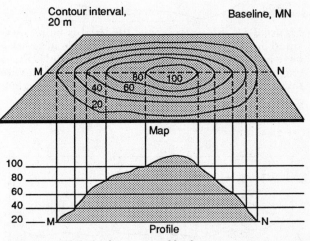

Figure 3-15. Making a profile from a contour map.

2. At the point where the baseline intersects a contour, mark the elevation of the contour.

3. Project a vertical line from each elevation point to the corresponding elevation line on the profile section shown below the map.

4. Then, join the elevated points to make the profile.

QUESTIONS

Directions (43–44): Base your answers to questions 43 and 44 on the information and temperature chart and on your knowledge of earth science.

The temperature data (°C) plotted on the chart below was taken at the same elevation and time in a room. Letters A through G represent specific locations in the room.

```
26•   25•   23•   21•   18•ⓔ
27• ⓐ26•   25•   23•   19•
28•ⓑ30•   27•ⓓ 24•   20•ⓕ
28•   29•   27•   22•   19•
27•ⓒ 27•   26•   20•   19•ⓖ
```

43. Which diagram best represents the 26°C isotherm?

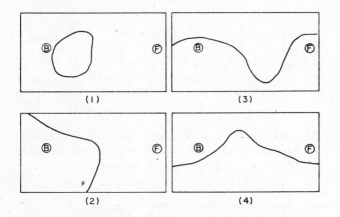

(1)   (3)

(2)   (4)

44. Which graph best represents the temperatures between B and F?

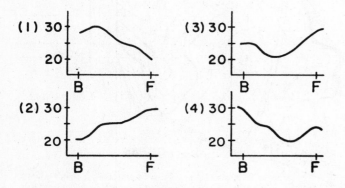

PROCESS OF INQUIRY SKILL

Determining a Gradient, or Slope. You can determine the rate of change of a value within a field by measuring the gradient. **Gradient**, or average slope, is the rate of change in field values between two points in a field. It is calculated by comparing the difference in field values at two points with the distance between those two points. For example, the average slope, or gradient, between any two points (A and B) on a mountain can easily be determined from a con-

tour map. If you know how many meters the mountain drops or rises between A and B in a given distance, you can calculate the average slope by using the following equation:

$$\text{slope} = \frac{\text{difference in elevation between A and B (m)}}{\text{distance between A and B (km)}}$$

Sample Problem

Calculate the average slope of a mountain trail from the 530-meter contour line to the 480-meter contour. The distance between these two elevations measures 4 kilometers.

Solution:

$$\text{slope} = \frac{\text{difference in elevation (m)}}{\text{distance between the points (km)}}$$

$$\text{slope} = \frac{530 \text{ m} - 480 \text{ m}}{4 \text{ km}}$$

$$\text{slope} = \frac{50 \text{ m}}{4 \text{ km}}$$

$$\text{slope} = 12.5 \text{ m/km}$$

QUESTIONS

45. A stream has a source at an elevation of 1000. meters. It ends in a lake that has an elevation of 300. meters. If the lake is 200. kilometers away from the source, what is the average gradient of the stream? (1) 1.5 m/km (2) 3.5 m/km (3) 10. m/km (4) 15 m/km

Directions (46–47): Base your answers to questions 46 and 47 on the diagram below which represents a contour map of a hill.

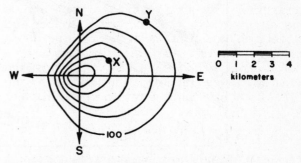

CONTOUR INTERVAL = 10 METERS

46. On which side of the hill does the land have the steepest slope? (1) north (2) south (3) east (4) west

47. What is the approximate gradient of the hill between points *X* and *Y*? [Refer to the *Earth Science Reference Tables*.] (1) 1 m/km (2) 10 m/km (3) 3 m/km (4) 30 m/km

What Is Our Model of the Earth?

25

Directions (48–49): Base your answers to questions 48 and 49 on your knowledge of earth science and on the topographic map shown below.

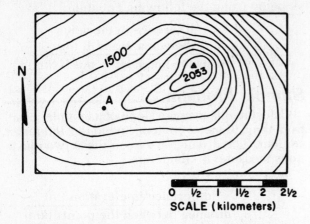

48. What is the most likely elevation of point *A*? (1) 1,250 (2) 1,650 (3) 1,750 (4) 1,850

49. Which section of the map shows the steepest gradient? (1) southeast (2) northeast (3) southwest (4) northwest

Directions (50–54): Base your answers to questions 50 through 54 on your knowledge of earth science, the *Earth Science Reference Tables,* and the topographic map below which represents a coastal landscape. The contour lines show the elevations in meters.

50. What is the approximate distance along the dirt road from points *G* to *H*? (1) 2.1 km (2) 2.6 km (3) 3.2 km (4) 4.0 km

51. What is the general direction of flow of the river between points *E* and *F*? (1) north to south (2) south to north (3) west to east (4) east to west

52. What is the elevation of the highest contour line shown on the map? (1) 140 m (2) 150 m (3) 155 m (4) 180 m

53. Which diagram best represents the profile along a straight line between points *C* and *J*?

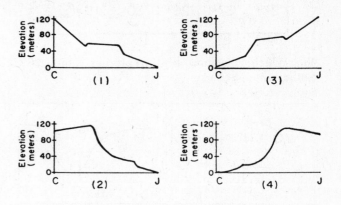

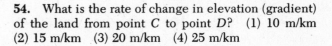

54. What is the rate of change in elevation (gradient) of the land from point *C* to point *D*? (1) 10 m/km (2) 15 m/km (3) 20 m/km (4) 25 m/km

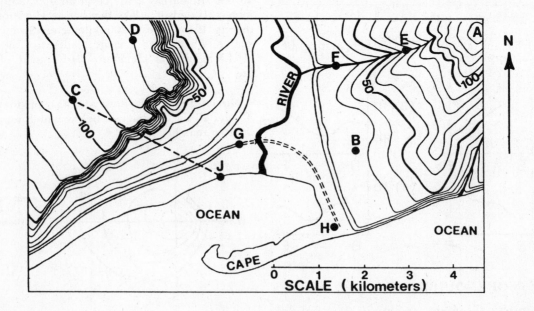

4 Earth Motions

MOTIONS OF CELESTIAL OBJECTS

To most observers, the night sky looks like a huge dome, or hemisphere, that extends down to the horizon in every direction. If an observer were to extend the dome of the sky so that it circles the entire earth, she or he would produce an imaginary sphere, the **celestial sphere**, on which all objects in the sky appear projected. A **celestial object**, such as the sun, the moon, a planet, or any distant object visible in the sky, generally appears to rise in the east and set in the west.

Most of the celestial objects appear to move along circular paths, or parts of circles called arcs of the celestial sphere. The apparent east-west motion of an object occurs at an angular rate of approximately 15° per hour (360°, or one rotation, in 24 hours). In the course of a 24-hour day, a star that is positioned near Polaris in the Northern Hemisphere will appear to move in a complete circular path about a point in the sky directly above the North Pole (the celestial North Pole). Other stars appear to move 15° per hour from east to west along arcs until they disappear below the horizon. See Figure 4-1.

Motion of the Stars and Planets.

The stars located over the earth's equator follow nearly the same path as the sun—rising in the east and setting in the west. Stars in the southern portion of the sky briefly arc across or appear over the horizon on their westward journey. Stars over the North Pole move in circles around Polaris. The motions of stars are all characterized by a circular motion of 15° per hour around the celestial North Pole.

The planets do not remain in fixed positions among the stars. In addition to their daily 15° per hour circular motion, they change their positions from night to night. Each planet has its own characteristic motion. Sometimes a planet drifts westward with respect to the stars, and sometimes a planet reverses its direction and moves eastward among the stars. The wandering motions of planets led ancient observers of the sky to recognize that these celestial objects were different from the "other" stars. In fact, the word planet means "wanderer."

Observations made over a period of time have shown that cyclical changes occur in the surface features of planets. Surface features also appear to move across the planets. Such evidence indicates that the other planets, as they revolve around the sun, must also rotate on their axes.

LOCATING A STAR ON THE CELESTIAL SPHERE

To locate a star on the celestial sphere, two measurements are needed. One measurement gives the altitude of the star, and the other measurement gives the star's azimuth.

The *altitude* of a star is a measurement of its angular height above the celestial horizon and is measured in degrees. See Figure 4-2. A star sighted directly over the head of an observer has an altitude of 90°. This point on the celestial sphere, which is directly overhead with respect to the observer, is called the zenith. The altitude of a star is always given with respect to the observer; therefore, it is different from one place to another, depending on the location of the observer on the earth.

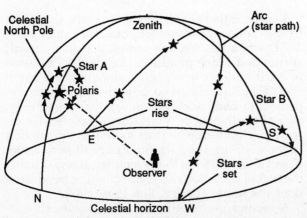

Figure 4-1. The celestial sphere.

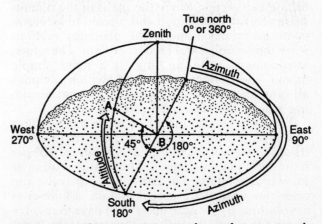

Figure 4-2. The star at Point A is located at an azimuth of 180° and an altitude of 45°. The observer is standing in the center, directly under the zenith.

The *azimuth* of a star is the angular measure of an arc of the celestial horizon beginning at true north and continuing clockwise until it intersects with the arc representing the star's altitude. See Figure 4-2. Altitude and azimuth provide the basis of an angular coordinate system that describes the location of a star on the celestial sphere.

THE GEOCENTRIC MODEL

Early civilizations were aware of how celestial objects, such as the sun and moon, moved through the sky from east to west. Because these people could not feel the earth moving, they considered the earth to be a stationary object located at the center of the universe around which all celestial objects revolved. Their model of the universe was **geocentric**, or earth-centered.

The geocentric model is able to explain the apparent motions of celestial objects from east to west by their revolution around the earth. To account for **retrograde motion** (the apparent backward motion of the planets, such as Mars), a system of circles called epicycles was invented and added to the model. A planet followed these small circles for retrograde motion. However, the geocentric model was always thought to be imperfect, for there is no natural reason for the epicycles. Another weakness of the geocentric model was its inability to explain certain terrestrial motions, such as rotation of the Foucault pendulum and the Coriolis effect, which are discussed on pages 28–29. Since the geocentric model never satisfactorily explained these apparent motions of celestial and terrestrial objects, it was eventually replaced by a superior model—the *heliocentric model*.

THE HELIOCENTRIC MODEL

Observations by Copernicus, Brahe, Kepler, Galileo, and other scientists in the 16th and 17th centuries eventually made the geocentric model difficult to accept. When the paths of the planets were carefully measured and plotted in an earth-centered model, some of the planetary motions were too complex and hard to explain. Therefore, astronomers prefer to support a more simple model, the **heliocentric model**, which includes all nine known planets (the solar system) revolving around the sun, and a rotating earth.

The heliocentric model includes two motions of the planet earth. Each day the earth spins on its **axis**—from west to east at the rate of 15° per hour (360° in 24 hours). This daily motion is known as **rotation**. The earth also *orbits* the sun once per **year**. This annual motion is known as **revolution**. If the earth takes 365¼ days to revolve around the sun, it revolves approximately 1° per day.

The heliocentric model of the solar system ex- plains retrograde motion without inventing special orbits (epicycles). For example, differences in the rates of revolution of the earth and Mars create the illusion of retrograde motion. See Figure 4-3. The earth sometimes moves ahead of Mars, causing Mars to appear to move backward with relation to the earth.

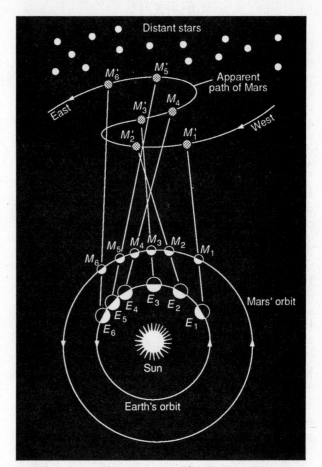

Figure 4-3. Retrograde motion of Mars. The earth moves in its orbit more rapidly than Mars. From positions E1 and E2 on the earth, Mars appears to move forward. From positions E3 and E4, Mars appears to move backward. From positions E5 and E6, Mars appears to move forward again.

Evidence for the rotation of the earth, exhibited in the heliocentric model, was not found until 1851, when the French scientist Jean Foucault suspended a long pendulum inside the Pantheon in Paris and set it swinging along a north-south line. Foucault observed how the pendulum appeared to change direction, as it swung freely, away from the north-south line in a clockwise direction. He interpreted this motion as the rotation of the earth underneath the **Foucault pendulum**. Foucault knew from the principles of physics that the actual direction of a free-swinging pendulum does not really change. See Figure 4-4.

A second piece of evidence of the earth's rotation can be observed in the circular patterns of

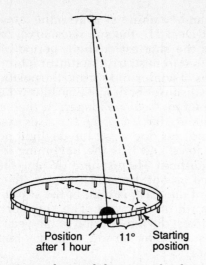

Figure 4-4. Foucault pendulum. At the latitude of Paris, the plane of the swinging pendulum appears, in one hour, to move 11° from the starting position. One full rotation takes about 36 hours.

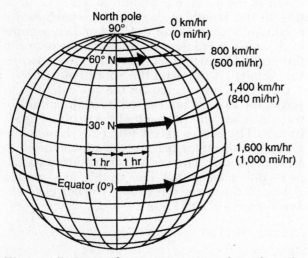

Figure 4-5. Rates of rotation at various latitudes. The linear speed of the earth's rotation decreases as an observer travels from the equator toward a pole. The angular rate of the earth's rotation is the same for all latitudes.

the ocean currents and in the circular wind patterns of the atmosphere. Because all places on the earth's surface do not rotate at the same speed (see Figure 4-5), objects, air masses, and ocean currents that move long distances are deflected from a straight-line path—they appear to curve. This deflection, known as the **Coriolis effect**, can be seen in the photographs of cloud patterns taken by satellites far above the earth. In the Northern Hemisphere, the deflection is to the right of the straight-line path. In the Southern Hemisphere, it is to the left. See Figure 4-6. The Coriolis effect will be discussed further in Topic 7.

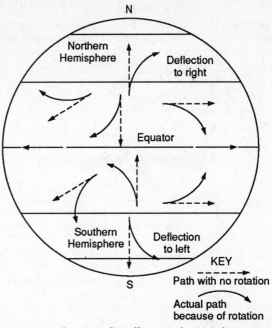

Figure 4-6. The Coriolis effect. In the Northern Hemisphere, winds and ocean currents are deflected to the right. In the Southern Hemisphere, the deflection is to the left. At the equator, there is no deflection.

THE APPARENT MOTIONS OF THE SUN

Our system of time is based upon the **apparent** motions of the sun. The motion of a celestial object, such as the sun, the moon, or a planet, through the sky is called *apparent motion* because the object is not really moving as it appears to be. The apparent rising and setting of the sun is actually caused by the earth's rotation. The **apparent solar day** is the interval of time during which the sun passes from its highest point on one day to its highest point on the next. It is measured from the apparent solar noon (when the sun is on the meridian) to the next apparent solar noon. Sometimes the sun's apparent motions are faster than average and sometimes slower, but the length of the solar day averages 24 hours. This is called the **mean solar day**.

Seasons. Because the earth revolves, the sun's pathway from east to west in the sky also changes on a yearly cycle. See Figure 4-7. In New York, the noon sun is high in the sky at the beginning of the summer. Through the next six months, summer and autumn, the noon position of the sun gets a little lower in the sky each day. While this happens, the sunrise position starts north of due east and moves slowly southward as each daylight period becomes a little shorter than the day before. At the *autumnal equinox* (about Sept. 23), the sun rises due east and sets due west. Daylight lasts for 12 hours, and it is the beginning of fall in the Northern Hemisphere.

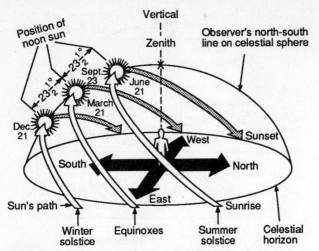

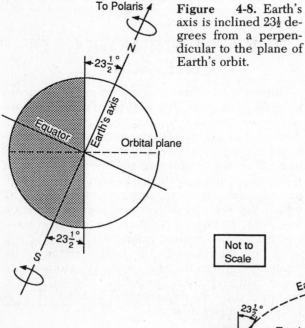

Figure 4-7. Path of the sun's apparent motion at latitude 40° N on the solstices and the equinoxes. The strongest rays from the sun are those that are most direct, when the sun is the highest in the sky. To the observer, the sun's path appears to change both daily and seasonally. It is noon for the observer when the sun crosses a north-south line through the sky (the observer's meridian).

Figure 4-8. Earth's axis is inclined 23½ degrees from a perpendicular to the plane of Earth's orbit.

At the beginning of winter, the *winter solstice* (about Dec. 21), the sun rises south of due east; this is the shortest daylight period of the year, measured from sunrise to sunset. Throughout the months of winter and spring, the positions of sunrise and sunset both move northward as the daylight periods become longer. At the *vernal equinox* (about March 21), the sun rises exactly in the east and sets due west; the daylight period is 12 hours long, and it is the beginning of spring in the Northern Hemisphere. When the *summer solstice* (about June 21) arrives, the sun rises north of due east, is high in the sky at noon, and sets north of due west. The summer solstice is the longest daylight period of the year, measured from sunrise to sunset; it is the beginning of summer.

Daylight Hours.

At equinox, the sun rises due east and sets due west. For all locations except the poles, daylight lasts 12 hours. At the equator throughout the year, there are 12 hours of daylight and 12 hours of night. As one gets closer to the poles, the amount of seasonal variation in the length of daylight increases until a maximum six months of daylight and six months of darkness is reached for all locations between the Arctic Circle and the North Pole or between the Antarctic Circle and the South Pole.

Of course, the changes in the sun's daily path across the sky are not caused by real motions of the sun. They are the result of the earth's spin on its axis. The earth's axis is tilted 23½° from a line perpendicular to the plane of the orbit of the earth around the sun. The earth also exhibits parallelism—this means that the earth's axis always points in the same direction. It never changes. See Figure 4-8 and Figure 4-9.

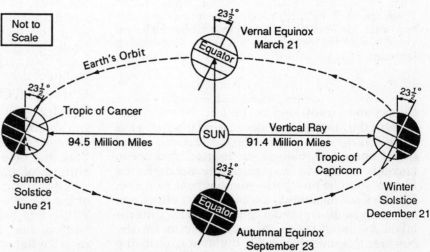

Figure 4-9. Throughout Earth's revolution around the sun, Earth's inclined axis and its parallelism (the axis always points in the same direction) are important in the regular change of seasons and the change in the length of day and night.

Reviewing Earth Science: Topic 4

1. In the geocentric model (the earth at the center of the universe), which motion would occur? (1) The earth would revolve around the sun. (2) The earth would rotate on its axis. (3) The moon would revolve around the sun. (4) The sun would revolve around the earth.

2. In its orbit around the sun, approximately how many degrees per day does the earth revolve? (1) 1° (2) 13° (3) 15° (4) 90°

3. In the geocentric model, which event is most difficult to explain? (1) the daily apparent motion of the sun (2) the daily apparent motion of the moon (3) the yearly apparent motion of the outer planets (4) the yearly apparent motion of the farthest stars

4. The apparent rising and setting of the sun as seen from the earth are caused by the (1) rotation of the sun (2) rotation of the earth (3) revolution of the earth (4) revolution of the sun

5. Which is the best evidence for the earth's rotation? (1) the rising of the sun (2) the changing of the seasons (3) the phases of the moon (4) the motion of a Foucault pendulum

6. Based on observations made in the Northern Hemisphere, which statement is the best supporting evidence that the earth rotates on its axis? (1) The stars appear to follow daily circular paths around Polaris. (2) The apparent solar diameter varies throughout the year. (3) The length of the daylight period varies throughout the year. (4) The seasons (spring, summer, fall, and winter) repeat in a cyclic pattern.

7. On March 21, two observers, one at 45° north latitude and the other at 45° south latitude, watch the "rising" sun. In which direction(s) must they look? (1) Both observers must look westward. (2) Both observers must look eastward. (3) The observer at 45° N. must look westward while the other must look eastward. (4) The observer at 45° S. must look westward while the other must look eastward.

8. Upon which frame of reference is time based? (1) the motions of the earth (2) the longitude of an observer (3) the motions of the moon (4) the real motions of the sun

9. From September to November, the sun's altitude at noon in the Northern Hemisphere (1) decreases (2) increases (3) remains the same

10. What causes the Coriolis effect? (1) high- and low-pressure belts (2) the earth's revolution (3) the equatorial calms (4) the earth's rotation

11. Why do stars appear to move through the night sky at the rate of 15 degrees per hour? (1) The earth actually moves around the Sun at a rate of 15° per hour. (2) The stars actually move around the center of the galaxy at a rate of 15° per hour. (3) The earth actually rotates at a rate of 15° per hour. (4) The stars actually revolve around the earth at a rate of 15° per hour.

12. What is the total number of degrees that the earth rotates on its axis during a 12-hour period? (1) 1° (2) 15° (3) 180° (4) 360°

13. Which diagram below best represents the illumination of the earth on the first day of summer in the Northern Hemisphere?

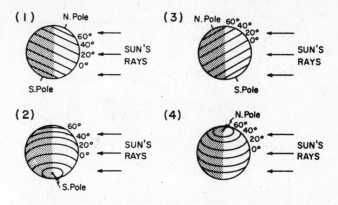

14. In New York State, between February and May, the number of daylight hours (1) decreases (2) increases (3) remains the same

15. The star Sirius is observed in the evening sky during the month of January. At the end of 3 hours, Sirius will appear to have moved (1) 60° (2) 45° (3) 3° (4) 0°

16. Which position in the diagram below best represents the earth on the first day of summer in the Northern Hemisphere?

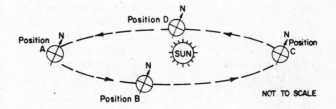

(1) A (2) B (3) C (4) D

17. The sun will be observed to rise north of east by an observer in New York State on (1) January 1 (2) March 1 (3) July 1 (4) October 1

Directions (18–19): Questions 18 and 19 are based on the diagram below, which represents the western horizon as viewed by an observer in New York State. A, B, C, D, and E are possible positions of sunset, and A and E represent the outermost limits beyond which sunset does not occur.

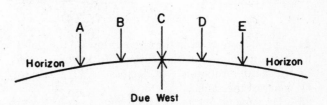

18. Which position most accurately indicates the position of sunset on May 6? (1) A (2) B (3) C (4) D

19. Which sunset position represents the day with the greatest number of daylight hours? (1) A (2) E (3) C (4) D

20. The diagram below shows the sun's maximum altitude (*C*) relative to a vertical stick in New York State on June 21. In which direction from the base of the stick does shadow *C'* point?

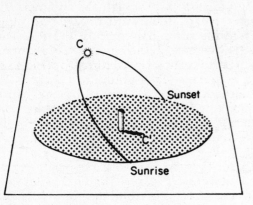

(1) north (2) south (3) east (4) west

21. In New York State, a recorded length of the shadow cast by a tree at noon each day from January to May will most probably indicate that the length of the shadow (1) continuously decreases (2) continuously increases (3) remains the same (4) increases and then decreases

22. New York State has several more hours of daylight in summer than in winter. Which statement helps explain this observation? (1) The earth is tilted on its axis. (2) The distance between the earth and the sun varies. (3) The diameter of the sun appears to change. (4) The speed of the earth in its orbit changes.

23. An observer in New York State took a time exposure photograph from 10 P.M. until midnight of the stars over the *northern* horizon. Which diagram best represents this photograph?

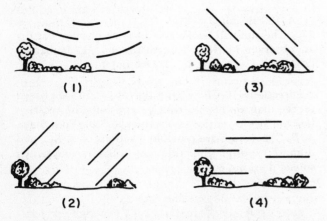

24. As one moves from the equator toward the poles, the velocity of the earth's surface, in km/hr, caused by the earth's rotation (1) decreases (2) increases (3) remains the same

25. How many degrees per hour must a satellite orbit in order to remain above the same spot on the equator? (1) 1 degree/hr. (2) 15 degrees/hr. (3) 24 degrees/hr. (4) 360 degrees/hr.

26. Planetary winds do *not* blow directly north or south because of (1) the Coriolis effect (2) gravitational force (3) magnetic force (4) centripetal force

Directions (27–31): Base your answers to questions 27 through 31 on your knowledge of earth science and the diagram below. The diagram represents the apparent path of the sun at three different dates during the year as it appears to an observer in New York State. The paths are labeled I, II, III and letters *A* through *G* are points on the paths. Path II occurs on March 21.

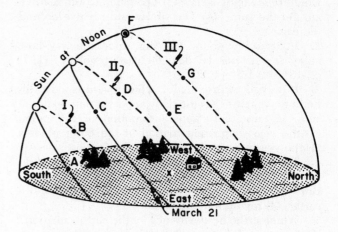

27. Which statement explains the apparent daily motion of the sun across the sky along path II? (1) The earth rotates on its axis. (2) The earth revolves around the sun. (3) The earth's axis is inclined to its orbit. (4) The earth's orbit is elliptical.

28. The angular distance along path II between points *C* and *D* is measured to be 90°. Approximately how much time would be required for the sun to move this distance? (1) 1 hour (2) 2 hours (3) 6 hours (4) 4 hours

29. What would be the position of the sun at 3 P.M. in December? (1) *A* (2) *B* (3) *E* (4) *G*

30. Which would be the approximate length of the daylight period for the observer when the sun travels along the entire length of path I? (1) 9 hours (2) 12 hours (3) 15 hours (4) 18 hours

31. The sun is at point *F*, which is the maximum altitude of the sun for the year. A vertical stick is placed at location *X*, and the stick's shadow is measured each noon for the next 30 days. During this time, the length of the shadow will (1) become shorter (2) become longer (3) remain the same

VERTICAL RAY

The earth's **seasons** can also be defined by the latitude at which a ray of sunlight, the **vertical ray**, strikes the earth's surface at an angle of 90°. The vertical ray always strikes the earth somewhere; and where it does, the sun is directly overhead. At this position, the sun is said to be at the *zenith*, or an altitude of 90°.

As the sun's daily path changes, so does the latitude that receives the vertical ray. The vertical ray moves seasonally between the *Tropic of Cancer* and the *Tropic of Capricorn*, at a rate of 23½° each season. The shifting of the sun's vertical ray from 23½° N to 23½° S means that only the area in

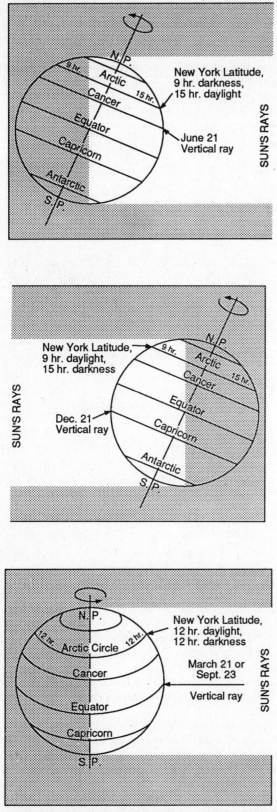

between those two latitudes will have a noon sun that reaches zenith sometime during the year.

During summer in the Northern Hemisphere, the vertical ray of sunlight strikes the earth north of the equator. But through the summer, it continually moves southward toward the equator, until, at the autumnal equinox, the noon sun is directly overhead at the equator. Throughout the autumn, the vertical ray continually moves southward from the equator until it reaches the **Tropic of Capricorn** ($23\frac{1}{2}°$ S), indicating the Northern Hemisphere's winter solstice. Then the vertical ray begins to move northward, crosses the equator again at the spring equinox, and reaches its most northerly point, the **Tropic of Cancer** ($23\frac{1}{2}°$ N), indicating the Northern Hemisphere's summer solstice. See Figure 4-10. Because the United States mainland is north of the Tropic of Cancer, the noon sun never is directly overhead at any time during the year. It never reaches the zenith in the United States; it is *always* seen to the south of an observer in New York. Refer back to Figure 4-7 on page 30. On what day of the year are the sun's rays most nearly vertical for the observer in the diagram? At noon on about June 21, the sun's rays are most nearly vertical for the observer in Figure 4-7.

ANGULAR DIAMETERS OF CELESTIAL OBJECTS

If you hold a ping-pong ball at arm's length, it looks rather small. But if the same ball is held close to your eye, it appears much larger. Although the size of the ball has not changed, the angular diameter of the ball has changed. **Angular diameter** is the angle formed between two sides of an object and your eye. The angular diameter of any object depends upon the actual size of the object and upon how far away the object is from the observer. The nearer an object is to an observer, the greater an object's angular diameter. For example, when you observe the sun, the moon, and the planets over a period of time, you will notice that they appear to change in size in a cyclic manner. The apparent change in size, or diameter, is due to a change in distance between each celestial object and the earth. The angular diameter of each celestial object changes periodically, but the real size, or diameter, of each celestial object stays the same.

Observations of the sun's angular diameter tell us that the earth is closest to the sun in January and farthest from the sun in July. Seasonal variations result from parallelism, the tilt of the earth's axis, and the earth's shape—not from earth-sun distance. The sun's angular diameter is larger in winter and smaller in summer. These observations tell us that the earth is closest to the sun in January and farthest from the sun in July.

Figure 4-10. How the vertical ray of sunlight strikes the earth's surface during the course of a year. And how day and night are distributed on Earth on the Northern Hemisphere's longest day (June 21) and its shortest day (Dec. 21). These days are the solstices. Day and night are equal in length everywhere on Earth only on the two equinoxes (about Sept. 23 and March 21).

QUESTIONS

32. Which graph best represents the relationship between latitude north of the equator and the length of the daylight period on March 21?

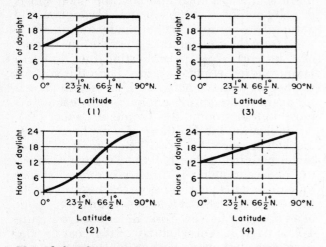

33. If the distance between the earth and the sun were increased, which change would occur? (1) The apparent diameter of the sun would decrease. (2) The amount of insolation received by the earth would increase. (3) The time for one Earth rotation (rotation period) would double. (4) The time for one Earth revolution (orbital period) would decrease.

34. How many days during the year is the sun directly overhead in New York State? (1) 1 (2) 2 (3) 0 (4) 4

35. In the diagram below, the direct rays of the sun are striking the earth's surface at 23½° N. What is the date shown in the diagram?

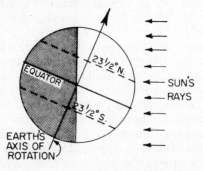

(1) March 21 (2) June 21 (3) September 23 (4) December 21

36. On December 21, at which latitude would an observer find the sun directly overhead? (1) 0° (2) 23½° North (3) 23½° South (4) 90° South

37. During a period of one year, what would be the greatest altitude of the sun at the North Pole? (1) 90° (2) 66½° (3) 23½° (4) 0°

38. The earth's axis of rotation is tilted 23½° from a line perpendicular to the plane of its orbit. What would be the result if the tilt was increased to 33½°? (1) an increase in the amount of solar radiation received by the earth (2) colder winters and warmer summers in New York State (3) less difference between winter and summer temperatures in New York State (4) shorter days and longer nights at the equator

39. For an observer at 23½° N. latitude, which graph best represents the relationship between the altitude of the sun above the horizon at solar noon and the month of the year?

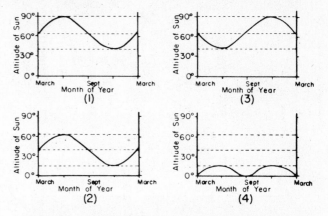
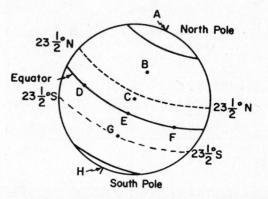

Directions (40–44): Base your answers to questions 40 through 44 on your knowledge of earth science and the diagram below which represents a view of the earth as seen from space. Locations *A* through *H* are on the earth's surface.

40. At which location would the altitude of Polaris (North Star) be the greatest? (1) *A* (2) *B* (3) *C* (4) *G*

41. When it is noon at location *E*, what time of day will it be at location *D*? (1) morning (2) noon (3) afternoon (4) night

42. At which two locations could the sun be directly overhead at local noon sometime during the same 24-hour period? (1) *B* and *C* (2) *C* and *E* (3) *D* and *F* (4) *E* and *G*

43. The distance between locations *C* and *B* is 3000 kilometers. When the sun is directly overhead at location *C*, what other measurement would be necessary to calculate the earth's circumference? (1) the distance from location *C* to the equator (2) the angle of a shadow cast by a vertical pole at *B* (3) the distance from *C* to *F* (4) the time of day at location *A*

44. The latitude of position *G* is 23½° S. During which months would the sun's vertical ray be moving northward between locations *G* and *E*? (1) January and February (2) April and May (3) July and August (4) October and November

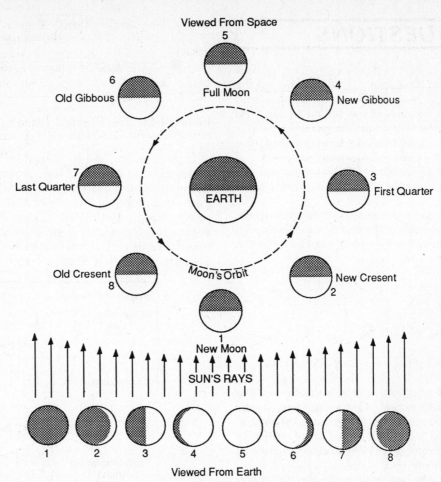

Figure 4-11. Phases of the moon. One-half of the moon's surface is always illuminated as it orbits the earth. Viewed from the earth, the moon's phases are seen as different portions of the illuminated half. When the moon is in position 1, an observer on the earth cannot see any part of the moon because the lighted half of the moon is facing the sun.

PHASES OF THE MOON

The apparent shape of the moon depends upon the changing relative positions of the earth, the sun, and the moon. As the moon completes one revolution around the earth each month (about 30 days), the growing and shrinking lighted area makes the moon appear to change in shape. When the moon and the sun are on the same side of the earth, the dark side of the moon faces the earth, and the illuminated side of the moon is not visible from the earth. This is the new moon phase. See Figure 4-11. When the moon's position is opposite the sun, a fully lighted moon, the full moon, is seen. And if the positions of the moon and the sun are 90° apart, half of the moon is lighted and half is in shadow (the quarter moon). Apparent changes in the shape of the moon, caused by light and shadow, are called the phases of the moon.

When the sun and the moon are on opposite sides of the earth, you might think that the moon would move into the earth's shadow. When the moon and the sun are on the same side of the

earth, you might think that the earth would pass through the shadow of the moon. These events do occasionally happen and are known as **eclipses** of the sun and the moon. Eclipses are rare, however, for the path of the moon's orbit is inclined about five degrees to the plane of the earth's orbit. See Figure 4-12. Therefore, the moon is usually above or below the plane of the earth's orbit when it passes in front of the sun or behind the earth.

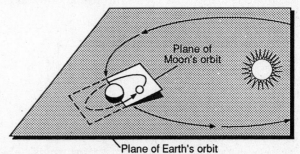
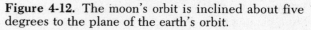

Figure 4-12. The moon's orbit is inclined about five degrees to the plane of the earth's orbit.

45. Which motion causes the moon to show phases when viewed from the earth? (1) the rotation of the moon on its axis (2) the revolution of the moon around the earth (3) the rotation of the sun on its axis (4) the revolution of the sun around the moon

46. As viewed from the earth, the moon's phases have shown which type of changes over the past 50 years? (1) noncyclic and predictable (2) noncyclic and unpredictable (3) cyclic and predictable (4) cyclic and unpredictable

47. The diagrams below represent photographs of the moon taken from earth at different times. Which photograph was taken when the moon was closest to the earth?

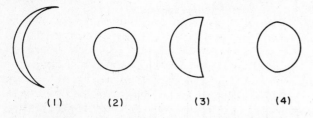

48. Which is the best indication that the moon's distance from the earth varies? (1) the apparent change in the shape of the moon (2) the apparent change in the diameter of the moon (3) the apparent change in the altitude of the moon (4) the apparent change in the color of the moon

49. Which diagram best represents the full-moon phase of the moon as seen from the earth?

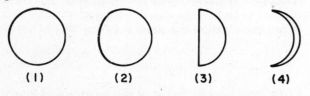

THE GEOMETRY OF ORBITS

The orbits of the planets that revolve around the sun look like flattened circles. The exact shape of an orbit, however, is an ellipse. An **ellipse** is defined by two fixed points called the foci (singular: **focus**) that lie on either side of the center of the *major axis*, a line through the widest part of an ellipse. See Figure 4-13. The orbits of the planets are ellipses with the sun at one focus. See Figure 4-14.

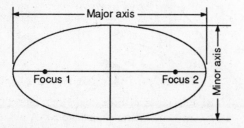

Figure 4-13. The major axis of an ellipse is a straight line passing through the two foci.

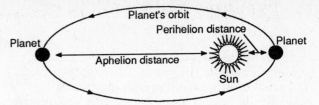

Figure 4-14. The elliptical shape of a planet's orbit with the sun at one focus. (Not to scale.)

If the two foci are located near the ends of the major axis, an ellipse is long and narrow, like the paths of many comets. At its most extreme elongation, an ellipse becomes a line. As the foci move closer together, the shape of an ellipse becomes more circular. A circle is a special kind of an ellipse in which the two foci come together at a single point. See Figure 4-15.

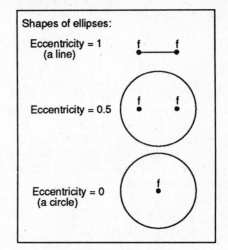

Figure 4-15. Shapes of ellipses.

You will find in the *Earth Science Reference Tables* the following formula that can be used to calculate the **eccentricity** (elongation) of an ellipse.

$$\text{eccentricity} = \frac{\text{distance between the foci}}{\text{length of the major axis}}$$

$$e = \frac{d}{L}$$

Sample Problem

Find the eccentricity of the ellipse in Figure 4-16. (The dots show the locations of the two foci. You will need a centimeter scale to measure the ellipse.)

Solution:

$$e = \frac{d}{L}$$

$$e = \frac{4 \text{ cm}}{5 \text{ cm}}$$

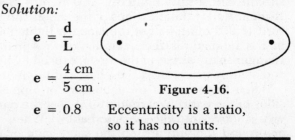

Figure 4-16.

$e = 0.8$ Eccentricity is a ratio, so it has no units.

KEPLER'S THREE LAWS OF MOTION

In 1609, the German astronomer Johannes Kepler formulated three laws to characterize the path, or **orbit**, of any satellite around its primary. (A **satellite** is an object that moves elliptically around another object, and the object that lies along the major axis of the ellipse is known as the **primary**.)

First Law.
The orbits of the planets are ellipses with the sun located at one focus of the ellipse. The other focus is located at a point in empty space.

Second Law.
A line between a planet and the sun sweeps over equal areas in space in equal periods of time. For example, in Figure 4-17, area A, which is short and wide, is equal to area B, which is long and narrow.

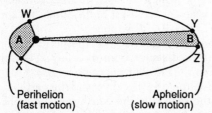

Perihelion (fast motion) **Aphelion** (slow motion)

Figure 4-17. Kepler's second law explains why a satellite's orbital velocity varies. Arc A and arc B show the motion of a satellite over equal periods of time. Distance wx is greater than distance yz. Areas A and B are equal. In equal time periods, a line between the satellite and its primary sweeps out equal areas.

While the areas within the orbit are equal, the distances along the path of the orbit are not equal. (The distance between w and x is greater than the distance between y and z.) In other words, a planet covers unequal distances in its orbit in equal periods of time; the **orbital speed** of a planet changes. When a planet is closest to the sun (**perihelion**), it moves fastest. When a planet is farthest from the sun (**aphelion**), it moves slowest.

Third Law.
The time it takes for a planet to orbit the sun is related to the average distance of that planet from the sun. The outer planets take longer to orbit the sun for two reasons: They have longer orbits through which to travel, *and* they also move slower in their orbits.

An exact mathematical statement of Kepler's third law holds that the square of the orbital period of a satellite (T^2) is proportional to the cube of the average distance from its primary (R^3). In mathematical terms,

$$T^2 \propto R^3$$

The above three laws describe the motions of any satellites in space, including the planets and their moons.

GRAVITY

The *law of universal gravitation* states that there is a force of attraction, F_g, between any two masses, m_1 and m_2. It is the force that holds all satellites in their orbits. The force of attraction (F_g) between two objects is directly proportional to the product of their masses (m_1m_2) and inversely proportional to the square of the distance between the centers of their masses (d^2). Mathematically,

$$F_g \propto \frac{m_1m_2}{d^2}$$

or

$$F_g = G\,\frac{m_1m_2}{d^2}$$

where G is the gravitational constant, which changes the proportion ($\propto$) into an equation ($=$).

The law of gravitation explains why the speed of a planet in its orbit around the sun changes. At perihelion, when the planet is closest to the sun, it moves faster because the gravitational force is greater at a closer distance. As the force increases, the acceleration (and, therefore, speed) increases. Recall that force is proportional to mass times acceleration, $F = ma$. Since the mass does not change, an increase in F would mean an increase in a. At aphelion, the distance is greater and the force is weaker; therefore, the acceleration of the planet's motion is reduced.

Example: If the distance between two objects is increased to three times its original value, what happens to the gravitational force between them?

Answer: The gravitational attraction varies as the inverse square of the distance. The distance ratio is 3 to 1. The square of 3 is 9, so the inverse square of 3 is $\frac{1}{9}$. Therefore the gravity becomes $\frac{1}{9}$ as great.

Example: How is the gravity between two objects affected by moving them from 10 m apart to 5 m apart (measured center to center)?

Answer: The distance ratio is $\frac{1}{2}$ since the distance is cut in half. The inverse square of $\frac{1}{2}$ is 4, so the gravity increases to 4 times the original amount.

Example: What would happen to the force of gravity between two objects if the mass of just one of them was doubled?

Answer: Gravity varies proportionally to the mass of either object. If the mass of one object is doubled, the gravitational attraction between them is also doubled.

Kinetic Energy and Potential Energy of the Planets.
A planet in orbit around the sun also goes through a transformation of energy because its orbit is elliptical. When it is closest to the sun, a planet moves fastest and has the most

kinetic energy. As it moves away from the sun, a planet's kinetic energy is reduced, and its *potential energy* increases. But the total amount of energy (potential plus kinetic) remains the same, even though there is a constant change back and forth from potential to kinetic energy all around the orbit. The total energy of the system is conserved. See Figure 4-18.

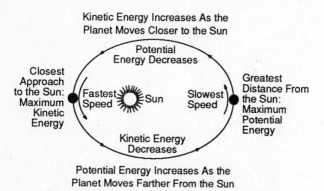

Figure 4-18. A planet orbits the sun.

The Changing Length of the Day.

Due to the changing speed of the earth in its orbit, the time from *solar noon* of one day (when the sun is at its highest point in the sky) to solar noon of the next day is seldom exactly 24 hours. As the earth moves in its orbit, it may have to spin a little more or less than 360° to return to the position at which the sun is at its highest point in the sky. See Figure 4-19. For example, in winter (at perihelion in early Jan.), when the earth moves the fastest in its orbit, the time from noon of one day to noon of the next day is more than 24 hours (by about 28 seconds). Our clocks are set to an average length of the day, or the *mean solar day*.

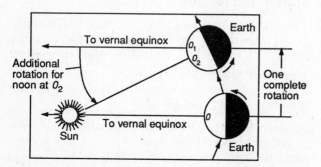

Figure 4-19. Length of apparent solar day. For an observer at O, the sun is directly overhead and it is noon. After the earth has made a complete rotation, the observer is at O_1. But the sun is not overhead until the observer arrives at O_2. The earth must rotate an additional amount to bring the observer in line with the sun again, when it is noon. The interval of time from O through O_1 to O_2 is one solar day.

50. When does local solar noon always occur for an observer in New York State? (1) when the clock reads 12 noon (2) when the sun reaches its maximum altitude (3) when the sun is directly overhead (4) when the sun is on the prime meridian

51. A sundial measures time based upon the position of the sun in the sky. This time is called (1) apparent solar time (2) standard time (3) Greenwich time (4) mean time

52. What is the relationship between apparent solar time and mean solar time? (1) Apparent solar time is always ahead of mean solar time by a constant amount. (2) Apparent solar time is always behind mean solar time by a constant amount. (3) The difference between apparent solar time and mean solar time varies with the seasons. (4) There is no difference between apparent solar time and mean solar time.

53. During which season in the Northern Hemisphere is the earth closest to the sun? (1) spring (2) summer (3) fall (4) winter

54. Who first suggested that the period of a planet is related to its distance from the sun? (1) Copernicus (2) Galileo (3) Kepler (4) Newton

55. When the orbital velocity of the earth is greatest, what is the season in the Northern Hemisphere? (1) spring (2) summer (3) fall (4) winter

56. During a ten-year period, which is a noncyclic change? (1) the moon's phases as seen from the earth (2) the earth's orbital velocity around the sun (3) the apparent path of the sun as seen from the earth (4) the impact of a meteorite on the earth

57. Which planetary model allows a scientist to predict the exact positions of the planets in the night sky over many years? (1) The planets' orbits are circles in a geocentric model. (2) The planets' orbits are ellipses in a geocentric model. (3) The planets' orbits are circles in a heliocentric model. (4) The planets' orbits are ellipses in a heliocentric model.

58. Why does the angular diameter of the sun, as seen from the earth, appear to be greater during our winter than summer? (1) The earth is closer to the sun during our winter. (2) The Northern Hemisphere is inclined toward the sun during our winter. (3) The sun expands during our winter. (4) The earth is revolving around the sun faster during our winter.

59. Planet X is revolving in an elliptical orbit around a star. A graph of the star's apparent angular diameter, as viewed from planet X, is shown below.

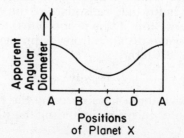

Which diagram would be the best model for showing planet X's elliptical orbit?

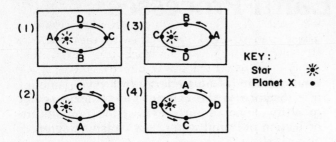

(1) Kinetic energy is increasing and potential energy is decreasing.   (2) Kinetic energy is decreasing and potential energy is increasing.   (3) Both kinetic and potential energy are decreasing.   (4) Both kinetic and potential energy are increasing.

65. The top views of four possible orbits for a planet revolving around a star are shown below. The distances from the star to each orbit are drawn to scale. In which orbit would the greatest changes in orbital velocity occur as the planet makes one revolution?

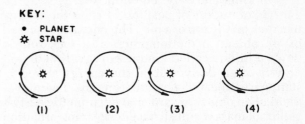

60. The earth reaches its greatest orbital speed when it is   (1) closest to the moon   (2) farthest from the moon   (3) closest to the sun   (4) farthest from the sun

61. As the distance between the earth and a satellite increases, the gravitational attraction between them will   (1) decrease   (2) increase   (3) remain the same

62. What is the exact shape of the earth's orbit around the sun?   (1) The orbit is a slightly eccentric ellipse.   (2) The orbit is a very eccentric ellipse.   (3) The orbit is an oblate spheroid.   (4) The orbit is a perfect circle.

63. The diagram below represents a planet orbiting a star. Lines are drawn from the star to four positions of the planet. The amount of time required to move between positions is indicated. Area X is equal to area Y. Why is the distance A-B greater than distance C-D?

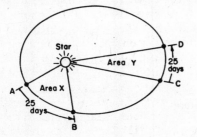

(1) The planet travels at a constant orbital velocity around the star.   (2) The planet travels the same number of degrees per hour.   (3) The length of a planet's day is the same throughout the year.   (4) The planet's orbital velocity is dependent on its distance from the star.

64. The diagram below represents a planet in orbit around a star. Which statement best describes how the planet's energy is changing as it moves from Point A to point B?

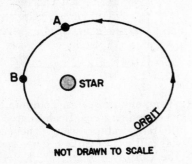

66. If the distance from earth to the sun were doubled, the gravitational attraction between the sun and earth would become   (1) one-fourth as great   (2) one-third as great   (3) twice as great   (4) four times as great

Directions (67–68): Base your answers to questions 67 and 68 on your knowledge of earth science, the *Earth Science Reference Tables,* and the diagram below. The diagram is a model of the orbit of an imaginary planet Q around a star. Points A, B, C, and D indicate four orbital positions of planet Q.

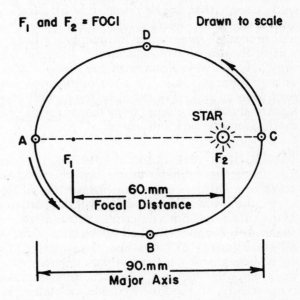

67. At which position in its orbit does planet Q have the greatest velocity?   (1) A   (2) B   (3) C   (4) D

68. What is the approximate eccentricity of planet Q's orbit? [*Use the Earth Science Reference Tables.*]   (1) 0.06   (2) 0.15   (3) 0.67   (4) 1.50

TOPIC 5 Energy in Earth Processes

ENERGY

Energy is the ability to do work. All events and processes on our planet involve energy. All forms of energy can be classified as either potential energy or kinetic energy. **Potential energy** is stored energy, or energy of position, such as the energy in a rock on the top of a hill. The energy possessed by an object in motion, such as a rock rolling down a hill, is called **kinetic energy**. Kinetic energy is often derived from the energy stored in stationary objects—potential energy. The movement of an object toward or away from the earth's center of mass results in an energy transformation from kinetic to potential or vice versa. For example, as an object rises above ground level (zero potential energy) to higher levels, its potential energy *increases* with each successive level. As the object falls, its potential energy *decreases*. During the fall, all of the object's potential energy is converted to kinetic energy. Thus, potential energy decreases as kinetic energy increases, while the total of potential and kinetic energy remains constant. As soon as the object reaches ground level, its potential energy becomes zero once again.

Thermal energy is the total potential and kinetic energy that can be released as heat from a substance or an object. Many events, changes, and processes in earth environments are the result of the transfer of heat energy (thermal energy). Heat always flows from a region of higher energy (energy source) to a region of lower energy (energy sink). For example, the earth is constantly absorbing energy from the sun while radiating energy back into space.

Measuring Kinetic Heat Energy.

When you use a thermometer to measure the **temperature** of a substance, you are measuring, in degrees, the average kinetic energy of the particles in the substance. For a description of temperature scales, see Figure 5-1. At all temperatures above **absolute zero** ($-273°$ Celsius), the particles of a substance are in constant vibrational motion—the greater the energy of vibration, the higher the temperature. In the kinetic theory of matter, kinetic heat energy is defined as the vibrational motion of particles in a substance or object.

Temperature is a measure of the average kinetic energy of the particles in a substance. It tells us how hot a substance is. Temperature, however, does not tell us the quantity of heat present. The quantity of heat represents the total kinetic and potential energy contained by all the particles of a substance. The unit used to measure the total quantity of heat energy in a given amount of substance is the calorie. One **calorie** is the quantity of heat required to raise the temperature of 1 gram of liquid water by 1 Celsius degree.

Temperature

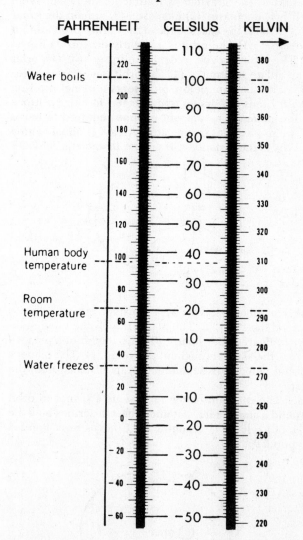

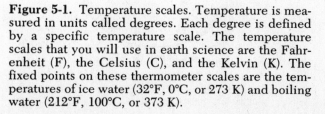

Figure 5-1. Temperature scales. Temperature is measured in units called degrees. Each degree is defined by a specific temperature scale. The temperature scales that you will use in earth science are the Fahrenheit (F), the Celsius (C), and the Kelvin (K). The fixed points on these thermometer scales are the temperatures of ice water (32°F, 0°C, or 273 K) and boiling water (212°F, 100°C, or 373 K).

40

1. Which energy transformation occurs as a rock falls freely from the top of a vertical cliff? (1) The rock's potential energy and kinetic energy decrease. (2) The rock's potential energy decreases and the rock's kinetic energy increases. (3) The rock's potential energy increases and the rock's kinetic energy decreases. (4) The rock's potential energy and kinetic energy increase.

2. During a volcanic eruption, a rock is thrown upward into the air from point *A* to point *B* as shown in the diagram below. Which graph below best represents the relationship between the height of the rock and its potential energy (*PE*) as it rises?

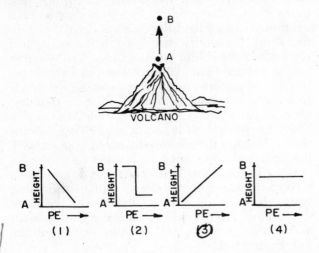

3. A rounded pebble moves from *A* through *D*, as shown. At which position does the pebble have the greatest kinetic energy?

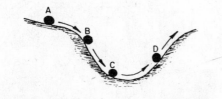

(1) *A*   (2) *B*   (3) *C*   (4) *D*

4. A temperature of 20.°C is equal to a temperature of (1) −7°F   (2) 36°F   (3) 68°F   (4) 293°F

5. A temperature of 104° Fahrenheit is equal to a temperature of (1) 40°C   (2) 72°C   (3) 104°C   (4) 136°C

6. A temperature of 80° Fahrenheit would be approximately equal to how many degrees on the Celsius scale? (1) 27   (2) 34   (3) 178   (4) 299

Specific Heat.

The quantity of heat required to raise the temperature of one gram of a substance by one Celsius degree is called its **specific heat**. Liquid water has the highest specific heat of the common substances in nature. For liquid water, the specific heat is 1. This means that adding 1 calorie of heat energy to 1 gram of liquid water will raise its temperature by 1 Celsius degree. It does not matter what the original temperature of the liquid water was. Its new temperature will be 1 Celsius degree higher.

Every substance has its own specific heat. The value of the specific heat is a property of the particular substance. Most substances have specific heats that have values less than 1. The lower the value of the specific heat, the less heat that has to be added to raise the temperature of one gram of the substance by one Celsius degree. Ice, or solid water, is an example of a substance with a specific heat less than 1. It would require less heat energy to raise the temperature of 1 gram of ice from −3°C to −2°C than it would to raise the temperature of 1 gram of liquid water from 10°C to 11°C.

Table 5-1 lists the specific heats of some other common substances. This information is available to you in the *Earth Science Reference Tables*. The unit of measure for specific heat is calories per gram degree Celsius (cal/g °C). Values for specific heat are directly proportional to the mass of the substance. The table states that it requires 0.03 calories to raise the temperature of 1 gram of lead by 1 Celsius degree. To raise the temperature of 100 grams of lead by 1 Celsius degree would require 100 times as much heat, or 3 calories.

Table 5-1. Specific Heats of Common Materials

Material	Specific Heat (cal/g °C)
Water	1.0
Ice	0.5
Water vapor	0.5
Dry air	0.24
Basalt	0.20
Granite	0.19
Iron	0.11
Copper	0.09
Lead	0.03

PROCESS OF INQUIRY SKILL

Calculating Changes in Heat Energy. The quantity of heat gained or lost by an object can be calculated with the following formula:

$$Q = m \times \Delta t \times C_p$$

where Q = Heat (calories)
  m = mass (grams)
  Δt = change in temperature (°C)
  C_p = specific heat (cal/g°-C)

The Greek letter delta (Δ) means "change in."

Sample Problems

1. Find the heat energy required to raise the temperature of 100 grams of liquid water by 5°C.
Solution:

$$Q = m \times \Delta t \times C_p$$

$$= 100 \text{ g} \times 5°C \times 1 \text{ cal/g-°C}$$

$$= 500 \text{ cal}$$

2. How much energy is released by 10 grams of iron that cools from 15°C to 12°C?
Solution:

$$Q = m \times \Delta t \times C_p$$

$$= 10 \text{ g} \times 3°C \times 0.11 \text{ cal/g-°C}$$

$$= 3.3 \text{ cal}$$

QUESTIONS

Answer questions 7 through 12 using the *Earth Science Reference Tables.*

7. If the same amount of heat energy is added to equal masses of each substance listed below, which substance would show the greatest increase in temperature?　(1) water　(2) basalt　(3) ice　(4) lead

8. What is the total amount of energy gained by a 100.-gram piece of basalt when it is heated from 20.0°C to 60.0°C?　(1) 40.0 calories　(2) 800. calories　(3) 4000 calories　(4) 6000 calories

9. How many calories of heat energy must be added to 5 grams of liquid water to change its temperature from 10°C to 30°C?　(1) 5 cal　(2) 20 cal　(3) 100 cal　(4) 150 cal

10. How many calories of heat energy must be added to 10. grams of iron to raise its temperature 10.C°?　(1) 0.11 cal　(2) 1.1 cal　(3) 11 cal　(4) 110 cal

11. Which material would require the most heat energy to increase the temperature of 1 gram of the material one Celsius degree?　(1) water　(2) ice　(3) basalt　(4) granite

12. Which material would require the greatest amount of heat energy to raise its temperature from 5°C to 10°C?　(1) 10 g of granite　(2) 10 g of dry air　(3) 10 g of lead　(4) 10 g of iron

Heat Flow.

Heat flows from a region of higher temperature (the **source**) to a region of lower temperature (the **sink**). Heat always flows from the warmer object to the cooler one. For example, the net flow of energy is from the sun to the earth, because the sun is hotter than the earth. The sun is the energy source, and the earth is the energy sink.

It is important to note that energy is not lost when heat flows. If the energy source appears to lose more energy than the energy sink gains,

some of the energy must have escaped into the environment.

The transfer of energy between two objects may be accomplished by conduction, convection, radiation, or by any combination of these processes. During **conduction**, energy is passed from molecule to molecule without the molecules themselves changing their relative positions. In conduction, energy is transferred by direct contact. Conduction works best in solids, although liquids and gases can also lose or gain energy by conduction. Metals are particularly good conductors of heat energy, because vibrational energy is quickly passed along from atom to atom in metals.

Convection involves the migration of particles, or the movement of particles, from one place to another. Convection works best in liquids and gases (fluids) that readily flow. Heat flow by convection is caused by differences in density within the fluid. Generally, the hot portion of a fluid rises while the colder portion sinks. A **convection cell** is a simple circulation pattern of a fluid motion that transfers energy. For example, when air in a room is heated by a wood stove or radiator, air near the stove is heated first, and it expands. Since the heated air is less dense, it rises toward the ceiling. In the meantime, air in contact with the cool walls becomes cooler and more dense, sinking to the floor. This cool air will then move toward the stove or radiator to replace the rising warm air. Continuous heat, supplied by the stove or radiator, will provide a steady circulation of air and distribute heat energy throughout the room. See Figure 5-2.

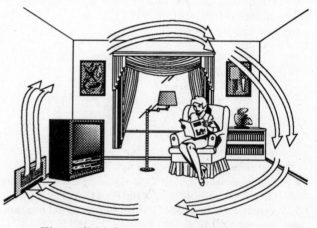

Figure 5-2. Convection currents in air.

All objects above the temperature of absolute zero contain vibrating molecules or atoms. As heat causes the atoms to vibrate, the electrical charges within the atoms also vibrate. This motion of the charges creates disturbances in the electromagnetic field that radiates from each atom. Heat **radiation** is an energy transfer by means of electromagnetic waves. Radiation is the fastest form of heat flow, and it is the only one that can penetrate a vacuum, such as deep space.

13. What method of energy transfer requires no medium for transfer? (1) conduction (2) convection (3) advection (4) radiation

14. During which process of energy exchange does cold air displace warmer air? (1) absorption (2) convection (3) conduction (4) radiation

15. Which statement is the best example of heat energy transfer by conduction? (1) Heat energy is transferred from the bottom to the top of a lake. (2) Heat energy is transferred from the surface soil to the rocks below. (3) Heat energy is transferred from the earth's surface to the upper atmosphere. (4) Heat energy is transferred from the sun to the earth.

16. Which diagram best represents the transfer of heat by convection in a liquid?

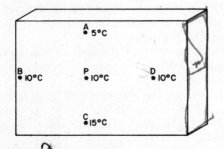

(1) (2) (3) (4)

17. The diagram below shows temperature values at various points in a solid piece of aluminum. Toward which point will heat flow from point P?

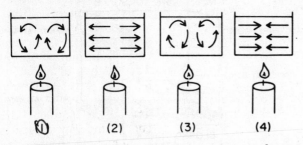

(1) A (2) B (3) C (4) D

18. Which example of heat transfer is due mainly to convection? (1) heat energy transferred by air moving from the earth's surface to the upper atmosphere (2) heat energy transferred by being reflected from a lake surface to the air above (3) heat energy transferred through a solid metal door (4) heat energy transferred from the sun to the earth

Directions (19–23): Base your answers to questions 19 through 23 on your knowledge of earth science, the *Earth Science Reference Tables*, and on the diagram and information below.

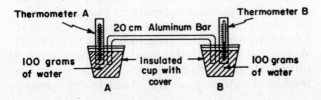

A student used the apparatus shown in the diagram above to perform an experiment. At the beginning of the experiment, the temperature of the water was 90°C in cup A and 10°C in cup B. The student took readings from the two thermometers for 14 minutes and recorded the following information:

Time (min)	Cup A Temperature (°C)	Cup B Temperature (°C)
0	90	10
2	87	10
4	84	10
6	81	11
8	78	13
10	75	15
12	72	17
14	69	19

19. Which graph best represents the relationship between time and the temperature of the water in cup A?

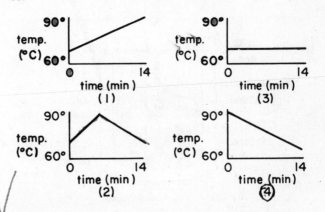

20. Which statement best explains why the amount of heat energy gained by cup B is less than the amount of heat energy lost by cup A? (1) Water heats more slowly than it cools. (2) The aluminum bar is losing some heat to the air. (3) The thermometer in cup A generated heat energy. (4) Heat energy flows from heat sinks to heat sources.

21. What was the amount of heat gained by the 100 grams of water in cup B during the 14 minutes? (1) 90 calories (2) 110 calories (3) 900 calories (4) 1,100 calories

22. The difference between the amount of heat energy lost by cup A and the amount of heat energy gained by cup B could be decreased by (1) replacing the 20-cm aluminum bar with a 10-cm aluminum bar (2) using more water in cup A (3) using metal cups instead of insulated cups (4) lowering the room temperature to 10°C

23. If all the heat lost by cup A were gained by cup B, what would be the highest possible temperature of the water in cup B? (1) 19°C (2) 40°C (3) 50°C (4) 80°C

PROCESS OF INQUIRY SKILL

Measuring Heat Flow in a Closed Energy System. A closed energy system is one in which heat energy can neither enter nor leave the system. A **calorimeter** is a closed energy system. See Figure 5-3. If two objects at different temperatures are placed together in a calorimeter, energy will flow from the object with the higher temperature to the object with the lower temperature. As a result, the temperature of the cooler object will rise, while that of the warmer object will fall. Eventually, thermal equilibrium will be established, and there will no longer be a net heat flow in either direction between the objects. If the calorimeter does not absorb or release a significant amount of energy, the law of conservation of energy requires that the energy lost by the warmer object equal the energy gained by the cooler object. The following example illustrates a method used in solving such a heat-exchange problem.

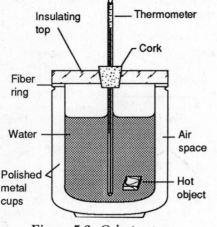

Figure 5-3. Calorimeter.

Sample Problem

A 0.2-kilogram mass of water is in a calorimeter at 15°C. A 0.1-kilogram piece of metal at 100°C is added. The final temperature of the mixture is 20°C. Calculate the specific heat of the metal. (Assume that the effect of the calorimeter is negligible.)

Solution:

$$\text{heat gain} = \text{heat loss}$$

$$\underset{\substack{\text{temp. rise} \\ \text{water}}}{m \times C_p \times \Delta t} = \underset{\substack{\text{temp. drop} \\ \text{metal}}}{m \times C_p \times \Delta t}$$

$$(0.2 \text{ kg})\left(1 \frac{\text{kcal}}{\text{kg-}°\text{C}}\right)(5 \text{ °C})$$

$$= (0.1 \text{ kg})(C_p \text{ metal})(80 \text{ °C})$$

$$C_p \text{ metal} = \frac{(0.2 \text{ kg})\left(1 \frac{\text{kcal}}{\text{kg-}°\text{C}}\right)(5 \text{ °C})}{(0.1 \text{ kg})(80°\text{C})}$$

$$C_p \text{ metal} = 0.125 \text{ kcal/kg-}°\text{C}$$

24. In a closed system, the amount of energy lost by a heat source (1) is less than the amount of energy gained by a heat sink (2) is greater than the amount of energy gained by a heat sink (3) equals the amount of energy gained by a heat sink

Directions (25–29): Base your answers to questions 25 through 29 on your knowledge of earth science, the *Earth Science Reference Tables,* and the diagram below. The diagram represents a closed energy system consisting of air and equal masses of copper, granite, and water in a perfectly insulated container. The temperatures were taken at the time the materials were placed inside the closed system.

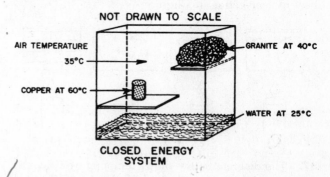

25. In this system, which material is a heat sink for another material? (1) The water is a heat sink for the air. (2) The copper is a heat sink for the granite. (3) The granite is a heat sink for the water. (4) The copper is a heat sink for the air.

26. Which material in the energy system has the highest specific heat? (1) copper (2) granite (3) dry air (4) water

27. The mass of the granite is 2000 grams. How much heat would have to be added to raise its temperature 20 C°? (1) 76 cal (2) 4000 cal (3) 5400 cal (4) 7600 cal

28. In the first day after the materials were placed in the system, the temperature of the water would probably (1) decrease (2) increase (3) remain the same

29. As time passes, the total energy in the system will (1) decrease (2) increase (3) remain the same

SOLAR RADIATION

The vast majority of energy used in earth processes can be traced back to radiation from the sun. For example, hydroelectric power, which is electricity obtained from generators at a dam or a waterfall, gets its energy from water that was evaporated, mostly from the oceans. During this process, evaporated water forms clouds that blow over land. As thunderstorms develop, rain is released from the clouds and falls back to the earth. Water is collected behind a dam and is then used to operate the turbines that generate electricity. Both evaporation and the wind in this process derived their energy from solar radiation. The only form of terrestrial energy that cannot be traced back to the sun is natural *radioactivity*, the spontaneous release of particles by a substance.

The sun radiates **electromagnetic energy** in a variety of forms of electromagnetic waves—from long-wave heat rays to short-wave radiations of ultraviolet light and X rays. The full range of this form of energy is known as the **electromagnetic spectrum**. See Figure 5-4. Most of the sun's energy that reaches the earth's surface arrives as infrared, visible, and ultraviolet light.

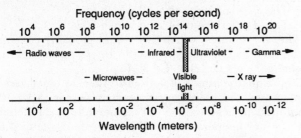

Figure 5-4. The electromagnetic spectrum.

Energy waves can be longitudinal (like sound waves) or transverse (like light waves). *Longitudinal* waves vibrate back and forth as they travel forward, like the coils of a compressed spring that suddenly are released. As a pulse of energy is transmitted along the spring, each loop of the spring vibrates along the same line as that in which the energy is moving. See Figure 5-5.

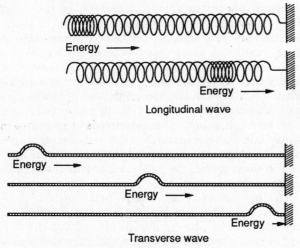

Figure 5-5. Energy waves.

Transverse waves vibrate side to side, or up and down, like waves on a rope as they travel forward. As energy pulses move along the rope, each part of the rope in turn moves up and down along a line perpendicular to the length of the rope.

Electromagnetic waves show the characteristics of transverse waves. The vibrations in one direction are the crests of the wave, and the op-posite vibrations are troughs. One **wavelength** is the distance between corresponding points on two successive crests or two successive troughs. A *cycle* consists of one crest and one trough. See Figure 5-6.

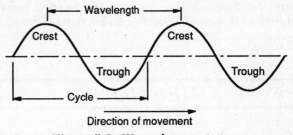

Figure 5-6. Wave characteristics.

Interaction of Visible Light With Matter.

Four interactions are possible whenever light strikes matter. When light strikes shiny surfaces, like metal or glass, it *reflects*, or bounces off, the shiny surface. Reflection is more likely when the radiation strikes the surface at a low angle. The still surface of a lake may reflect light like a mirror. If light strikes small particles suspended within a transparent medium, it will *scatter*. Light rays are randomly reflected from suspended particles, like cloud droplets. Light moving from one medium to another is often bent or *refracted*. Refraction in the atmosphere happens when light slows down as it enters the denser atmosphere near the earth's surface.

Radiation can also be *absorbed* by matter. For example, sunlight (with strong, short wavelengths) is absorbed by the surface of the earth and then reradiated back into space as infrared rays (with longer wavelengths). See Figure 5-7.

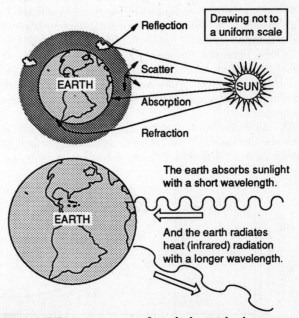

Figure 5-7. Interaction of sunlight with the atmosphere.

The ability of a surface to reflect or to absorb radiation in the form of light depends upon several factors. Rough surfaces absorb light better than smooth surfaces, and dark-colored surfaces absorb light better than light-colored surfaces. Surfaces that absorb radiation the best are also surfaces that reradiate energy the best; *a good absorber is a good radiator.* Black is the best absorber of radiant energy, and it is also the best radiator.

QUESTIONS

30. What is the major source of energy for the earth? (1) electrical storms   (2) radioactive decay of earth materials   (3) the sun   (4) thermal currents in the mantle

31. By which process does starlight travel through space?   (1) absorption   (2) conduction   (3) convection   (4) radiation

32. The various forms of electromagnetic energy are distinguished from one another by their   (1) temperature   (2) wavelengths   (3) longitudinal wave properties   (4) speed of travel

33. At which temperature will an object radiate the greatest amount of electromagnetic energy? [Refer to the *Earth Science Reference Tables.*]   (1) 0° Fahrenheit   (2) 5° Celsius   (3) 10° Fahrenheit   (4) 230° Kelvin

34. As the earth's surface absorbs solar energy and then radiates it, the wavelength of the outgoing energy will have   (1) decreased   (2) increased   (3) remained the same

35. Two identical objects are painted different colors, one black and the other white. If both objects are placed in the sunlight, the amount of energy absorbed by the black object compared to the amount absorbed by the white is   (1) less   (2) greater   (3) the same

36. How does the amount of heat energy reflected by a smooth, dark-colored concrete surface compare with the amount of heat energy reflected by a smooth, light-colored concrete surface?   (1) The dark-colored surface will reflect less heat energy.   (2) The dark-colored surface will reflect more heat energy.   (3) The dark-colored surface will reflect the same amount of heat energy.

37. The graph below represents the relationship between the intensity and wavelength of the sun's electromagnetic radiation. Which statement is best supported by the graph?

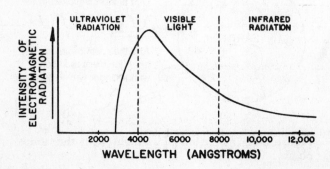

(1) The infrared radiation given off by the sun occurs at a wavelength of 2,000 angstroms.   (2) The maximum intensity of radiation given off by the sun occurs in the visible region.   (3) The infrared radiation given off by the sun has a shorter wavelength than ultraviolet radiation.   (4) The electromagnetic energy given off by the sun consists of a single wavelength.

38. Four trays, each containing sand at the same temperature but with different characteristics, were placed on a sunny windowsill. The type of sand in each tray is listed below:

Tray 1—light-colored sand which is dry
Tray 2—light-colored sand which is wet
Tray 3—dark-colored sand which is dry
Tray 4—dark-colored sand which is wet

After 30 minutes, which tray would probably contain the sand that had undergone the *greatest* temperature change?   (1) 1   (2) 2   (3) 3   (4) 4

39. Equal volumes of soil and water, at equal temperatures, are placed near a radiant heater. After 10 minutes of heating, the soil temperature is 34°C and the water temperature is 27°C. Ten minutes after the source of heat is withdrawn, the soil temperature is 32°C and the water temperature is 26°C. Which conclusion is most logical?   (1) A good reflector of heat is a good absorber of heat.   (2) A good reflector of heat is a good radiator of heat.   (3) A good absorber of heat is a good radiator of heat.   (4) A good absorber of heat is a poor radiator of heat.

STATES OF MATTER

Substances found naturally on the earth exist in three **phases** or *states of matter*. In the *solid* state, the particles (atoms or molecules) of many substances are rigidly held in a three-dimensional network known as a *crystal lattice*. Water in the solid phase is known as ice or snow. The molecules in ice are held in place by strong intermolecular bonds. Although these molecules can vibrate, they are not free to move over and around each other. The symmetrical patterns of snowflakes are caused by the regular arrangements of the molecules and their rigid bonding. When these bonds are broken, the snow will melt to become a liquid.

In the *liquid* state, water molecules are attracted to each other but not bonded rigidly in a crystal lattice. They move freely within the liquid. Unlike ice, liquid water will take the shape of the container in which it is resting. The liquid phase of water is the most abundant form of water on the earth, and it is found primarily within the earth's oceans. If enough heat energy is supplied to break the attractive forces between liquid water molecules, the liquid will change into a gas.

Water molecules in the *gaseous* state move freely through space. The shape and volume of any gas is determined by the shape and volume of its container. Water vapor is a colorless, odorless gas that makes up roughly 1% of the earth's atmosphere. If additional heat energy is added to a gas, it may change to a plasma, in which the vibrational energy is so great that electrons are no longer able to remain with a specific atom. Although plasma is not found naturally on the earth, it is the most abundant state of matter in the universe because it exists within the stars, like our sun.

Changes in Phase.

If you start with a one-gram sample of ice and gradually add heat to it, you can observe the changes in phase that occur as heat energy is added to the sample. As the temperature of the ice approaches its **melting temperature**—0°C, water molecules held in their fixed positions in the ice vibrate more and more rapidly. Heat supplied to the sample at its melting temperature does not raise the temperature of the molecules. It is used to break them loose from their positions in the solid. The heat is completely used in bringing about the change of phase before any of it can be used to raise the temperature of the newly formed liquid water. The quantity of heat required to change one gram of solid into liquid at its melting temperature is called the **heat of fusion**. The heat of fusion of ice is 80 calories per gram.

Once all of the molecules have been freed from their rigid positions in the solid, the sample will have changed completely into a liquid. When additional heat is added to the gram of liquid water, the vibrational energy of the molecules of liquid will increase. To raise the temperature of 1 gram of liquid water from 0°C to 100°C (the **boiling temperature** of water) will require 100 calories, or 1 calorie per gram per Celsius degree.

At its boiling point, the water will remain at 100° Celsius while an additional 540 calories of heat are absorbed. This additional heat is used to pull apart liquid water molecules to form water vapor, a gas. The quantity of heat required to change one gram of liquid into gas at its boiling point is called the **heat of vaporization**. The heat of vaporization of liquid water is 540 calories per gram. As in melting, the temperature did not rise during the phase change. See Figure 5-8. The amount of heat required for each change of phase is a property of the substance being heated. The heat of vaporization and the heat of fusion are called **latent** (hidden or not observable) **heat** because the heat required for these phase changes does not change the temperature of the substance.

When energy is released from matter, the matter will condense or freeze. Consider what happens as very hot water vapor loses energy. The temperature of the water vapor will decrease to 100° Celsius. At this point the water vapor begins to change into liquid water. A release of heat energy (540 calories per gram) turns the water vapor into a liquid while the temperature remains constant. This change in phase is known as **condensation**.

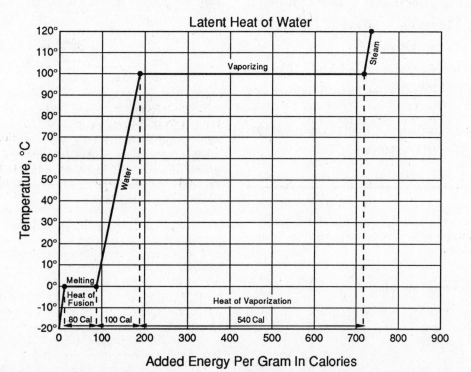

Figure 5-8. Changes of state of water. In changing to liquid water at 0°C, 1 gram of ice absorbs 80 calories (heat of fusion). In reaching the boiling point at 100°C, 1 gram of water absorbs 100 calories. In changing to vapor at 100°C, 1 gram of water absorbs 540 calories (heat of vaporization).

Energy in Earth Processes

After the water condenses, it will continue to decrease in temperature until the liquid cools to the **freezing temperature**, 0° Celsius, and starts to change into ice. The release of heat energy (80 calories per gram) turns the liquid into a solid while the temperature remains constant. Any additional release of heat energy will cool the ice to a lower temperature—below 0°C.

It is important to note that the energy needed to melt a sample is the same as the energy released when the sample freezes. This is also true of vaporization and condensation. The energy that must be added to vaporize any quantity of liquid is equal to the energy released when the same amount of vapor condenses to make a liquid.

Certain substances, like dry ice (solid carbon dioxide) undergo another type of phase change. **Sublimation** is a direct change from a solid to a gas or from a gas to a solid without the liquid phase occurring.

The following examples show you how to calculate the latent heat of water during a phase change.

Sample Problems

1. How much energy is needed to change 5 grams of ice at 0°C into water at 0°C?

Solution:

Heat (calories) = m (mass) × heat of fusion

$$H = 5 \text{ g} \times 80 \text{ cal/g}$$

$$= 400 \text{ cal}$$

2. How much energy is released when 10 grams of water vapor condenses?

Solution:

Heat (calories) = m (mass) × heat of vaporization

$$H = 10 \text{ g} \times 540 \text{ cal/g}$$

$$= 5,400 \text{ cal}$$

QUESTIONS

40. As heat energy is added to an open container of boiling water, the temperature of the boiling water will (1) decrease (2) increase (3) remain the same

41. An observer noted that even though the ice on a pond was melting, the temperature of the liquid water in the pond remained constant until all the ice melted. Which statement best explains this observation? (1) The angle of insolation is not great enough. (2) The daylight hours are longer than the nighttime hours. (3) The nighttime hours are longer than the daylight hours. (4) The heat energy is being used to change the solid ice to liquid water.

42. Latent heat of vaporization is released when (1) ice melts (2) water freezes (3) water evaporates (4) water vapor condenses

43. If equal masses of water in various phases (states) are compared, which phase will contain the greatest amount of stored energy (latent heat)? (1) solid ice (2) liquid water (3) water vapor

44. How many calories of latent heat would have to be absorbed by 100 grams of liquid water at 100°C in order to change all of the liquid water into water vapor at 100°C? (1) 100 cal (2) 1000 cal (3) 8000 cal (4) 54,000 cal

45. A sample of water undergoes the phase changes from ice to vapor and back to ice as shown in the model below. During which phase change does the sample gain the greatest amount of energy?

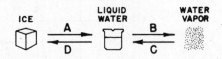

(1) A (2) B (3) C (4) D

46. Based on the *Earth Science Reference Tables*, what is the total amount of energy required to melt 100 grams of ice at 0°C to liquid water at 0°C? (1) 5400 cal (2) 8000 cal (3) 54,000 cal (4) 80,000 cal

TOPIC 6 Insolation and the Earth's Surface

INSOLATION

The earth receives nearly all of its energy from the sun. The sun's electromagnetic energy that reaches the earth is called **insolation** (INcoming SOLar radiATION). The intensity (strength) of insolation depends upon several factors, such as the angle of insolation, the duration of insolation, and the type of surface the insolation strikes.

Angle of Insolation.

The **angle of insolation** is a measure of how high the sun is in the sky. As the sun rises and sets, the angle of insolation changes constantly. It is measured from the horizon up to the position of the sun. The noon sun has the greatest angle of insolation, and, therefore, noon has the greatest intensity of insolation per unit area. In the morning and in the afternoon, when the sun is lower in the sky, the sunlight is less direct and less intense. See Figure 6-1.

The angle of insolation at a given place also changes seasonally. In the Northern Hemisphere, the lowest angle of insolation is reached at the winter solstice (about Dec. 21), the intermediate angle at the vernal and autumnal equinoxes (about March 21 and Sept. 23), and the highest angle at the summer solstice (about June 21).

Because the earth is spherical, each latitude on the earth has a different angle of insolation, as shown in Figure 6-2. As the seasons progress, only one latitude within the tropics ($23\frac{1}{2}°$ N to $23\frac{1}{2}°$ S) will receive the vertical ray at noon each day. As shown in Figure 6-2, the vertical ray strikes the earth's surface at an angle of 90°. Sunlight is most intense at this angle because the sun's energy is concentrated in the smallest possible area. At all other latitudes, slanting rays of sunlight strike the earth's surface at acute angles and are weaker in intensity, distributing their energy over a larger area than the vertical ray. See Figure 6-2. For all locations north of the Tropic of Cancer ($23\frac{1}{2}°$ N), the most direct and most intense insolation occurs at noon on the summer solstice (about June 21).

The vertical ray, which always strikes the earth somewhere in the tropics ($23\frac{1}{2}°$ N to $23\frac{1}{2}°$ S), accounts for high average temperatures in the tropical zone. The low angle (tangential) rays that strike the earth in the Arctic zone ($66\frac{1}{2}°$ N to 90° N) and in the Antarctic zone ($66\frac{1}{2}°$ S to 90° S) account for the low average temperatures in these zones.

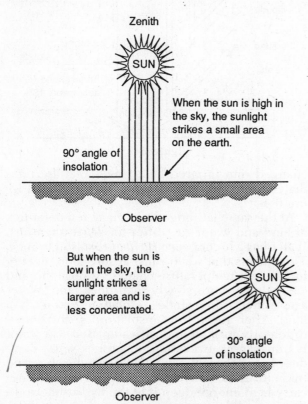

Figure 6-1. Angle of insolation and intensity of insolation. The lower the sun is in the sky, the less concentrated the sunlight. This is because the sun's rays are spread out over a larger area when the angle of insolation is low. When the sun is near the horizon, the sunlight must travel a greater distance through the atmosphere. This also reduces the strength of sunlight when the angle of insolation is low.

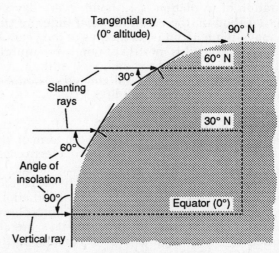

Figure 6-2. Angles of insolation at different latitudes on equinox. As the degree of latitude increases the angle of insolation and the intensity of insolation decrease. (If the vertical ray is at the equator, it is either the vernal or autumnal equinox.)

Table 6-1. Insolation and Latitude

Location	Latitude	Date	Sun's Noon Elevation	Hours of Daylight
North Pole	90° N	March Equinox	0°	24*
		June Solstice	23½°	24
		September Equinox	0°	24*
		December Solstice	—	0
New York City	41° N	March Equinox	49°	12
		June Solstice	72½°	15
		September Equinox	49°	12
		December Solstice	25½°	9
Equator	0°	March Equinox	90°	12
		June Solstice	66½°	12
		September Equinox	90°	12
		December Solstice	66½°	12
South Pole	90° S	March Equinox	0°	24*
		June Solstice	—	0
		September Equinox	0°	24*
		December Solstice	23½°	24

* On these dates, the sun circles along the horizon at both poles.

Duration of Insolation.

The **duration of insolation** is the length of time (from sunrise to sunset), or daylight period, that the sun appears in the sky. A section of the earth's surface receives the most heat energy when the sun is highest in the sky and when the duration of insolation is the greatest. Generally, as the angle of insolation and the duration of insolation increase, temperatures at the earth's surface increase.

In the Northern Hemisphere, the greatest duration of insolation occurs at the summer solstice. The further north you go, the longer the daylight period at this time. For example, at the end of June, the sun is in the sky for the whole day (24 hours) at locations north of the Arctic Circle. At locations south of the Arctic Circle, the duration of sunlight is less at this time. At the equator, the duration of insolation is 12 hours every day. At any location on the earth, the total time the sun is above the horizon is six months of the year. At the North Pole, this means six months of sunlight followed by six months of darkness. At the Equator, it means 12 hours of sunlight and 12 hours of darkness each day. See Table 6-1.

Absorption of Insolation.

Most of the sun's energy reaches the earth in the form of visible light, because light is the kind of electromagnetic radiation that can best penetrate the earth's protective atmosphere. High-energy radiations, like X rays and gamma rays, are absorbed by ozone and other gases in the upper atmosphere. Long-wave radiations, like *infrared* rays, are absorbed by water vapor and carbon dioxide in the atmosphere. Visible light wavelengths, however, readily penetrate the earth's atmosphere. See Figure 6-3. Upon reaching the surface of the earth, visible light waves are absorbed, scattered, or reflected. Some of the absorbed energy is

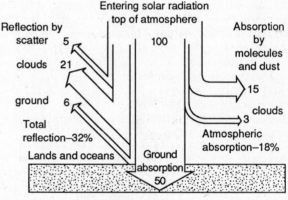

Figure 6-3.

changed into infrared heat waves that are reradiated back into the atmosphere at night. See Figure 6-4.

At the same latitude, the average temperatures of land and water can differ for several reasons. Water has a higher *specific heat* than soil or rock. This means that water must absorb more energy for a given temperature change; it heats up and cools down more slowly than does land. Water also reflects low-angle insolation better than land. After absorption, insolation is distributed differently in land and in water. Because water is transparent, insolation penetrates water more deeply and more quickly than it can be absorbed by land. Also, convection currents in the water carry heat energy deep into the hydrosphere. In the ground, heat energy can travel only by conduction. Thus, the same amount of insolation travels through a greater volume of water than land. The result is that land heats up faster and cools down faster than water.

Some of the insolation that is absorbed by the earth heats the earth to a higher temperature, but most of it is converted into latent potential en-

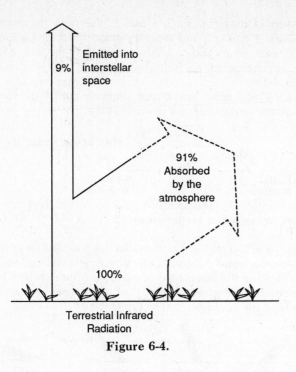

Figure 6-4.

ergy. During the melting of ice and snow or evaporation of seawater, a great deal of energy is used for a change of state. Each gram of water that evaporates absorbs 540 calories of energy. The newly formed water vapor carries potential energy into the atmosphere. It is the most important reservoir of potential energy in the atmosphere.

Reflection of Insolation.
The presence of clouds in the atmosphere is one factor that reduces the heating effects of insolation. Clouds reflect from 30–60% of the light falling on them. They can absorb another 5–20%. In addition to reflection and absorption from clouds, some incoming solar radiation is reflected from the surface of the earth. The lower the angle of insolation, the greater the reflection of solar rays. More reflection also occurs when the land is light in color or covered by snow or ice.

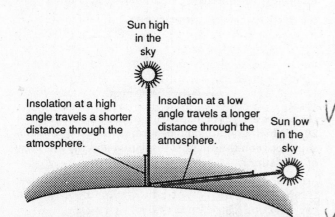

Figure 6-5. Insolation at a high angle travels a short distance through the atmosphere. Insolation at a low angle travels a long distance through the atmosphere.

Insolation and the Earth's Surface

While the North and South Poles receive the same total duration of insolation as the equator, the temperatures are much lower at the poles. There are three reasons for this. First, the snow at the poles reflects much of the insolation back into space. Second, the sun is always low in the sky, so the sunlight is more spread out and less concentrated than it is at the equator. Finally, when the sun is low in the sky the sunlight must travel a greater distance through the earth's atmosphere. Within the atmosphere, much of the insolation is reflected, refracted, or absorbed. Therefore, radiation of reduced strength reaches the ground at the poles. See Figure 6-5.

Scattering of Insolation.
The random reflection of insolation off rough surfaces is called *scattering*. Tiny particles of airborne solids and liquids, such as dust, pollen, pollutants, and water droplets are called **aerosols**. By scattering insolation, aerosols reduce its intensity. Some aerosols, like certain hairsprays and room deodorizers, however, contain fluorocarbons which participate in chemical reactions that destroy the ozone layer of the atmosphere. As a result, *ultraviolet* rays gain greater access to the surface of the earth. People who are exposed to greater amounts of ultraviolet rays face an increased risk of developing skin cancer.

QUESTIONS

1. Electromagnetic energy that reaches the earth from the sun is called (1) insolation (2) conduction (3) specific heat (4) terrestrial radiation
2. As the amount of reflection caused by dust particles in the atmosphere increases, the amount of insolation reaching the earth's surface (1) decreases (2) increases (3) remains the same
3. Which graph best illustrates the relationship between the altitude of the noontime sun and the insolation?

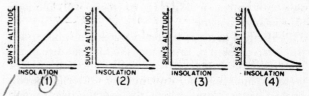

4. In New York State, ski trails that are constructed on a north-facing slope usually retain their snow later in the spring than those on a south-facing slope. This is chiefly because (1) the northern slope is protected from the prevailing south winds (2) the southern slope has darker soil (3) snowfall is greater on the northern slope (4) the rays of the sun are more direct on southern slopes
5. As the number of degrees of latitude from the equator increases, the yearly average temperature generally (1) decreases (2) increases (3) remains the same

6. Compared to polar areas, why are equatorial areas of equal size heated much more intensely by the sun? (1) The sun's rays are more nearly perpendicular at the equator than at the poles. (2) The equatorial areas contain more water than the polar areas do. (3) More hours of daylight occur at the equator than at the poles. (4) The equatorial areas are nearer to the sun than the polar areas are.

7. The diagrams below represent flat horizontal surfaces at four different locations on the earth. The arrows represent the sun's rays striking each location at noon on March 21. Which location is farthest from the equator?

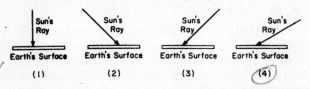

8. Which latitude on the earth would receive the highest average yearly insolation per square meter of surface if the atmosphere were completely transparent at all locations? (1) 90° N. (2) 23½° N. (3) 0° (4) 23½° S.

9. In the diagram below, a vertical post casts shadows A, B, C, and D at four different times during the day. Which shadow was cast when this location was receiving the greatest intensity of insolation?

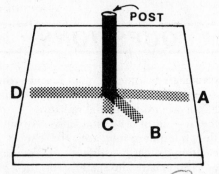

(1) shadow A (2) shadow B (3) shadow C (4) shadow D

10. As the angle between the sun's rays and the earth's surface approaches 90°, the amount of *insolation* per unit area will (1) decrease (2) increase (3) remain the same

11. If equal areas of land and water are subjected to the same amount of insolation, the temperature of the land will rise more quickly than the temperature of the water. Which does *not* explain this? (1) The specific heat of water is greater than the specific heat of most earth materials. (2) Some insolation is converted into potential energy by evaporation of water. (3) The insolation penetrates deeper in water than in most earth materials. (4) The density of most earth materials is greater than that of water.

12. For which date and location will the longest duration of insolation normally occur? (1) June 21, at 60° N. (2) June 21, at 23½° N. (3) December 21, at 60° N. (4) December 21, at 23½° N.

13. In New York State, summer is warmer than winter because in summer, New York State has (1) more hours of daylight and is closer to the sun (2) more hours of daylight and receives more direct insolation (3) fewer hours of daylight but is closer to the sun (4) fewer hours of daylight but receives more direct insolation

14. The diagram below represents the path of the sun across the sky during a particular day.

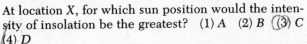

At location X, for which sun position would the intensity of insolation be the greatest? (1) A (2) B (3) C (4) D

15. Each of the sunbeams in the diagrams below contains the same amount of electromagnetic energy and is striking the same type of surface. Which surface is receiving the greatest amount of energy per unit area where the sunbeam strikes the surface?

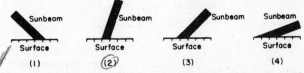

16. The addition of dust to the atmosphere by volcanic eruptions will most likely increase the amount of (1) radiant energy reflected by the atmosphere (2) insolation absorbed at the earth's surface (3) solar radiation absorbed by the oceans (4) ultraviolet rays striking the earth's surface

17. Which statement best describes how the insolation changes in New York State from May 21 through June 21? (1) Intensity and duration both decrease. (2) Intensity and duration both increase. (3) Intensity decreases and duration increases. (4) Intensity increases and duration decreases.

18. In New York State, the longest period of insolation occurs on or about (1) January 21 (2) March 21 (3) June 21 (4) August 21

19. The diagram represents a ray of sunlight striking the earth at point P. Angle A is the angle between the ray and the surface of the earth at point P. As angle A increases, the intensity of insolation at point P will

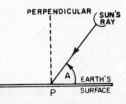

(1) decrease (2) increase (3) remain the same

20. Which graph below best represents the relationship between the angle of insolation and the intensity of insolation?

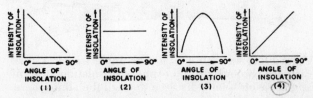

TERRESTRIAL RADIATION

During terrestrial radiation, energy waves emitted from the surface of the earth are longer in wavelength than energy waves in the range of visible light emitted from the sun. The longer infrared heat waves radiated by the earth are absorbed by gases like carbon dioxide and water vapor and remain trapped in the atmosphere. See Figure 6-6A. This process is called the **greenhouse effect** because the glass of a greenhouse traps heat in a similar way.

In a greenhouse, the short wavelengths of energy from the sun (visible light) pass through the glass and into the greenhouse. When the light strikes objects inside the greenhouse, it is absorbed; the energy is then given off as long-wave infrared rays, or heat. As the objects reradiate heat outward, the glass reflects the longer infrared heat waves back into the greenhouse where they heat the air. Thus, the temperature inside a greenhouse is usually warmer than the temperature of the air outside. See Figure 6-6B.

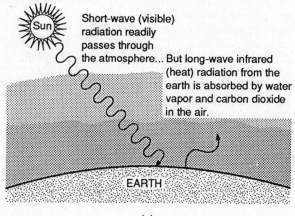

Short-wave (visible) radiation readily passes through the atmosphere... But long-wave infrared (heat) radiation from the earth is absorbed by water vapor and carbon dioxide in the air.

EARTH

(a)

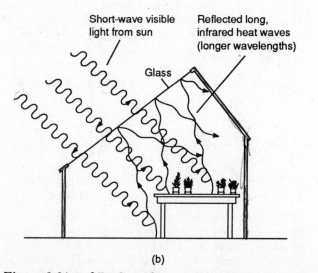

Short-wave visible light from sun — Reflected long, infrared heat waves (longer wavelengths)

Glass

(b)

Figure 6-6A and B. Greenhouse effect. Short waves of light are transmitted, but longer waves of heat are reflected back into the greenhouse.

In the atmosphere, the greenhouse effect occurs all over the earth's surface and makes the earth a comfortable place to live. However, some scientists believe that the greenhouse effect may increase to a dangerous level in the future. As a result of industrial processes and deforestation, scientists believe that the amount of carbon dioxide in the air will increase to very high levels. This carbon dioxide gas will, in turn, trap more and more heat rays and cause critical changes in climate.

The Insolation-Temperature Lag.

A lag exists between the time of greatest intensity of insolation and the time of highest air temperature. Why? Because insolation energy is first absorbed by the earth's surface and then reradiated as heat energy that warms the air. Consider a 24-hour period. At sunrise, the earth is cool, but it becomes warmer as it absorbs solar radiation throughout the morning hours. At noon, the incoming radiation reaches a maximum. For the next two or three hours, the earth continues to absorb more energy than it radiates. Thus, the air temperature continues to rise. By mid-afternoon, the earth reaches an equilibrium between the incoming energy and the outgoing radiation. At this point, the highest air temperature is reached. After this, the earth radiates more energy than it receives from the sun and the net loss of energy causes the earth to cool off. This cooling period continues until slightly after sunrise the next morning. See Figure 6-7. The time delay between maximum or minimum insolation and maximum or minimum air temperature is known as the **insolation-temperature lag**.

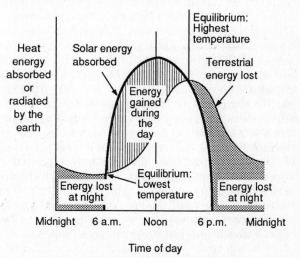

Heat energy absorbed or radiated by the earth — Solar energy absorbed — Equilibrium: Highest temperature — Energy gained during the day — Terrestrial energy lost — Energy lost at night — Equilibrium: Lowest temperature — Energy lost at night

Midnight — 6 a.m. — Noon — 6 p.m. — Midnight

Time of day

Figure 6-7. The daily energy balance.

Seasonal variations in air temperatures also occur. As with the daily cycle, average monthly temperatures depend upon the balance between insolation and terrestrial radiation. The highest average monthly temperatures do not come in June when the noon sun is the highest in the sky in the Northern Hemisphere and when the hours

Insolation and the Earth's Surface

of sunlight are the longest. The maximum temperatures lag behind the insolation cycle by about a month. This is because the earth continues to absorb more energy than it radiates to space for about a month after the summer solstice. Maximum and minimum monthly temperatures occur when there is a **radiative balance** between insolation and terrestrial radiation. See Figure 6-8.

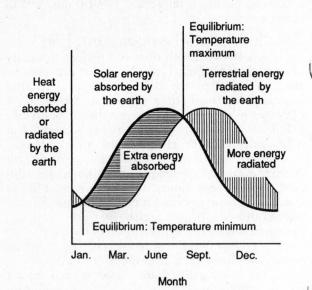

Figure 6-8. The annual energy balance.

Long-Range Radiative Balance.

Seasonal changes in air temperature are a result of insolation and terrestrial radiation being out of balance. When the earth receives more energy than it radiates into space, the earth's temperature will rise, as it does in the spring and summer. If the terrestrial radiation is greater, however, the temperature of the earth will go down. Measurements of the temperature of the earth show that the energy gain and loss of the earth are roughly equal over a period of 10 years, meaning that the earth's temperature is relatively stable from decade to decade. However, evidence shows that the earth's temperature has been out of balance for periods of thousands of years. An important result of this long-range imbalance between insolation and terrestrial radiation has been the periodic advances of the continental glaciers, at least four times in the past million years. These cold glacial climates are followed by warmer periods in cycles of about one hundred thousand years.

QUESTIONS

21. What happens to radiant energy that strikes the earth's crust?   (1) It is completely absorbed.   (2) It is completely reflected.   (3) It is partially absorbed and partially reflected.   (4) It is changed from long wavelengths to short wavelengths.

22. In New York State, when do the highest air temperatures for the year usually occur?   (1) a few weeks before maximum insolation is received   (2) a few weeks after maximum insolation is received   (3) at the time that maximum insolation is received

23. During which month does the *minimum* duration of insolation occur in New York State?   (1) February   (2) July   (3) September   (4) December

24. In New York State on a summer day, at which time and location would the highest air temperature most likely occur?   (1) 10 A.M. at a beach   (2) 2 P.M. at a plowed field   (3) noon on the ocean   (4) noon within a forest

25. Adding more carbon dioxide to the atmosphere increases the amount of   (1) radiant energy reflected by the earth   (2) radiation from the sun absorbed by the oceans   (3) radiation from the earth absorbed by the atmosphere   (4) ultraviolet rays striking the earth

26. In which region of the electromagnetic spectrum is most of the outgoing radiation from the earth?   (1) infrared   (2) visible   (3) ultraviolet   (4) X ray

27. Some scientists have theorized that an increased concentration of carbon dioxide will cause an increase in the worldwide atmospheric temperature. This theory is based on the fact that carbon dioxide is   (1) a good absorber of infrared radiation   (2) used by plants in photosynthesis   (3) necessary for precipitation to occur   (4) produced by the respiration of plants and animals

28. Electromagnetic energy that is being given off by the surface of the earth is called   (1) convection   (2) insolation   (3) specific heat   (4) terrestrial radiation

29. What is the usual cause of the drop in temperature that occurs between sunset and sunrise at most New York State locations?   (1) strong winds   (2) ground radiation   (3) cloud formation   (4) heavy precipitation

30. Which model best represents how a greenhouse remains warm as a result of insolation from the sun?

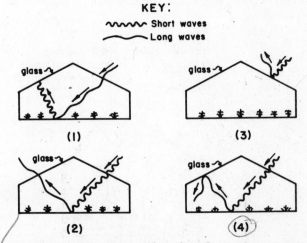

31. Some scientists predict that the increase in atmospheric carbon dioxide will cause a worldwide increase in temperature. Which could result from this increase in temperature?   (1) Continental drift will increase.   (2) Isotherms will shift toward the equator.   (3) Additional landmasses will form.   (4) Icecaps at the earth's poles will melt.

32. Between the years 1850 and 1900, records indicate that the earth's mean surface temperature showed little variation. This would support the inference that (1) the earth was in radiative balance (2) another ice age was approaching (3) more energy was coming in than was going out from the earth (4) the sun was emitting more energy

Directions (33–37): Base your answers to questions 33 through 37 on the information on the graph below and on your knowledge of earth science. The graph represents variations in mean surface air temperature, radiant energy absorbed from the sun, and radiant energy lost by the earth during the same one-year period at a location in New York State.

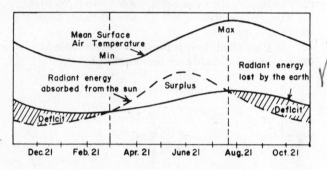

33. During which month is the temperature highest? (1) Aug. (2) Dec. (3) Feb. (4) June

34. Compared to the time of minimum temperature, the time of minimum energy absorbed from the sun was (1) the same (2) 3 months earlier (3) 4 months later (4) 3 months later

35. On this graph either a minimum or maximum mean surface air temperature occurred at the same time that (1) a radiative balance had been reached (2) the mean energy absorbed from the sun was increasing (3) the surplus and deficit were both at maximum (4) the mean energy radiated by the earth was unchanged

36. The line on the graph that represents the mean surface air temperature is most similar to the kind of line that would be plotted to represent actual air temperature changes occurring in Albany, New York, for a period of (1) one hour (2) one day (3) one week (4) one month

37. The graph indicates that the maximum mean surface air temperature occurs about a month after the time when maximum radiant energy is absorbed from the sun. Which is the most probable cause for this time difference? (1) Energy from the sun controls the earth's surface temperature which in turn controls the surface air temperature. (2) At the time when the radiant energy absorption is greatest, the earth is not at the point where it is closest to the sun. (3) The radiant energy lost by the earth has not yet reached a maximum at that time. (4) As there is an increase in the amount of radiant energy absorbed, there is a comparable increase in the amount of radiant energy lost.

Directions (38–42): Base your answers to questions 38 through 42 on your knowledge of earth science, the

Earth Science Reference Tables, and the diagram below. The diagram represents a hot-air solar collector consisting of a wooden box frame, an absorber plate, a glass cover, and insulation.

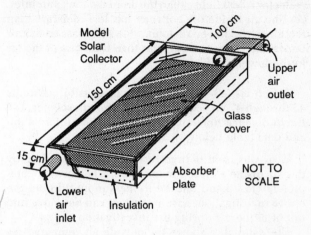

38. The solar collector is placed outside in sunlight, facing south and tilted 40° from the horizontal. At which position of the sun would the collector receive the most intense solar radiation?

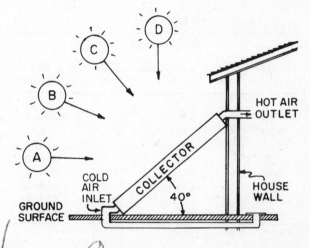

(1) *A* (2) *B* (3) *C* (4) *D*

39. The main purpose of the insulation behind the absorber plate is to (1) decrease the amount of energy lost through the back of the collector (2) decrease the amount of energy received by the collector (3) increase the amount of energy reflected by the absorber plate (4) increase the rate of energy transfer through the absorber plate

40. Which paint should be used on the absorber plate if it is designed to absorb the greatest possible amount of insolation? (1) red paint (2) white paint (3) yellow paint (4) black paint

41. What is the primary function of the glass cover? (1) It reduces the amount of insolation entering the collector. (2) It increases the heat that is lost by convection to the outside air. (3) It allows short wavelengths of radiation to enter, but reduces the amount of long-wavelength radiation that escapes. (4) It allows all wavelengths of radiation to pass through in either direction.

Insolation and the Earth's Surface

42. Why does the air usually enter the collector at the lower air inlet and leave the collector at the upper air outlet? (1) The air inside the collector is cooler than the air in the lower air inlet. (2) The air inside the collector is less dense than the air in the lower air inlet. (3) The air inside the collector has less moisture than the air in the lower air inlet. (4) The mass of the air inside the collector is greater than the mass of the air in the lower air inlet.

Directions (43–47): Base your answers to questions 43 through 47 on your knowledge of earth science, the *Earth Science Reference Tables*, and the information and data table below.

A car was used to investigate the heat absorbed by the air inside a closed automobile. The car was completely closed and left out in the sunlight during the entire investigation. Assume that air can *not* move into or out of the car during the investigation.

The data table shows the outside air temperatures beneath the car, the air temperatures inside the passenger compartment, and the sky conditions during the investigation.

Data Table

Clock Time (P.M.)	Air Temperature (°C)		Sky Conditions
	Outside	Inside	
2:10	24	30	cloudy
2:15	24	33	cloudy
2:20	24	38	cloudy
2:25	24	40	cloudy
2:30	24	41	cloudy
2:35	24	42	sunny
2:40	24	43	cloudy
2:45	24	43	cloudy
2:50	24	43	cloudy

43. By which process does most of the insolation pass through the car's windows? (1) compression (2) conduction (3) convection (4) radiation

44. What was the rate at which the inside air temperature changed during the first five minutes of the investigation? (1) 0.3 C°/min (2) 0.6 C°/min (3) 3.0 C°/min (4) 5.0 C°/min

45. The air temperature inside the car did *not* increase above 43°C, because during the last ten minutes, the (1) sky cover began to clear (2) insolation was absorbed by the inside air at a higher rate (3) density of the air inside the car was equal to the air density outside the car (4) air inside the car was losing heat at the same rate that it was gaining heat

46. The color of the car's interior is black. What would probably have happened to the temperature readings inside the car if the car's interior were white? (1) The temperature readings would have been lower. (2) The temperature readings would have been higher. (3) The temperature readings would have been the same.

47. Which graph best represents the relationship between time and inside air temperature?

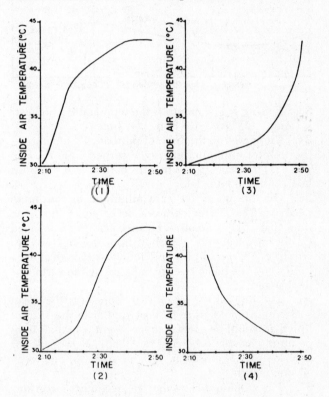

TOPIC 7 Energy Exchanges in the Atmosphere

WEATHER

Insolation is unevenly distributed over the earth. Although the energy of sunlight is concentrated near the equator and less concentrated at the poles, the earth's atmosphere helps to distribute this energy over the surface of the earth. Within the lowest atmospheric layer, the troposphere, energy exchanges occur which cause the weather. The **weather** is defined as the local condition of the atmosphere and the short-term changes in this condition. Weather is described by the measurement of **atmospheric variables**, such as temperature, pressure, winds, and moisture content.

Air Temperature. Air molecules in the atmosphere receive energy either directly from the sun, as the sunlight heats the air, or indirectly from the sun, as the air is warmed by terrestrial radiation or by contact with the ground. Air temperature is a measure of the average kinetic vibrational energy of air molecules in the atmosphere at a given place and time. Air temperature is measured with a thermometer, whose units of measure are usually degrees Celsius or degrees Fahrenheit.

What causes changes in air temperature? Changes in the temperature of the earth, which affect air temperature, are directly related to both the duration and the angle of insolation. For example, the warmest weather occurs in the summer, when the days are long and the sun is high in the sky. By reflecting insolation back into space, clouds can reduce the heating of the atmosphere. By changing from vapor to water (condensation), water droplets in the air can contribute great quantities of heat energy to the atmosphere. Air temperature also changes when the atmosphere picks up heat energy by the conduction of heat from warm land and water surfaces and by the friction between moving air masses and the ground.

Atmospheric Pressure. **Atmospheric pressure** is a measure of the force exerted by the atmosphere. Changes in atmospheric pressure result from changes in the temperature and the moisture content of the air and from changes in elevation.

If you plot two graphs—air temperature against time and air pressure against time—you will find that air temperature is inversely proportional to air pressure. See Figure 7-1. This relationship can be explained by recalling that gases expand when they are heated and contract when they are cooled. For example, air expands when it is

heated. As a result, hot air is less dense than cool air. As air is heated, the change in density of air causes the atmospheric pressure to decrease. Increasing air temperature decreases atmospheric pressure. Conversely, as air is cooled, the change in density of air causes the atmospheric pressure to increase. Decreasing air temperature increases atmospheric pressure.

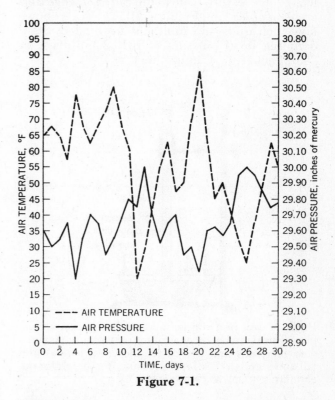

Figure 7-1.

Atmospheric pressure is also a function of **humidity**, or *moisture* content of the air. Although liquid water is quite heavy, water vapor is very light. When comparing the two gases, water vapor is lighter than dry air. Hot air can hold a lot of water vapor. As water evaporates into the air on a hot day, the light water vapor displaces the heavier air molecules. As the air becomes more humid, the air gets lighter and the atmospheric pressure decreases. Places with high humidity and hot temperatures are generally places of low atmospheric pressure. Conversely, cold air can hold little water vapor. Therefore, places with low humidity and cold temperatures are generally places of high atmospheric pressure.

Atmospheric pressure also depends upon elevation. Air pressure is caused by the weight of the atmosphere above you. If you move to a higher elevation, atmospheric pressure decreases because there is less air above you. About ⅔ of the weight of the atmosphere is below an elevation of 6,000 meters. Above this, the air becomes very thin and the atmospheric pressure is very low.

PROCESS OF INQUIRY SKILL

Measuring Atmospheric Pressure. Instruments used for measuring atmospheric pressure are called barometers. A simple mercury barometer is shown in Figure 7-2A. Atmospheric pressure is determined by reading the height of the mercury column in the barometer. The barometer's scale may be in centimeters or in inches. You can convert a measurement made in inches into metric units of pressure called millibars (mb) by using the Pressure scale in the *Earth Science Reference Tables*. See Figure 7-2B. The scale shows how inch units and millibars are related. Standard sea level pressure is 1013.2 millibars, or 29.92 inches, or 1 atmosphere.

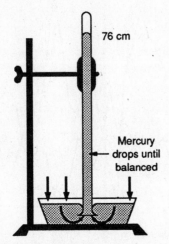

Figure 7-2A. In a simple mercury barometer, atmospheric pressure balances a column of mercury. As pressure increases and decreases, the column rises and falls. At standard sea level pressure, the height of the column is about 76 centimeters.

Example 1: According to the *Earth Science Reference Tables*, an air pressure of 30.15 inches of mercury is equal to   (1) 1017 mb   (2) 1019 mb   (3) 1021 mb   (4) 1023 mb

Answer: 3

Example 2: According to the *Earth Science Reference Tables*, an atmospheric pressure of 978 millibars is equal to   (1) 28.76 inches of mercury   (2) 28.88 inches of mercury   (3) 28.92 inches of mercury   (4) 29.00 inches of mercury

Answer: 2

Example 3: According to the *Earth Science Reference Tables*, an atmospheric pressure of 1019 millibars is equal to   (1) 31.05 inches of mercury   (2) 30.15 inches of mercury   (3) 30.09 inches of mercury   (4) 30.00 inches of mercury

Answer: 3

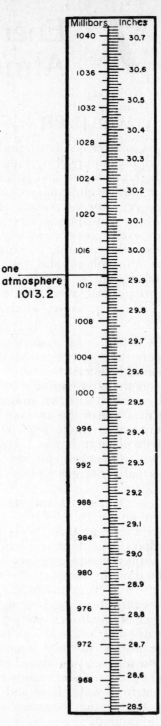

Figure 7-2B. Atmospheric pressure scale.

WIND

Wind can be described as the flow of air roughly parallel to the surface of the earth. Wind is the horizontal component of convection and moves heat with the moving air. Energy that is unevenly distributed over the earth is transported by winds. For example, near the poles, where the sun is always low in the sky, the ground is cold. Snow and ice reflect much of the insolation that reaches the surface of the earth in the polar regions. But near the equator, where the noon sun is high in the sky, insolation is stronger. The circulation of the winds helps to distribute this energy from regions of surplus energy to regions of energy deficit.

The speed of the wind is determined by the differences in atmospheric pressure. Wherever the air pressure gradient is the greatest, the winds will be the strongest. The **pressure gradient** is the rate of change in air pressure between two points on a map. For example, on a weather map that shows an air pressure field with isobars (lines that connect points of equal atmospheric pressure), the fastest winds will occur where the isobars are the closest to each other. This is the location with the greatest air pressure gradient. See Figure 7-3.

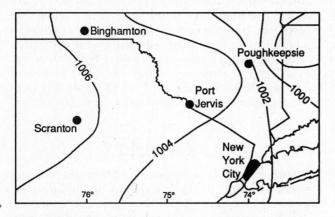

Figure 7-3. The strongest winds on this map will occur near Poughkeepsie. The isobars are the closest together in that area indicating the greatest pressure gradient.

The direction of the wind is controlled by two factors: the atmospheric pressure gradient and the Coriolis effect. Winds always blow from regions of high pressure to regions of low pressure. For example, in areas near the equator where low-density, warm, moist air produces rising air currents, regions of perpetual low pressure exist. In areas near the poles, where dense, cold, dry air produces descending air currents, regions of high pressure exist. The greater the pressure gradient between the regions, the faster the winds will blow. However, because of the earth's rotation, the winds are deflected to the right of the pressure gradient path in the Northern Hemisphere and to the left of the pressure gradient path in the Southern Hemisphere. This deflection is known as the *Coriolis effect*. See Figure 7-4.

Although the Coriolis effect causes the winds to curve to the right as they blow out of a high-pressure system, the winds cannot continue to curve to the right as they enter a low-pressure system. So the winds must curve to the left as they

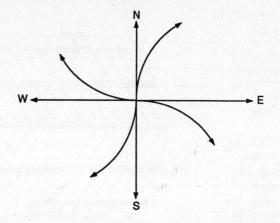

Figure 7-4. The Coriolis effect causes the winds to curve to the right in the Northern Hemisphere. Remember that a curve to the right must be a right turn with respect to the direction of travel. If the wind is blowing toward you, a curve to the right will go to *your* left. The curves on this diagram are all curves to the right.

blow into a low-pressure system. This creates a clockwise circulation of air around and out of a high-pressure system and a counterclockwise circulation of air around and into a low-pressure system. See Figure 7-5.

The winds are also responsible for moving surface ocean currents. Most of the surface currents of the oceans move in nearly the same direction as the prevailing winds because the surface currents are driven, in part, by these winds.

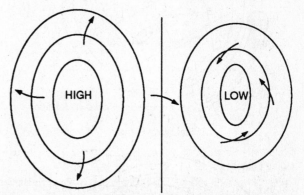

Figure 7-5. Wind direction and the Coriolis force. Winds move in a clockwise outspiral around high-pressure systems. Winds move in a counterclockwise inspiral around low-pressure systems.

Planetary Wind Belts. If the earth were stationary, the wind patterns on the earth would be simple. Cold air would sink at the poles and flow along the surface of the earth toward the equator. As the winds approached the equator, they would be warmed by direct sunlight and by contact with the warm surface of the earth. Surface winds would also pick up water vapor by evaporation. At the equator, the winds would flow upward and then back to the poles—making two great convection cells over the earth (one in

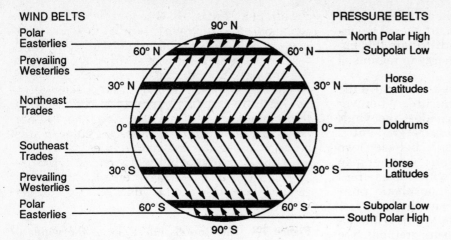

WIND BELTS

Polar Easterlies — 90° N
Prevailing Westerlies — 60° N
Northeast Trades — 30° N
Southeast Trades — 0°
Prevailing Westerlies — 30° S
Polar Easterlies — 60° S
90° S

PRESSURE BELTS

North Polar High — 60° N
Subpolar Low
Horse Latitudes — 30° N
Doldrums — 0°
Horse Latitudes — 30° S
Subpolar Low — 60° S
South Polar High

Figure 7-6. Winds always move from high-pressure systems into low-pressure systems. For example, the doldrums is a low-pressure belt at the equator in which warmed air is constantly rising. The horse latitudes (bands occurring between 30°N and 30°S) are belts of high pressure in which cooled air begins to sink downward. Consequently, a pressure gradient exists between the horse latitudes and the doldrums that causes the winds to move from a high-pressure region to a low-pressure region.

each hemisphere). However, the earth's rotation makes actual wind patterns more complex. The Coriolis effect causes the winds to be deflected to the right in the Northern Hemisphere and to the left in the Southern Hemisphere. As a result, the two convection cells mentioned above break into six convection cells—three in each hemisphere. When the convection cells interact, they produce the doldrums (weak winds at the equator), the trade winds, the prevailing westerlies, and the polar easterlies. These wind zones are called the **planetary wind belts**. See Figure 7-6. Note that between the wind zones are regions in which the air is sinking into a high-pressure area or rising out of a low-pressure area. These zones of rising and sinking air join the wind belts and winds in the upper atmosphere to create a system of atmospheric convection cells. See Figure 7-7.

MOISTURE

Humidity is a measure of the moisture, or water vapor content, of the air. Humidity is often expressed in terms of the dew-point temperature and the vapor pressure of water. The **dew point** is the temperature to which the air must be cooled to reach saturation. At **saturation**, the air holds as much water vapor as it can at that temperature. If the air is cooled below the dew-point temperature, water vapor will condense out of the air as dew, fog, or frost. However, if the dew-point temperature is well below the air temperature, the air will feel dry.

As the air temperature and the dew-point temperature approach each other, the humidity of the air, as well as the probability of precipitation, increases. The difference between these two temperatures can become smaller in either of two ways: (1) the moisture content of the air can increase, thus raising the dew-point temperature closer to the air temperature or (2) the air temperature can drop, thus bringing air temperature down closer to the dew-point temperature. (Note: although the dew point is a temperature, the only way to change the dew point is by adding water vapor to, or by taking water vapor out of the air.)

PROCESS OF INQUIRY SKILL

Using a Sling Psychrometer to Measure Dew Point. A sling psychrometer consists of two thermometers mounted on a narrow frame which has a handle used to whirl the thermometers through

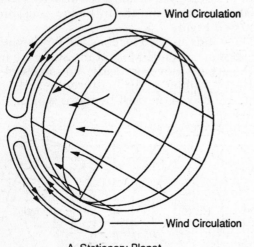

Wind Circulation

Wind Circulation

A. Stationary Planet

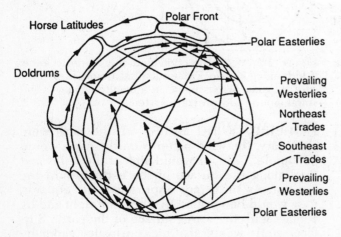

Horse Latitudes
Polar Front
Doldrums
Polar Easterlies
Prevailing Westerlies
Northeast Trades
Southeast Trades
Prevailing Westerlies
Polar Easterlies

B. Rotating Earth

Figure 7-7. Two models of atmospheric circulation.

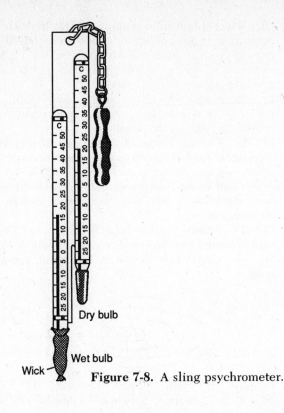

Dry bulb

Wet bulb

Wick

Figure 7-8. A sling psychrometer.

the air. See Figure 7-8. One thermometer always remains dry. The other has a cloth sock (wick) over its bulb that is moistened before it is used.

After a psychrometer is whirled around for a few minutes, both thermometers should be read. Evaporation of water from the wick will have lowered the temperature reading on the wet-bulb thermometer only if the air is less than 100 percent saturated. The drop in temperature in such a case is called the wet-bulb depression.

Using the dew-point temperature chart below and the two thermometer readings on the psychrometer, you can find the dew-point temperature.

Example: What is the dew-point temperature if the dry-bulb reading is 20°C and the wet-bulb reading is 17°C?

Solution: To find the dew-point temperature:

1. Calculate the wet-bulb depression (dry-bulb temperature minus wet-bulb temperature). In this problem, the wet-bulb depression is 3°.
2. Find the dry-bulb reading on the chart (see Figure 7-9) by looking along the horizontal line next to 20°C. Then find the 3° vertical line and trace it up to the 20° horizontal line.

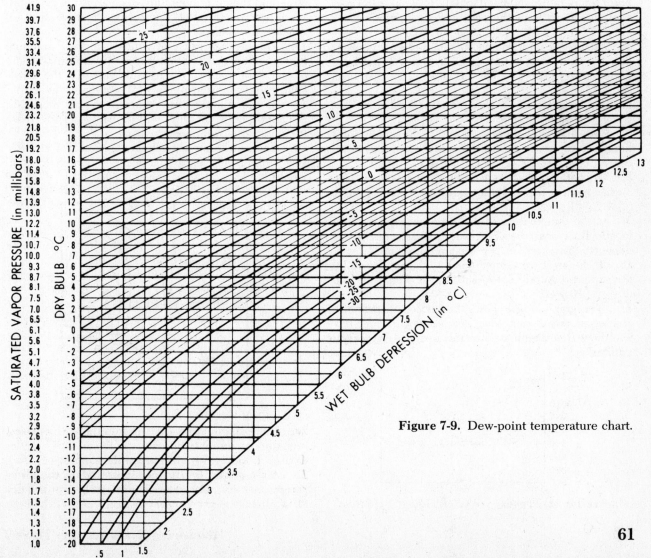

Figure 7-9. Dew-point temperature chart.

SATURATED VAPOR PRESSURE (in millibars)

DRY BULB °C

WET BULB DEPRESSION (in °C)

61

3. Where the two lines intersect, a third line (a diagonal line) shows the value of the dew-point temperature, which is namely 15°C. This means that air at 20°C must be cooled to 15°C to become saturated. The dew-point temperature can be read from the numbers in the center of the chart or from the dry-bulb numbers to the left.

QUESTIONS

1. According to the Dew-point Temperature Chart in the *Earth Science Reference Tables*, what is the dew point if the air temperature is 13°C and the wet-bulb temperature is 9°C? (1) −14°C (2) 0°C (3) 5°C (4) 9°C

2. What is the approximate dew-point temperature if the dry-bulb temperature is 26°C and the wet-bulb temperature is 21°C? (1) 5°C (2) 12°C (3) 18°C (4) 23°C

3. What is the approximate dew-point temperature if the dry-bulb temperature is 19°C and the wet-bulb temperature is 13°C? (1) 12°C (2) 8°C (3) 7°C (4) −25°C

4. The dew-point temperature of the air is determined to be 10°C. If the accepted value for the dew-point temperature on that day is 12°C, what is the percent deviation from the accepted dew-point value? (1) 16.7% (2) 2.0% (3) 13.9% (4) 83.3%

5. What is the approximate dew-point temperature if the dry-bulb temperature is 25°C and the wet-bulb temperature is 20°C? (1) 7°C (2) 11°C (3) 17°C (4) 20°C

6. Which is a form of precipitation? (1) frost (2) snow (3) dew (4) fog

7. If the air temperature were 20°C, which dew-point temperature would indicate the highest water vapor content? (1) 18°C (2) 15°C (3) 10°C (4) 0°C

8. At what temperature would ice crystals form from air that has a dew-point temperature of −6°C? (1) 6°C (2) 0°C (3) −2°C (4) −6°C

9. As the temperature of the atmosphere at a given location increases, the air pressure will most likely (1) decrease (2) increase (3) remain the same

10. If the air were saturated at 15°C, what would be the vapor pressure? (1) 7.5 mb (2) 12.5 mb (3) 15.0 mb (4) 16.9 mb

11. The graph below shows the surface air pressure at a certain city during a five-day period. On which day was the warmest air mass probably over the city for the entire day?

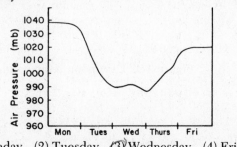

(1) Monday (2) Tuesday (3) Wednesday (4) Friday

12. Winds blow from regions of (1) high air temperature to regions of low air temperature (2) high air pressure to regions of low air pressure (3) high precipitation to regions of low precipitation (4) convergence to regions of divergence

13. As an isobar bends around a low-pressure area, the pressure along this line will (1) decrease (2) increase (3) remain the same

14. On a weather map of the United States, the indicated movement of air in a low-pressure system is (1) toward the center and clockwise (2) toward the center and counterclockwise (3) out from the center and clockwise (4) out from the center and counterclockwise

15. The diagram below shows the isolines of air pressure around a low-pressure center. On which side of the low-pressure center will the wind speed be greatest?

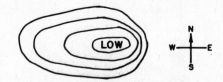

(1) north (2) south (3) east (4) west

16. As the difference between the dew-point temperature and the air temperature decreases, the probability of precipitation (1) decreases (2) increases (3) remains the same

17. The primary cause of winds is the (1) unequal heating of the earth's atmosphere (2) uniform density of the atmosphere (3) friction between the atmosphere and the lithosphere (4) rotation of the earth

18. As the amount of moisture in the air increases, the atmospheric pressure will probably (1) decrease (2) increase (3) remain the same

19. The map below represents a portion of an air pressure field at the earth's surface. At which location would the highest wind speed occur?

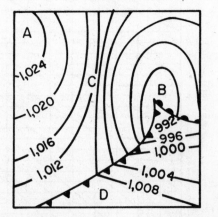

(1) A (2) B (3) C (4) D

20. If the amount of water vapor in the air increases, then the dew-point temperature of the air will (1) decrease (2) increase (3) remain the same

21. Air pressure is usually highest when the air is (1) cool and dry (2) cool and moist (3) warm and dry (4) warm and moist

62   *Reviewing Earth Science: Topic 7*

22. In a certain area the air temperature and the dewpoint temperature are approaching the same value. The air pressure is decreasing and the cloud cover is increasing. What atmospheric change is most likely occurring in this area? (1) Warm, moist air is moving into the area. (2) Warm, dry air is moving into the area. (3) Cold, dry air is moving into the area. (4) A cold front has just passed through this area.

23. For a location in central New York State, which would *least* likely change during a one-week period? (1) the atmospheric pressure, in millibars (2) the elevation, in meters (3) the temperature, in degrees Celsius (4) the relative humidity, in percent

24. An observer recorded the barometric pressure while traveling up the west side of a mountain and down the other side. Which graph best represents the probable air pressure changes that were observed?

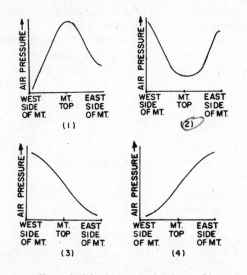

25. Air will probably have its highest density when it is (1) warm and moist (2) warm and dry (3) cold and moist (4) cold and dry

26. Which factor is most directly related to wind velocity? (1) dew point (2) relative humidity (3) cloud type (4) pressure gradient

27. The table below shows the noontime data for air pressure and air temperature at a location over a period of one week.

WEATHER DATA RECORDED AT NOON

Date	Nov. 9	Nov. 10	Nov. 11	Nov. 12	Nov. 13	Nov. 14	Nov. 15
Air Temperature (°C)	1	6	0	−2	−4	5	10
Air Pressure (millibars)	1024	998	1015	1021	1030	1013	?

Based on the data provided, which air pressure would most likely occur at noon on November 15? (1) 987 millibars (2) 1015 millibars (3) 1017 millibars (4) 1022 millibars

28. Which combination of air temperature and dewpoint temperature would most likely occur in humid air? (1) air temperature 10°C, dew-point temperature −4°C (2) air temperature 15°C, dew-point temperature 3°C (3) air temperature 24°C, dew-point temperature 23°C (4) air temperature 26°C, dew-point temperature 10°C

29. Which drawing best illustrates the general result that the earth's rotation would have on the direction of the wind as it moves away from the center of a high-pressure system in the Northern Hemisphere?

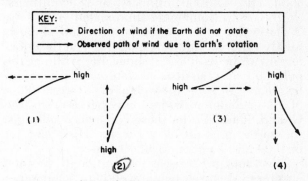

Directions (30–34): Base your answers to questions 30 through 34 on your knowledge of earth science and the diagram below. The diagram represents the general circulation of the earth's atmosphere and the earth's planetary wind and pressure belts. Points *A* through *F* represent locations on the earth's surface.

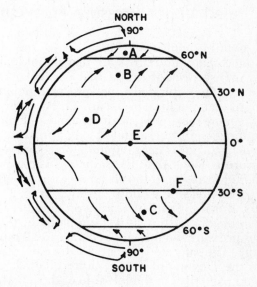

30. The curving paths of the surface winds shown in the diagram are caused by the earth's (1) gravitational field (2) magnetic field (3) rotation (4) revolution

31. Which location might be in New York State? (1) A (2) B (3) C (4) D

32. Which location is experiencing a southwest planetary wind? (1) A (2) B (3) C (4) F

33. Which location is near the center of a low-pressure belt where daily rains are common? (1) E (2) B (3) F (4) D

34. The arrows in the diagram represent energy transfer by which process? (1) conduction (2) radiation (3) convection (4) absorption

Energy Exchanges in the Atmosphere

VAPOR PRESSURE

The weight of the atmosphere causes our atmospheric pressure. Since air is composed of a variety of gases mixed together, the whole atmospheric pressure is the sum of the partial pressures of each of these gases. Air is about 78% nitrogen, therefore the partial pressure of nitrogen alone is about 78% of the total atmospheric pressure. Normal air pressure is roughly 1000 millibars, so the partial pressure of nitrogen gas is about 78% of 1000 millibars, or 780 millibars. (Millibars are commonly abbreviated "mb.")

The water vapor content of the atmosphere is highly variable. In warm, moist air near the equator, it can be as high as about 4%; while at the poles, the air is so dry that water vapor makes up less than $\frac{1}{10}$ of 1% of the weight of the air. A figure of 1% is common in the temperate areas of the United States. Under these common conditions, the partial pressure of water vapor is about 1% of 1000 millibars, or about 10 mb.

The **vapor pressure** is the portion of the total air pressure caused by the weight of water vapor alone. The water vapor content of the air is sometimes called the **absolute humidity**. It is convenient to express absolute humidity in terms of the vapor pressure. Absolute humidity is most commonly expressed as a vapor pressure, in millibars.

Saturated Vapor Pressure and Actual Vapor Pressure.
The air is seldom completely full of moisture. If it is, we say the air is saturated. Saturated air is air that is holding as much moisture as it can at that particular temperature. The saturated vapor pressure depends upon the temperature of the air. The warmer the air, the more moisture that air can hold and, therefore, the greater the saturated vapor pressure. Of course, if the air is not saturated, the actual vapor pressure is lower than the saturated vapor pressure. For example, if the air temperature is 10°C, the vapor pressure could be as high as 12.2 millibars. But if the air is unsaturated, holding only half as much moisture as it could hold, the actual vapor pressure would only be 50% of 12.2 mb, or 6.1 mb. The saturated vapor pressure can be read from the Dew-point Temperature chart, Figure 7-9, on page 61. On the left side of this chart are two columns. The column of numbers on the right is the Celsius air temperature column. Next to these numbers are the saturated vapor pressure values at each temperature. By reading this chart you can see that at a temperature of 20°C, the air could hold enough moisture to make the vapor pressure 23.2 mb.

Saturation as a Dynamic Equilibrium.
When you think of saturated air, you may think that the air cannot absorb any more moisture. This is only partly true. In fact, saturated air can absorb more moisture, but only if it loses the same amount of moisture. Saturated air in contact with a water surface is in a state of dynamic equilibrium. While there is no *net* evaporation from the water surface, there is an exchange of water molecules at the air-water interface. As the most energetic water molecules escape into the air, an equal number of water vapor molecules condense into the liquid. At saturation, evaporation and condensation are in balance.

PROCESS OF INQUIRY SKILL

Calculating Relative Humidity. When calculating relative humidity, the saturation vapor pressure is used, as shown in the example that follows. **Relative humidity** is the ratio between the actual amount of water vapor in the air and the maximum amount of water vapor the air can hold at a given temperature. See Figure 7-10. If the relative humidity is 50%, the air is half filled to capacity with moisture. At 100% relative humidity, air is filled to capacity or saturated with moisture.

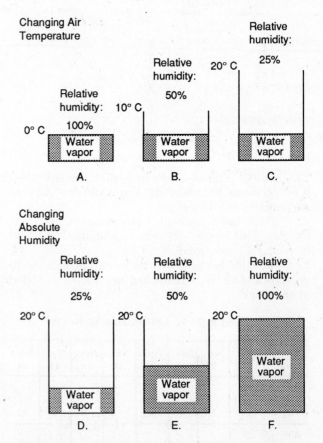

Figure 7-10. The effects of changing air temperature and of changing the moisture content of the air. In diagrams A–C, you can see that the air can hold more moisture as it gets warmer. If moisture is not added to the air, the relative humidity decreases as the temperature increases. In diagrams D–F, the temperature remains constant. As moisture is added to the air, the relative humidity increases.

To find relative humidity, you must determine the ratio between the saturation vapor pressure of the dew-point temperature and the saturation vapor pressure of the air temperature.

$$\text{relative humidity (percent)} = \frac{\text{saturation vapor pressure at dew-point temperature}}{\text{saturation vapor pressure at air temperature}} \times 100\%$$

A psychrometer and a dew-point chart supply the information needed to find relative humidity.

Sample Problems

1. What is the relative humidity when the dry-bulb reading is 25°C and the dew point is 15°C?

Solution:

a. At a dew point of 15°C, the saturation vapor pressure is 16.9 millibars.

b. At a dry-bulb temperature (air temperature) of 25°C, the saturation vapor pressure is 31.4 millibars.

c.

$$\text{relative humidity} = \frac{\text{saturation vapor pressure at dew-point temperature}}{\text{saturation vapor pressure at air temperature}} \times 100\%$$

$$\text{relative humidity} = \frac{16.9 \text{ mb}}{31.4 \text{ mb}} \times 100\%$$

$$\text{relative humidity} = 54\%$$

2. If the air temperature is 10°C and the dew-point temperature is 0°C, what is the approximate relative humidity? (1) 100% (2) 50% (3) 35% (4) 0%

Answer: 2

3. The air temperature is 7°C and the dew point is 2°C. What is the approximate relative humidity? (1) 30% (2) 50% (3) 70% (4) 90%

Answer: 3

THE EFFECTS OF ELEVATION CHANGES ON ATMOSPHERIC VARIABLES

Changes in the physical properties of the atmosphere, such as water vapor content, atmospheric pressure, and temperature, when changes occur in elevation, are shown by three graphs in the *Earth Science Reference Tables*. See Figure 7-11. For example, the temperature graph shows that the atmosphere of the earth has been divided into four layers based upon changes in air temperature. Within the troposphere (the bottom 12 kilometers of the atmosphere) temperature decreases with increasing elevation. Because it is the lowest layer where air pressure and air density are the greatest, the troposphere contains most of the mass of the earth's atmosphere.

Above the troposphere is the stratosphere. Unlike the temperature trend within the troposphere, the air becomes warmer with increasing elevation in the stratosphere. Within the next layer, the mesosphere, the air temperature drops with increasing elevation. The highest layer is the thermosphere. The air temperature increases with altitude within the thermosphere until the air becomes so thin that it is difficult to measure its temperature.

The other two graphs show that both water vapor content and air pressure decrease within all layers of the atmosphere as you go higher above the earth.

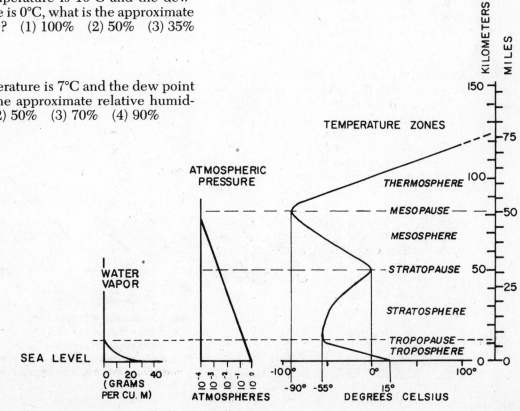

Figure 7-11.

ENERGY IN THE ATMOSPHERE

The atmosphere gets nearly all of its energy either directly or indirectly from the sun. Sunlight warms the air directly during the day, giving it kinetic heat energy. The sun also warms the earth which, in turn, gives off infrared (heat) radiation. Carbon dioxide and water vapor within the atmosphere absorb this long-wave radiation. The atmosphere is also warmed by contact with the surface of the earth. Friction between the winds and the surface of the earth provides additional heat.

The atmosphere absorbs and releases great amounts of energy as moisture enters the air and forms clouds. When water evaporates, the evaporating water carries at least 540 calories per gram into the atmosphere as latent potential energy. When water vapor condenses, the forming clouds release kinetic heat energy, which warms the air.

The principal source of water in the atmosphere is the oceans. However, water also evaporates from water held within the ground and from plants. Evaporation from plants is known as *transpiration*. The total evaporation from the ground, from open water (oceans, lakes, rivers), and from plants is called *evapotranspiration*.

Evaporation is different from boiling in that it takes place well below the boiling temperature. When water boils at 100° Celsius, a large portion

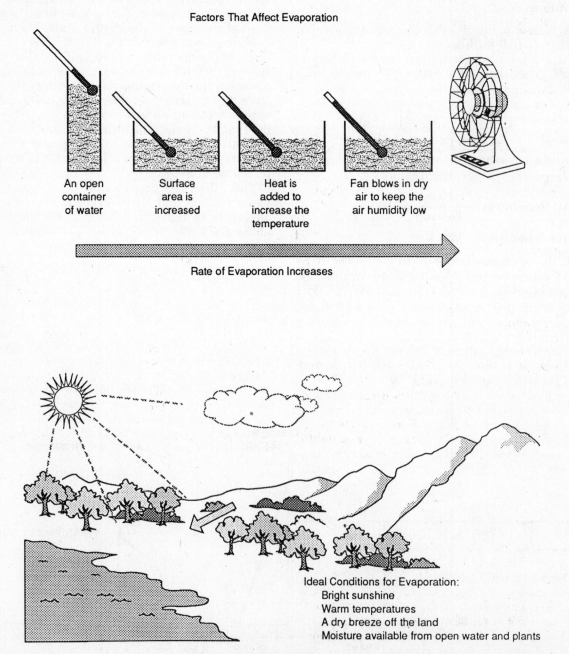

Figure 7-12.

of the water molecules have enough energy to break away from surrounding water molecules and enter the gaseous state. However, even in water well below the boiling temperature, some water molecules still have enough energy to escape from the water surface. Remember that the temperature of matter is the *average* kinetic energy of the molecules. Some molecules have more energy than others. The most energetic molecules escape, leaving less energetic molecules behind. For this reason, evaporation is a cooling process. As the most energetic molecules escape, the average temperature of the molecules decreases because the evaporating molecules carry their energy into the air and leave the cooler molecules behind.

The amount of water vapor that the air can hold is directly related to the temperature of the air. For each 10°C increase in temperature, the air can hold about twice as much water vapor.

Rates of Evaporation.
The rate at which water evaporates depends upon the availability of heat energy, the moisture content of the air, and the amount of water surface exposed to the air. Wind is also important because it moves in fresh, dry air as the air over the water surface becomes more moist.

Energy used for evaporation can be supplied from the kinetic heat energy of the evaporating liquid, from the energy of air molecules, or from an outside source, such as the sun. Added heat energy causes an increase in the rate of evaporation.

Dry air can absorb more moisture than moist air. At any given temperature, there is a limit to the amount of water vapor the air can hold. Dry air, at a specified temperature, can absorb more moisture before it reaches that limit. If there is no wind, the air in contact with a water surface may become saturated and evaporation will stop. A breeze is needed to provide more dry air so that evaporation can continue.

The amount of evaporation is directly related to the exposed water surface area. A quart of water will evaporate much more quickly from a shallow pan than it will from a narrow bottle. When the exposed surface area of water is increased, it will evaporate more quickly. See Figure 7-12.

QUESTIONS

35. Which atmospheric condition will cause the greatest amount of evaporation from the surface of a lake? (1) calm, dry, cold (2) moist, cold, windy (3) calm, moist, hot (4) dry, hot, windy

36. The primary source of moisture for the atmosphere is the earth's (1) ground water (2) vegetation (3) rivers and lakes (4) oceans

37. As the amount of water vapor in an air mass increases, the potential energy of the air mass will (1) decrease (2) increase (3) remain the same

38. Which graph best represents the effect that heating has on air density in the troposphere?

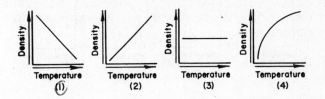

39. According to Figure 7-9 on page 61, which graph best represents the relationship between the saturated vapor pressure and the dry-bulb temperature?

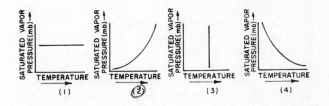

40. Which graph best shows the relationship between atmospheric pressure and water vapor content at the earth's surface?

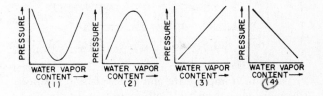

41. Moisture is evaporating from a lake into stationary air at a constant temperature. As more moisture is added to this air, the rate at which water will evaporate will probably (1) decrease (2) increase (3) remain the same

42. The rate of evaporation of water can be increased by (1) increasing the amount of moisture in the air (2) decreasing the temperature of the water (3) increasing the temperature of the air (4) decreasing the circulation of the air

43. In the diagram below, at which location would the vapor pressure of the air most likely be greatest?

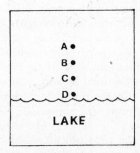

(1) A (2) B (3) C (4) D

---

44. According to the *Earth Science Reference Tables*, which graph best represents the relationship between the altitude and the amount of water vapor in the atmosphere?

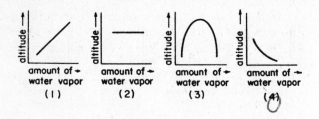

(1)   (2)   (3)   (4)

45. There will most likely be an increase in the rate at which water will evaporate from a pond, if there is a decrease in the   (1) wind velocity   (2) temperature of the air   (3) moisture content of the air   (4) altitude of the sun

46. According to the *Earth Science Reference Tables*, the greatest atmospheric pressure occurs in the   (1) troposphere   (2) stratosphere   (3) mesosphere   (4) thermosphere

47. All of the glass containers shown below contain the same amount of water and are receiving the same amount of heat energy. In a given amount of time, the most water will evaporate from which container?

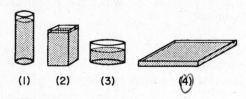

(1)   (2)   (3)   (4)

48. The air temperature and the wet-bulb temperature were measured and both were found to be 18°C. Two hours later, measurements were taken again and the air temperature was 20°C, while the wet-bulb temperature remained 18°C. The relative humidity of the air during those two hours   (1) decreased   (2) increased   (3) remained the same

49. A cloud may form when moist air rises because (1) the air pressure increases   (2) the air is cooled to its dew point or below   (3) the dew point increases (4) additional water vapor is added to the air

50. A balloon carrying weather instruments is released at the earth's surface and rises through the troposphere. As the balloon rises, what will the instruments generally indicate? [Refer to the *Earth Science Reference Tables*.]   (1) a decrease in both air temperature and air pressure   (2) an increase in both air temperature and air pressure   (3) an increase in air temperature and a decrease in air pressure   (4) a decrease in air temperature and an increase in air pressure

51. The energy gained by water during evaporation is later released by the water vapor during the process of   (1) transpiration   (2) convection   (3) melting   (4) condensation

52. As the vapor pressure increases, the amount of water that evaporates into the air   (1) decreases   (2) increases   (3) remains the same

Directions (53–57): Base your answers to questions 53 through 57 on your knowledge of earth science, the *Earth Science Reference Tables*, and the drawing below. The drawing represents five positions of a balloon after being released from a ship. The drawings of the balloon are not to scale compared to the altitude distances, but are to scale with each other.

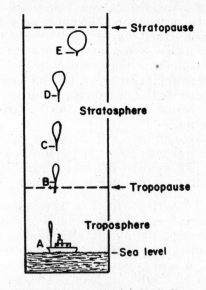

53. Which position represents the balloon when it is about 12 kilometers above sea level?   (1) A   (2) B   (3) D   (4) E

54. Why is the balloon's appearance at position E different from the balloon's appearance at position A? (1) There is a partial vacuum inside the balloon at A, but not at E.   (2) There is more gas inside the balloon at A than at E.   (3) The outside air temperature is lower at E than at A.   (4) The outside air pressure is lower at E than at A.

55. At which position would the warmest surrounding air temperature most likely be found?   (1) A   (2) B   (3) C   (4) D

56. Which graph best represents the relative amounts of water vapor found in the atmosphere at the different balloon positions?

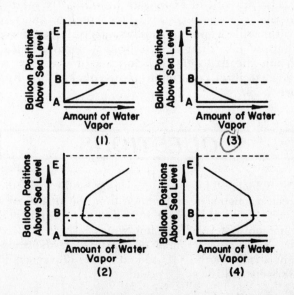

57. In order to make the balloon rise, the density of the gas put inside the balloon must be (1) less than the density of the air at sea level (2) more than the density of the air at sea level (3) the same as the density of the air at sea level

Directions (58–62): Base your answers to questions 58 through 62 on the diagram below, and on your knowledge of earth science. Write the *number* of the word or expression that best completes *each* statement or answers *each* question.

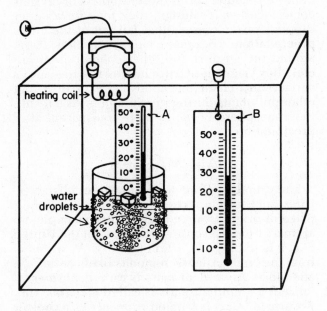

The sealed plastic container contains two Celsius thermometers, one of which is in a glass cup containing ice and water. A heating coil is available to vary the temperature of the sealed container.

58. What is the temperature of the air in the box? (1) 23.0°C (2) 25.0°C (3) 28.0°C (4) 29.0°C

59. Why have droplets of water formed on the outside of the glass cup? (1) Glass cups always accumulate water droplets on the outside when they are filled with water. (2) The air near the glass cup has become saturated. (3) Water has seeped through the pore spaces in the glass cup. (4) The relative humidity of the air near the glass cup is approaching 0%.

60. If the water droplets have just appeared on the glass cup, what is the dew-point temperature? (1) 6.5°C (2) 23°C (3) 28°C (4) 50°C

61. If the experiment were repeated with thermometer *B* reading 16.0°C and it was determined that the dew-point temperature was 7.0°C, what should be the relative humidity of the air in the box? [Refer to the reference tables for the relative humidity equation.] (1) 16% (2) 23% (3) 55% (4) 85%

62. The cup of water is removed and the box resealed. If the heating coil is used to raise the temperature of the air in the box, the dew-point temperature in the box would (1) decrease (2) increase (3) remain the same

Energy Exchanges in the Atmosphere

ADIABATIC TEMPERATURE CHANGES

Adiabatic Cooling: The Formation of Clouds.
A **cloud** is a large group of water droplets so small that they remain suspended in the air. Clouds form by condensation when moist air is cooled below its dew point. Condensation releases energy, so the formation of clouds is an important process that releases latent energy into the atmosphere.

To form a cloud, there must be a warm, moist mass of air. This mass of air, because of its higher temperature and because of its greater vapor content, will be lighter than surrounding air. As a result of its decreased density, it will tend to rise within the atmosphere. As it rises, the air mass will expand because of decreased pressure. This expansion results in fewer collisions of air molecules within the air mass—hence, a lower temperature (adiabatic cooling). The change in the temperature of a gas caused by expansion (cooling) or compression (warming) is called an **adiabatic temperature change**. No outside heat is involved in an adiabatic change in temperature of a gas.

If the mass of moist air is cooled below its dew point and if there are particles of dust or other surfaces (**condensation nuclei**) on which the water can condense, a cloud will form. If condensation occurs below 0° Celsius, the cloud will be composed of tiny ice crystals that have formed by sublimation—a process in which water vapor changes directly into tiny ice crystals. Most winter clouds and even very high summer clouds are composed of ice crystals that are too small to fall toward the ground.

Adiabatic Warming.
Adiabatic warming occurs when a cold air mass descends to lower altitudes and is compressed by surrounding air. Compression decreases the space between air molecules in the cold air mass. As a result, a greater number of collisions occur among air molecules as the air descends. In the process, the average kinetic energy of the air mass rises which, in turn, causes the temperature of the air mass to rise.

Wet and Dry Adiabatic Lapse Rates.
The rate at which air cools as it rises and expands is called the *adiabatic lapse rate*. Moist air cools slowly because, as it rises and expands, condensation (cloud formation) releases energy back into the air to slow its cooling. The moist (wet) adiabatic cooling rate averages about 0.6°C per 100 meters.

Dry air cools quickly because, as it rises and expands, water vapor is not present to condense and slow its cooling. The dry adiabatic cooling rate is 1°C per 100 meters. The wet adiabatic lapse rate is always lower than the dry adiabatic cooling rate because latent energy is released as water vapor condenses. See Figure 7-13.

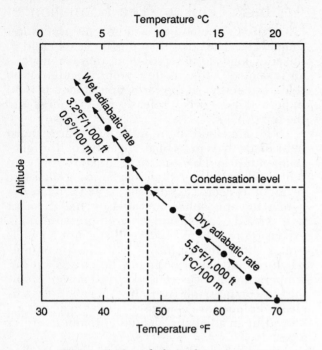

Figure 7-13. Adiabatic lapse rates.

When moist winds blow over a mountain range, we often see the effects of the difference between the wet and the dry adiabatic lapse rates. As the moist air rises on the windward side of the mountains, the energy released in cloud formation (condensation) causes the air to cool slowly. By the time the air reaches the top of the mountains, it has lost most of its moisture content due to precipitation. However, as the winds blow down the lee side of the mountains, the dry air warms up very quickly and absorbs moisture, causing relatively warm and dry conditions on the leeward side of the mountains. See Figure 7-14.

The coastal ranges of the American Northwest illustrate these conditions very well. Wet, cool weather is common along the coast. The mountains receive a great deal of rain and snow as the air rises over the mountains. Inland, on the downwind side of the mountain ranges, the climate is dry and warmer.

PRECIPITATION

Cloud droplets and ice crystals are small enough to remain suspended by air currents indefinitely. However, if these droplets or crystals come together (**coalesce**), they may form larger droplets or ice crystals that fall out of the air as **precipitation**. Because cloud droplets form around bits of dust and other condensation nuclei, they bring these particles down to the earth's surface and clean the atmosphere of dust and other pollutants during precipitation. As a result, the atmosphere becomes more transparent after precipitation.

AIR MASSES

Large bodies of air tend to take on characteristics, such as temperature and humidity, of their place of origin (**source region**). For example, an air mass from the southwestern part of the United States is likely to be warm and dry. An air mass from the North Atlantic region is likely to be cold and moist. An arid air mass is called *continental* (c), and a humid air mass is called *maritime* (m). A warm air mass is labeled *tropical* (T), a cool air mass is labeled *polar* (P), and an extremely cold air mass is labeled *arctic* (A). See Figure 7-15.

Meteorologists (scientists who study the weather) have specified two-letter codes to identify the temperature and humidity characteristics of air masses. Each one has a small letter followed by a capital letter. These codes are listed in the *Earth Science Reference Tables*.

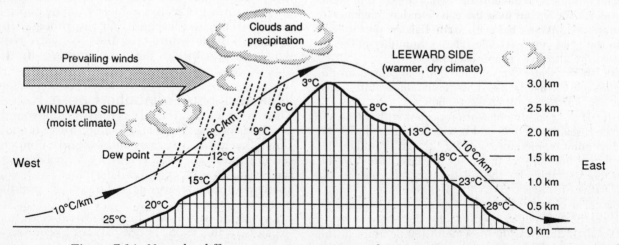

Figure 7-14. Note the differences in precipitation and in temperatures on the two sides of this mountain.

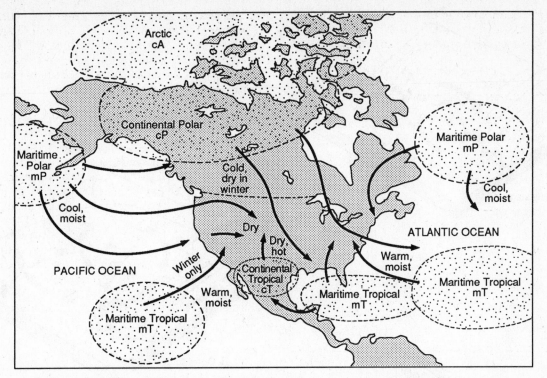

Figure 7-15. The arrows show the usual paths taken by air masses that affect weather in the United States.

cA continental arctic: an extremely cold, dry air mass which may have originated over the artic region of northwestern Canada, especially in the winter

cP continental polar: a cold, dry air mass, which may have originated over central Canada

cT continental tropical: a warm, dry air mass, which may have originated over Mexico or the American Southwest desert region

mT maritime tropical: a warm, moist air mass, which may have originated over the Gulf of Mexico

mP maritime polar: a cold, moist air mass, which may have originated over the North Atlantic Ocean or North Pacific Ocean

Cyclones.
A **cyclone** is a *low pressure system*. Because winds blow into a cyclone, the *converging* air brings together different air masses. When heavy, cool and dry air masses come together with lighter, warm and moist air masses, the lighter air masses are pushed aloft. As the warm and moist air is pushed upward, adiabatic cooling causes cloud formation and precipitation. For this reason, cyclones are associated with unstable weather and precipitation. Note that as the winds blow into a cyclone, they circulate counterclockwise. Figure 7-16 shows four stages in the development of a mid-latitude cyclone.

Weather Fronts.
The boundaries between air masses are known as **fronts**. Weather fronts are associated with cyclones because cyclones draw in different air masses. There are four kinds of fronts. See Figure 7-17. *Warm fronts* bring warm and often moist air. Because warm air is relatively light, it is often lifted up over a retreating cool air mass. A long, lasting rain occurs as a warm front approaches. A *cold front* brings cold, dense, and often dry air. The dense cold air wedges under a retreating warm air mass. Warm air is pushed rapidly upward, cumulus clouds form, and brief, but intense, precipitation occurs as a cold front approaches.

When a rapidly moving cold front overtakes a warm front, the warm air between the two cold air masses will be completely lifted above the surface, producing an *occluded front*. Finally, a stationary front is a nonmoving boundary between warm and cold air masses. Commonly, the winds along a *stationary front* are blowing in opposite directions, but the interface, or boundary, between the air masses does not move.

Anticyclones.
An **anticyclone** is a *high pressure system*. Anticyclones are zones of *divergence* because the winds blow out of an anticyclone. An anticyclone is a single mass of dense air that is spreading out; therefore, no weather fronts develop in an anticyclone. Remember, in the Northern Hemisphere, as the winds blow out of an anticyclone, the Coriolis force causes them to curve to the right in a clockwise direction. See Figure 7-18.

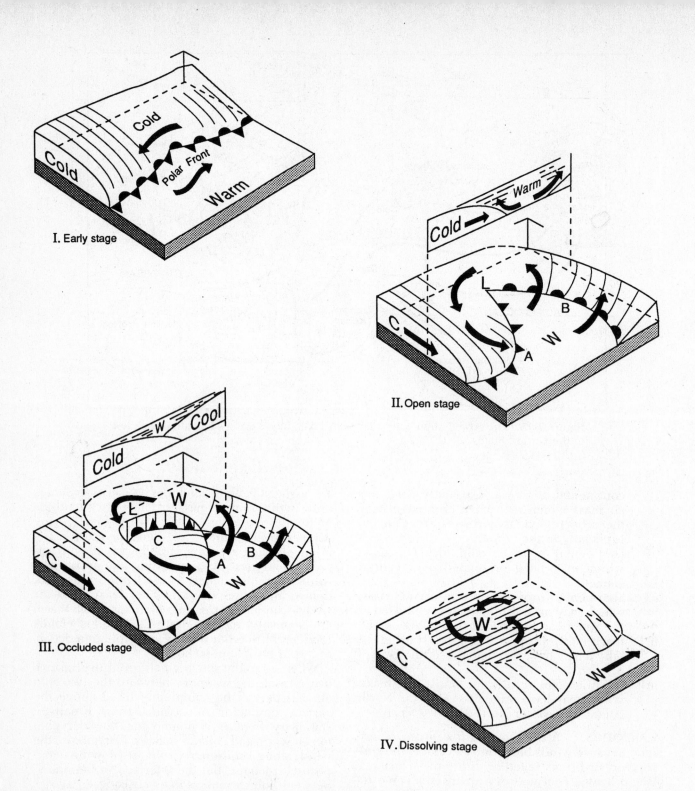

Figure 7-16. Four stages in the development of a mid-latitude cyclone. *I.* A swirl begins to develop as winds blow in opposite directions along a stationary front. (This may be a polar front that separates a cold, Canadian air mass from warmer air to the south.) *II.* The cold, dry, and more dense air begins to close in on the warmer and more moist air mass. Note the appearance of the cold front (A) and the warm front (B). Cloud formation and precipitation will tend to take place in front of the warm front (B) and along the cold front (A) where warm, moist air is cooled as it is pushed aloft. (Note the cross-sectional profile above the three-dimensional diagram.) *III.* The cold front (A) has overtaken the warm front (B) to produce an occluded front (C) where the whole warm air mass has been pushed up. Cloudy weather and precipitation can be found along all three fronts. *IV.* A portion of the warmer air mass is isolated as the swirl closes in. This isolated portion of the warmer air mass will lose its identity as it is absorbed by the cold air mass. At the dissolving stage of cyclonic development, the life of the cyclone usually ends. However, the early stage may develop, in which case the life cycle of the cyclone will take place all over again.

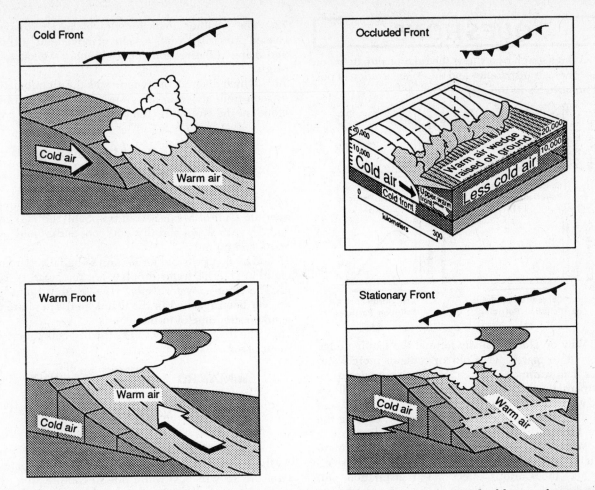

Figure 7-17. Four types of weather fronts. *Cold fronts* pass quickly. An advancing mass of cold air pushes warmer, more moist air aloft, often causing adiabatic cooling, rapid cloud formation, and intense precipitation. Summer cold fronts sometimes bring thunderstorms, followed by cool, dry weather and high atmospheric pressure. A cold front may pass in a matter of an hour or two. A *warm front* is produced when warm air flows in to replace a retreating cold air mass. As the warmer, more moist air rises over the cooler air, adiabatic cooling causes the formation of high, wispy clouds followed by thickening clouds and steady precipitation. The passage of a warm front may take several days and bring in warm, hazy weather conditions with relatively low atmospheric pressure. An *occluded front* is produced when an advancing cold air mass pushes a lighter warm air mass completely above the ground. Occluded fronts are commonly associated with large areas of rainy, unsettled weather. A *stationary front* occurs where the winds blow in opposite directions along a boundary between warm and cold air masses. The front is called stationary because the boundary is not moving.

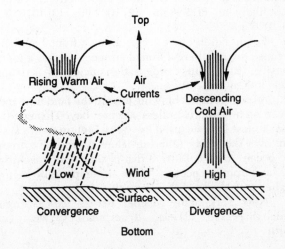

Figure 7-18. High- and low-pressure systems as zones of convergence and divergence. A low-pressure system is a zone of convergence. Rising warm, moist air at the center of the low causes winds and air masses to blow into the low-pressure system. The rising air also causes adiabatic cooling, cloud formation, and precipitation. The descending air within an anticyclone turns a high-pressure system into a single mass of cool, dry air that spreads across the surface of the earth.

Energy Exchanges in the Atmosphere

63. Which graph best shows the relationship between atmospheric transparency and the concentration of pollution particles in the air?

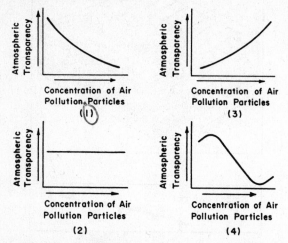

64. Why do clouds usually form at the leading edge of a cold air mass? (1) Cold air contains more water vapor than warm air does. (2) Cold air contains more dust particles than warm air does. (3) Cold air flows over warm air, causing the warm air to descend and cool. (4) Cold air flows under warm air, causing the warm air to rise and cool.

65. Which natural process removes small pollutant particles from the atmosphere? (1) the greenhouse effect (2) the Coriolis effect (3) transpiration (4) precipitation

66. Condensation of water vapor in the atmosphere is most likely to occur when a condensation surface is available and (1) a strong wind is blowing (2) the temperature of the air is below 0°C (3) the air is saturated with water vapor (4) the air pressure is rising

67. Where is precipitation most likely to occur? (1) near the frontal surface between two air masses (2) in descending air currents (3) on the leeward slopes of mountains (4) near the center of a high-pressure area

68. A strong surface wind is blowing from city A toward city B. City B has a barometric pressure of 1013 millibars. The barometric pressure of city A would most likely be (1) 988 mb (2) 1002 mb (3) 1013 mb (4) 1026 mb

69. Precipitation often occurs along a frontal surface because the air along a frontal surface (1) has a high density (2) contains condensation nuclei (3) is rising (4) is low in humidity

70. A cool breeze is blowing toward the land from the ocean on a warm, cloudless summer day. This condition is most likely caused by (1) a high-pressure system over the land (2) a hurricane approaching from the ocean (3) a cold front that is slowly approaching the land from the ocean (4) the air temperature being higher over the land than over the ocean

71. New York State weather usually comes from which direction? (1) east (2) northeast (3) west (4) north

72. The weather characteristics of an air mass are caused primarily by its (1) rate of movement (2) size and shape (3) direction of movement (4) geographic origin

73. Which diagram best represents the air circulation as seen from above in a high-pressure center (anticyclone) in the Northern Hemisphere?

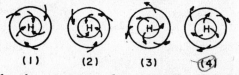

74. The characteristics of an air mass which formed over the Gulf of Mexico would probably be (1) cool and dry (2) warm and dry (3) cool and humid (4) warm and humid

75. Why is it possible for no rain to be falling from a cloud? (1) The water droplets are too small to fall. (2) The cloud is water vapor. (3) The dew point has not yet been reached in the cloud. (4) There are no condensation nuclei in the cloud.

76. The diagram below shows the direction of movement of air over a mountain.

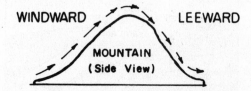

As the air moves down the leeward side of the mountain, the air will (1) warm due to compression (2) warm due to expansion (3) cool due to compression (4) cool due to expansion

77. As a parcel of air moves up a mountainside and expands, the temperature of the air will (1) decrease (2) increase (3) remain the same

78. Which fact explains why the moist adiabatic lapse rate is less than the dry adiabatic lapse rate? (1) Air pressure in clouds does not allow air to expand. (2) Condensation is a warming process. (3) Evaporation is a cooling process. (4) Water vapor is lighter than dry air.

79. An air mass originating over the North Pacific Ocean would most likely be (1) continental polar (2) continental tropical (3) maritime polar (4) maritime tropical

80. How does air circulate within a cyclone (low-pressure area) in the Northern Hemisphere? (1) counterclockwise and toward the center of the cyclone (2) counterclockwise and away from the center of the cyclone (3) clockwise and toward the center of the cyclone (4) clockwise and away from the center of the cyclone

81. A mT air mass would most likely originate over which type of Earth surface? (1) cold and moist (2) warm and moist (3) cold and dry (4) warm and dry

82. At which location will a low-pressure storm center most likely form? (1) along a frontal surface between different air masses (2) near the middle of a cold air mass (3) on the leeward side of mountains (4) over a very dry, large, flat land area

83. The diagram below represents a cross-sectional view of air masses associated with a low-pressure system. The cold frontal interface is moving faster than the warm frontal interface. What usually happens to the warm air that is between the two frontal surfaces?

(1) The warm air is forced over both frontal interfaces. (2) The warm air is forced under both frontal interfaces. (3) The warm air is forced over the cold frontal interface but under the warm frontal interface. (4) The warm air is forced under the cold frontal interface but over the warm frontal interface.

84. On a weather map, an air mass that is very warm and dry would be labeled (1) mP (2) mT (3) cP (4) cT

85. As a sample of very moist air rises from sea level to a higher altitude, the probability of condensation occurring in that air sample will (1) decrease (2) increase (3) remain the same

86. Compared to a maritime tropical air mass, a maritime polar air mass has (1) lower temperature and less water vapor (2) lower temperature and more water vapor (3) higher temperature and less water vapor (4) higher temperature and more water vapor

87. Two weather stations are located near each other. The air pressure at each station is changing so that the difference between the pressures is increasing. The wind speed between these two locations will probably (1) decrease (2) increase (3) remain the same

88. An air mass from the Gulf of Mexico, moving north into New York State, has a high relative humidity. What other characteristics will it probably have? (1) warm temperatures and low pressure (2) cool temperatures and low pressure (3) warm temperatures and high pressure (4) cool temperatures and high pressure

89. An air mass located over the central United States will most likely move toward the (1) northeast (2) northwest (3) southeast (4) southwest

Directions (90–94): Base your answers to questions 90 through 94 on your knowledge of earth science and the diagram below which shows a mountain. The prevailing wind direction and air temperatures at different elevations on both sides of the mountain are indicated.

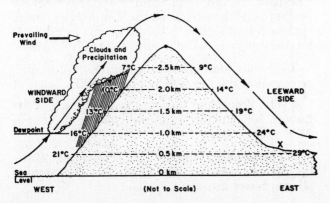

90. What would be the approximate air temperature at the top of the mountain? (1) 12°C (2) 10°C (3) 0°C (4) 4°C

91. On which side of the mountain and at what elevation is the relative humidity probably 100%? (1) on the windward side at 0.5 km (2) on the windward side at 1.5 km (3) on the leeward side at 1.0 km (4) on the leeward side at 2.5 km

92. How does the temperature of the air change as the air rises on the windward side of the mountain between sea level and 0.5 kilometer? (1) The air is warming due to compression of the air. (2) The air is warming due to expansion of the air. (3) The air is cooling due to compression of the air. (4) The air is cooling due to expansion of the air.

93. Which feature is probably located at the base of the mountain on the leeward side (location X)? (1) an arid region (2) a jungle (3) a glacier (4) a large lake

94. The air temperature on the leeward side of the mountain at the 1.5-kilometer level is higher than the temperature at the same elevation on the windward side. What is the probable cause for this? (1) Heat stored in the ocean keeps the windward side of the mountain warmer. (2) The insolation received at sea level is greater on the leeward side of the mountain. (3) The air on the windward side of the mountain has a lower adiabatic lapse rate than the air on the leeward side of the mountain. (4) Potential energy is lost as rain runs off the windward side of the mountain.

SYNOPTIC WEATHER MAPS

Weather maps that show a variety of atmospheric field quantities are known as **synoptic weather maps**. See Figure 7-19. Synoptic maps may show information about temperature, air pressure, precipitation, and other weather conditions at a particular time and over a large geographic area. The temperature field is shown by *isotherms*, and the field of air pressure is shown by lines of constant air pressure known as *isobars*. Because most weather systems move across the United States from west to east, synoptic weather maps provide information that can be used in making weather predictions. Some symbols used in describing weather conditions are shown in Figure 7-20.

Interpreting Information Shown at a Weather Station.

Because so much information must be recorded at each of the stations on a weather map, the information is shown in an abbreviated form (synoptic). Each type of measurement is shown at a prescribed position next to the circle that shows the geographic location of the reporting station. See Figure 7-21.

How to interpret the information recorded at weather stations on a synoptic weather map:

1. The circle in Figure 7-21 shows the geographic location of the weather station. The cloud cover is shown by the amount of the circle that is dark. This example shows a 75% cloud cover.

Energy Exchanges in the Atmosphere

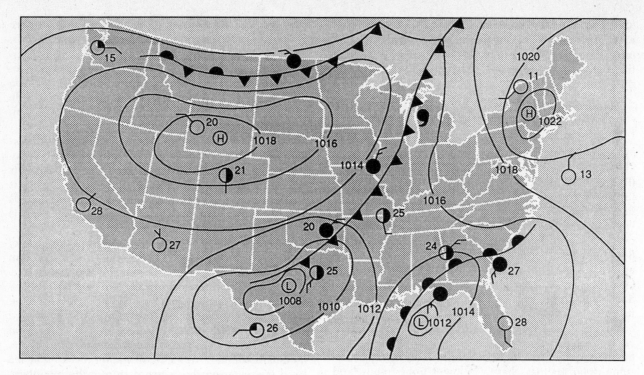

Figure 7-19. A synoptic weather map.

Present Weather
Symbols

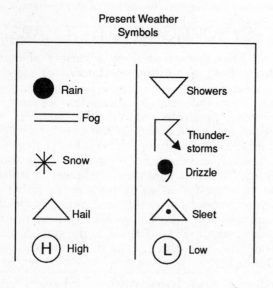

● Rain	▽	Showers
═ Fog		Thunder-storms
✳ Snow	● Drizzle
△ Hail	△ Sleet
Ⓗ High	Ⓛ Low

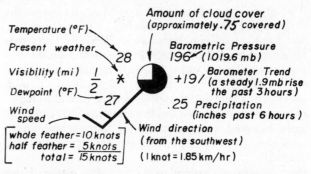

Figure 7-21. A weather station model.

Temperature (°F)
Present weather
Visibility (mi)
Dewpoint (°F)
Wind speed

Amount of cloud cover
(approximately .75 covered)
Barometric Pressure
196 (1019.6 mb)
+19/ Barometer Trend
(a steady 1.9 mb rise
the past 3 hours)
.25 Precipitation
(inches past 6 hours)
Wind direction
(from the southwest)
(1 knot = 1.85 km/hr)

whole feather = 10 knots
half feather = 5 knots
total = 15 knots

2. The line connected to the circle shows the direction *from which* the wind is blowing. This example shows a wind from the southwest. (Winds are always shown and named by the direction from which the wind has come and not by the direction toward which the wind is going.) The feathers show the wind speed. Each whole feather is 10 knots (10 nautical miles per hour), and each half feather 5 knots. In this example 1½ feathers means a wind of approximately 15 knots.

3. The air temperature in degrees Fahrenheit is shown at the top left; here it is 28°F.

4. The dew-point temperature is shown at the bottom left. In this example, the dew point is 27°F.

5. The symbol at the left side of the circle shows the present weather. The symbol in the example above shows snow.

Front Symbols

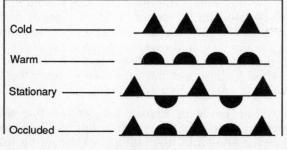

Cold ————	▲▲▲▲
Warm ————	⬤⬤⬤
Stationary ———	▲⬤▲⬤
Occluded ————	▲⬤▲▲

Figure 7-20.

6. The number next to the symbol for present weather shows the atmospheric visibility in miles; here it is ½ mile.

7. At the top right is a three-digit code showing the air pressure. To decode, a "9" or a "10" must be added in front of the code numbers, and a decimal point must be placed before the final digit. When the first digit is less than 5 add a 10. However, if the first digit is 5 or greater add a 9. For example, 196 millibars equals 1019.6 millibars. And 979 millibars equals 997.9 millibars. The final recording must result in a number that is close to the normal reading for air pressure which is about 1000 millibars.

8. The number to the right of the circle shows the change in air pressure over the past three hours. (Again, a decimal point must be added.) The line to the right of the number shows how the air pressure has changed. This one shows a steady increase of 1.9 millibars. A decreasing air pressure foretells the coming of clouds and rain. A rising air pressure means improving weather.

9. The number below the change in air pressure shows the amount of precipitation in inches over the past six hours. In this example, 25 hundredths of an inch of snow has fallen in 6 hours.

Some weather stations may display more or less information, but it will always be displayed in the format shown here.

Weather Predictions.
Based upon measurements of weather variables and weather patterns, meteorologists can make predictions of weather in the future. Such predictions have become increasingly reliable as more and more data have become available, and as computers have enabled meteorologists to process the data. Weather predictions are often expressed as a *probability* of occurrence. For example, if the present conditions have led to rainfall three out of four times in the past (¾), then the probability of rainfall is 75%.

QUESTIONS

95. The arrows on the diagram below represent surface wind directions on a weather map. The points represent the locations of four weather stations in the Northern Hemisphere. Which weather station probably has the *lowest* air pressure?

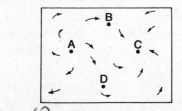

(1) A (2) B (3) C (4) D

Directions (96–97): Base your answers to questions 96 and 97 on the weather map shown below.

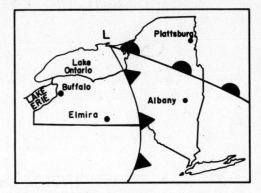

96. Which city is located in the warmest air mass? (1) Buffalo (2) Elmira (3) Albany (4) Plattsburg

97. Which city has most recently experienced a change in wind direction, brief heavy precipitation, and a rapid drop in air temperature? (1) Buffalo (2) Plattsburg (3) Albany (4) Elmira

98. A weather station records a barometric pressure of 1013.2 millibars. Which diagram below would best represent this weather station on a weather map? [Refer to the *Earth Science Reference Tables*.]

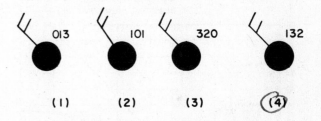

Directions (99–101): Base your answers to questions 99 through 101 on your knowledge of earth science and on the diagram below which represents a coastal region with wind direction as indicated.

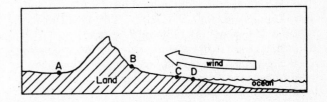

99. Which best explains the direction of the wind? (1) the land being cooled during a clear night (2) more water vapor in the air over the ocean than in the air over the land (3) low pressure over the land, and high pressure over the ocean (4) warm currents in the ocean

100. In the diagram, heat energy is being transferred by the wind from the ocean to the land mainly by the process of (1) convection (2) conduction (3) radiation (4) insolation

101. If the wind indicated in the diagram shows the prevailing wind direction, which location probably records the highest annual precipitation? (1) A (2) B (3) C (4) D

102. The diagram below shows four points on a map with their positions relative to a low-pressure weather system. Which point is most likely having heavy precipitation?

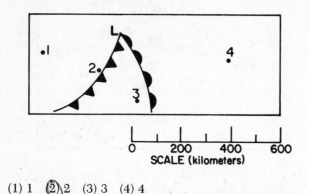

(1) 1   (2) 2   (3) 3   (4) 4

Directions (103–107): Base your answers to questions 103 through 107 on your knowledge of earth science, the *Earth Science Reference Tables*, and the graph below which shows the air temperature and dew-point temperature over a 24-hour period for a location in New York State.

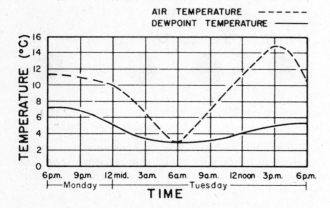

103. When was the air at ground level saturated with water vapor?   (1) 6 P.M. Monday   (2) 6 A.M. Tuesday   (3) 3 P.M. Tuesday   (4) 12 noon Tuesday

104. According to the weather map information in the *Earth Science Reference Tables*, which weather station model best represents the weather conditions at this location at 9 P.M. on Monday?

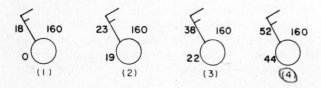

105. The air's capacity to hold water vapor was greatest at   (1) 6 P.M. Monday   (2) 6 A.M. Tuesday   (3) 3 P.M. Tuesday   (4) 12 noon Tuesday

106. If the trends shown continued, the air temperature at 7 P.M. Tuesday was probably about   (1) 8°C   (2) 2°C   (3) 11°C   (4) 14°C

107. The relative humidity at midnight was approximately   (1) 10%   (2) 40%   (3) 50%   (4) 70%

Directions (108–112): Base your answers to questions 108 through 112 on your knowledge of earth science, the *Earth Science Reference Tables*, and the map below which represents a weather system located over the central United States. Letters *A, B, C, D,* and *E* locate weather stations on the map.

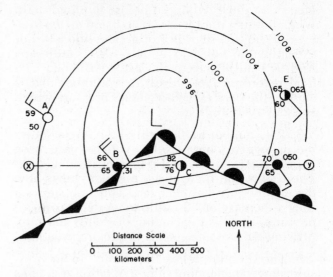

108. What is the air pressure at weather station *A*?   (1) 1069 mb   (2) 1064 mb   (3) 1004 mb   (4) 1000 mb

109. Which weather station is experiencing clouds, heavy precipitation, and rapidly decreasing air temperature?   (1) *A*   (2) *B*   (3) *E*   (4) *D*

110. In which diagram do the arrows best represent the wind direction in the weather system?

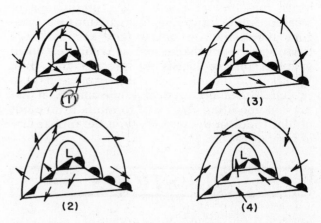

111. Which diagram best represents a cross section of the earth's atmosphere showing the fronts between air masses as they would appear along line x–y?

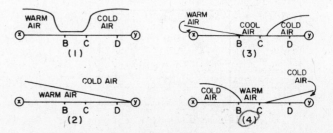

TOPIC 8 Moisture, Energy Budgets, Environmental Change

THE WATER CYCLE

The earth has a limited water supply that is constantly being recycled between the oceans, atmosphere, and land in a process called the **water cycle**. During this recycling process, water enters the atmosphere by evaporation and transpiration (evapotranspiration), which are fueled by energy from the sun. Water then condenses and returns to the earth's surface as precipitation. Precipitation that does not freeze, evaporate, or run off the land into streams **infiltrates** (sinks into) the ground and becomes **groundwater**. See Figure 8-1.

About 98% of the water on our planet is found in the oceans. The glaciers that exist near the poles of the earth account for most of the remaining water. Only about 0.6% of the earth's water exists within the ground, as groundwater. Unlike the oceans, groundwater is mostly fresh water; and unlike the glaciers, it is in the liquid state. Plants need groundwater for growth. Groundwater is also an important source of water for our homes, industry, and agriculture.

Groundwater Zones. After infiltrating soil, groundwater occupies distinct zones. See Figure 8-2. Gravity pulls much of the groundwater down into the **zone of saturation**. In the saturated zone, all spaces, cracks, and other openings in soil and rock grains become completely filled with water. Water will stop sinking deep into the soil once it has reached a layer of solid rock underneath the saturated zone that it cannot pass through (impermeable bedrock, as shown in Figure 8-2).

After all water has sunk to the zone of saturation, a boundary develops where the saturated zone meets the layer of particles above it. This boundary at the upper level of the saturated zone is called the **water table**. The zone between the water table and the surface of the soil is called the **zone of aeration**. In the aerated zone, air and some groundwater (known as *capillary water*) are present between spaces and cracks in soil and rock grains. The roots of plants in the root zone draw upon this water for plant growth.

Factors That Affect the Storage and Movement of Groundwater.
The amount of water in the ground and the movement of water through the ground are controlled by the characteristics of the soil and rock found near the surface. Water is able to infiltrate the ground when there are many openings, or pores, between ground particles for the water to pass through. Almost all materials on the earth's surface are porous, or have pores. The number of pores in a material compared with its volume is called **porosity**. It is porosity, or the percentage of empty space, that determines how much water a sample of rock can hold. See Figure 8-3.

The porosity of a loose material, such as soil, largely depends upon shape, packing, and the mixture of sizes of the soil particles. The most

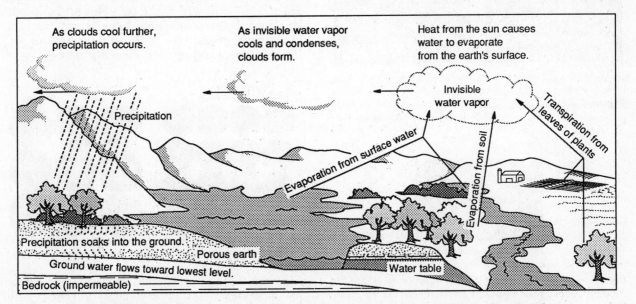

Figure 8-1. The water cycle is made up of a combination of processes that recycle the earth's water.

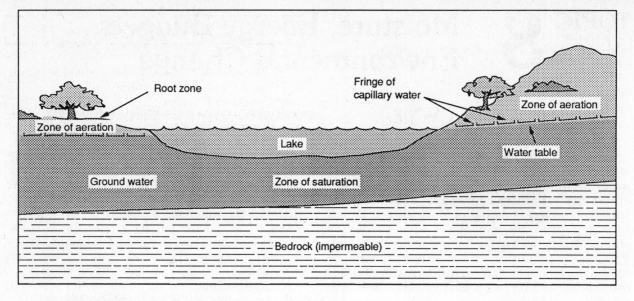

Figure 8-2. In the zone of saturation, all spaces between soil grains are filled with water. In the zone of aeration, all spaces between soil grains contain both air and water that plants use for growth.

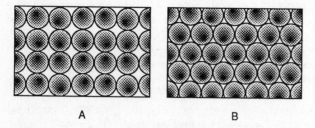

Figure 8-3. Pore spaces, capable of holding water, among round-shaped particles can account for about one-third of the total volume of a sample.

A   B

Figure 8-4. Because of the difference in the packing arrangement, soil sample B has less pore space than does sample A. Therefore, A is more porous than B.

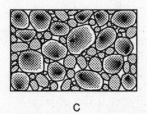

C

Figure 8-5. The porosity of soil sample C is greatly reduced because it contains particles of mixed sizes. In this sample, the smaller particles can fill the spaces between the larger ones.

porous soils are those that contain round particles that are all of the same size (**well sorted**) and that are not closely packed. The more closely packed the particles of soil are, the less porous the soil; the less closely packed the particles of soil are, the more porous the soil. See Figure 8-4.

Flattened and angular soil grains, such as clay particles, can pack closely together; therefore, most clay soils have little pore space and a low porosity. A soil that is composed of a mixture of particle sizes also has a low porosity because its smaller particles can fit into spaces between its larger particles. See Figure 8-5.

It is important to note that particle size alone does not affect the porosity of a soil. For example, when two well-sorted samples of different soils are taken—one with large particles and one with small particles—both may have about the same porosity, especially if their soil particles are similarly shaped and packed. See Figure 8-6.

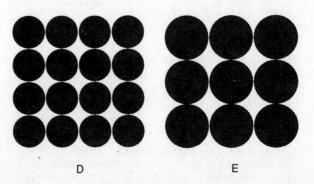

D   E

Figure 8-6. The well-sorted, small-grained soil (D) and the well-sorted, large-grained soil (E) have equally high porosities, especially since their soil particles are similarly shaped and packed.

Some rocks have low porosities because of a cementlike material that reduces pore space between particles. See Figure 8-7. Nonporous rocks, such as limestone, can become permeable (able to transmit water) because of the formation of cracks through which water can pass. See Figure 8-8.

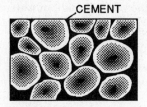

CEMENT

Figure 8-7. The presence of a natural cement material between particles reduces the porosity of this rock material.

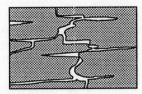

Figure 8-8. A rock with low porosity can become permeable because of cracks and fissures that develop during its formation.

Permeability is the ability of a soil to transmit water. The rate of permeability, or how fast water can pass through a soil, depends on the size of the pores and how the pores are connected. For example, soils with high permeabilities, such as sand, have large pores that are well connected. Water flows through the pores with little resistance. Soils with low permeabilities, such as clay, have small pores that are not well connected. Water in very small pores moves slowly and clings to the surfaces of nearby soil particles.

Infiltration of water will continue if the surface of a soil is permeable, if a soil is unsaturated, or if both conditions exist. However, surface **runoff** will occur when rainfall exceeds the permeability rate of a soil, when a soil is saturated, or when the slope (gradient) of a soil's surface is too great to allow infiltration to occur. Infiltration is also affected by temperature. At temperatures below 0°C, water within a soil will freeze, thus preventing further infiltration.

Capillarity is the ability of a soil to draw water upward into tiny spaces between soil grains. Soils composed of very small particles show the most capillary uptake. Capillary water moves upward against the force of gravity because of the attraction between water molecules and the surfaces of the soil particles. Capillarity, therefore, occurs most frequently in soils with small particles because these soils have more surface area per unit volume for water to cling to than do soils with large particles. Capillary water is water available for plants to draw through their roots. Figure 8-2 shows a fringe of capillary water.

1. As the amount of precipitation on land increases, the level of the water table will probably (1) fall (2) rise (3) remain the same
2. As groundwater flows from gravel into sand, its rate of flow will probably (1) decrease (2) increase (3) remain the same
3. A rock with a high porosity will probably (1) be resistant to weathering (2) be composed of large grains (3) have a large percentage of space between particles (4) have a small percentage of rounded particles
4. Which graph best represents the relationship between porosity and particle size for soil samples of uniform size, shape, and packing?

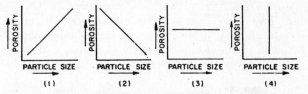

5. Assuming a constant land slope, the greatest infiltration of water into the earth will occur when the surface is (1) permeable and saturated (2) permeable and unsaturated (3) impermeable and saturated (4) impermeable and unsaturated
6. Surface runoff will *not* occur when (1) rainfall exceeds the permeability rate (2) the pore spaces are filled (3) infiltration exceeds rainfall (4) the slope of the surface is too great to allow infiltration
7. Which factor has the *least* effect on the rate of surface runoff? (1) amount of rainfall (2) permeability rate (3) surface slope (4) capillary action
8. During a rainstorm, when is surface runoff *least* likely to occur? (1) when the permeability rate of the soil equals the rainfall rate (2) when the pore spaces of the ground are saturated with water (3) when rainfall rate exceeds the permeability rate of the soil (4) when the slope of the surface is too great for infiltration to occur
9. Which is most important in determining the amount of groundwater that can be stored within a rock? (1) the rock's geologic age (2) the rock's hardness (3) the rock's porosity (4) the rock's color
10. Surface runoff will generally be greatest when the (1) rainfall is light and the ground is permeable (2) infiltration rate is greater than the rainfall rate (3) slope of the land is too great to permit infiltration (4) ground is permeable and unsaturated
11. When rain falls on a soil surface, flooding at that location would most likely occur if the (1) soil surface is permeable (2) soil surface is covered with vegetation (3) soil pore spaces are filled to capacity (4) infiltration rate exceeds the precipitation rate
12. Why does water move very slowly downward through clay soil? (1) Clay soil is composed of low-density minerals. (2) Clay soil is composed of very hard particles. (3) Clay soil has large pore spaces. (4) Clay soil has very small pore spaces.

13. Which graph most nearly represents the change in the infiltration rate of surface water as the soil temperature rises from −10°C through the freezing point to +10°C?

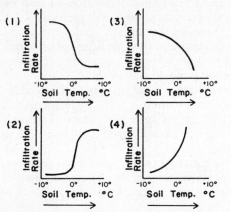

14. Two equal areas *A* and *B* each contain a sample of uniform size sediments as shown in the diagram below. Compared to the porosity of sample *A*, the porosity of sample *B* will be (1) less (2) greater (3) the same

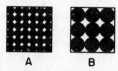

15. All the tubes below are the same except for the size of the soil particles inside. When water is poured into the tubes it will pass down through which tube the fastest?

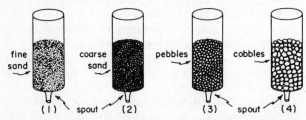

16. Which property of loose earth materials most likely increases as particle size decreases? (1) capillarity (2) infiltration (3) permeability (4) porosity

17. In which tube will capillary action be the greatest?

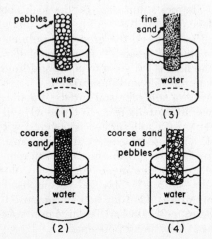

Directions (18–22): For *each* sentence in questions 18 through 22, write the *number* of the word, *chosen from the list below*, which is most closely related to that sentence.

(1) Capillarity (2) Permeability (3) Porosity

18. Water moves freely downward through upper portions of the soil most of the time.

19. There is the same amount of water in a saturated cubic meter of sand as there is in a saturated cubic meter of clay.

20. Water is *not* able to flow through all earth materials at the same rate.

21. Water movement increases as particle size decreases.

22. Water moves upward within the aeration zone.

WATER FOR STREAM FLOW

During and immediately after precipitation, streams receive water from overland flow. Even during dry periods when there is no ground runoff, however, many streams continue to flow. In these dry periods, stream water may come from the ground. For example, in regions where groundwater and precipitation are plentiful, water will seep into the streams where the water table comes to the surface at the streambed.

In dry climates, groundwater may be recharged by water flowing from the streams into the ground. See Figure 8-9.

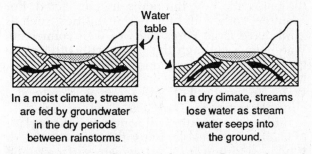

In a moist climate, streams are fed by groundwater in the dry periods between rainstorms.

In a dry climate, streams lose water as stream water seeps into the ground.

Figure 8-9. Groundwater and stream flow in dry and moist climates.

Rainfall and Stream Flow.

Streams and rivers do not respond immediately to rainfall, for most precipitation falls on the ground and then must flow over the ground as runoff to reach a stream. Therefore, a time lag occurs between maximum precipitation and maximum stream discharge. See Figure 8-10. Several other factors determine how quickly and how strongly streams respond to precipitation. If precipitation falls as snow, if the gradient of the land is low (little slope), or if a great deal of vegetation blocks overland flow, streams will respond more slowly. Large rivers respond slowly because most runoff must flow a great distance to reach the rivers. Small streams and streams in mountain areas where the land is steep and rocky respond quickly to rainfall. Less of a time lag exists be-

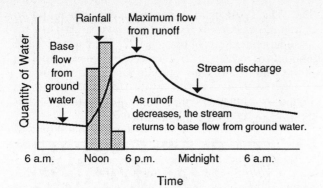

Figure 8-10. How a stream responds to precipitation. The greatest stream flow occurs after the time of maximum precipitation. A greater time lag occurs for large streams and streams in forested regions than for small streams and streams in urban areas.

tween maximum precipitation and maximum discharge. Also, runoff is very rapid and very brief in regions with buildings, paved streets, and parking lots.

QUESTIONS

23. Stream discharge would normally be highest during a period of (1) recharge (2) deficit (3) usage (4) surplus

24. During a dry summer, stream discharge is primarily controlled by the (1) supply of groundwater in the area of the stream (2) loss of capillary water through evapotranspiration (3) shape of the stream channel (4) amount of vegetation on the banks of the stream

25. As the groundwater supply during a drought (dry) period decreases, the amount of stream discharge will normally (1) decrease (2) increase (3) remain the same

26. Over several years, the graph of the velocity of stream flow for a point in a river of New York State will probably (1) decrease at a regular rate (2) increase at a regular rate (3) remain constant (4) vary in a cyclic manner

Base your answers to questions 27 and 28 on the graph below which represents the relationship between the time of year and the average monthly discharge of a stream located in New York State.

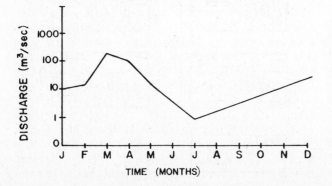

27. According to the graph, when will maximum surface runoff occur? (1) February through April (2) April through June (3) June through August (4) October through December

28. The stream discharge in June most likely occurred during a period of (1) minimum evapotranspiration (2) maximum groundwater surplus (3) groundwater recharge (4) groundwater depletion

ENVIRONMENTAL POLLUTION

Pollution can be defined as too much of any substance or of any form of energy in the environment that harms people or the plants and animals upon which people depend. Pollution comes from a variety of sources. Individuals cause pollution by littering and by contributing to smog when they discharge waste materials, such as smoke and exhaust fumes, from their homes and cars. Communities cause pollution by releasing sewage into rivers and lakes. Industries cause pollution by burying dangerous chemicals in the ground, by dumping chemicals into streams, lakes, and oceans, and by releasing effluents from industrial furnaces. All of these forms of pollution have resulted from our growing technology-based economy.

Many of the most serious forms of pollution exist in heavily populated regions. The concentration of pollutants usually varies directly with the population density. For example, the concentration of water pollutants in rivers, lakes, and groundwater increases in the vicinity of population centers. Air pollution also tends to vary directly with population density.

Our use of fossil fuels has created great amounts of carbon dioxide gas, which is released into the atmosphere. Because water vapor and carbon dioxide are good absorbers of heat (infrared) radiation, they trap heat energy in the atmosphere. For example, insolation can penetrate the air to warm the surface of the earth. However, when the heated earth then reradiates the energy back toward space, the longer-wave heat rays are absorbed by carbon dioxide and water vapor and cannot escape into space. As a result, some scientists believe the radiative equilibrium of the earth may be upset, possibly causing the earth's climates to become warmer.

Acid rain is created when factories and automobiles release particles and gases rich in the oxides of sulfur and nitrogen. These substances dissolve in water in the clouds and form acid rain that falls to the earth with precipitation. Acid rainfall has caused the rapid corrosion of buildings, and it has caused some soils and lakes to become so acidic that native plants and animals cannot live in them.

Inorganic wastes in the water, such as mercury and other chemicals, may concentrate in the bodies of fish and make the fish unfit for human consumption. In larger quantities, these chemicals make the water dangerous to play or swim in. If inorganic wastes are discharged into the ground, they can make ground water unfit for human consumption and for other uses. Although it is possible to purify water by filtration, by treatment with other chemicals, and by distillation, these methods are costly.

Organic Pollution.
Organic wastes in water, such as sewage and fertilizers, can promote the growth of **aerobic bacteria** that use dissolved oxygen in freshwater rivers and lakes. Most organic wastes result from fertilizers that wash off the land, from the waste products of farm animals, and from the incomplete sewage treatment of human wastes. Aerobic bacteria deplete the water of dissolved oxygen and lead to the growth of **anaerobic bacteria** that can live in water without dissolved oxygen. In the end, the water is unable to support a normal community of plants and animals.

Energy Pollution.
Various forms of energy pollution can adversely affect the environment. For example, electrical power plants release heated water into lakes and streams. This heated water can decrease the ability of our streams and lakes to hold dissolved oxygen. At the same time, heated water can cause fish to die because their cold-blooded bodies cannot adjust to rapid temperature changes. In other instances, energy pollution occurs when nuclear power plants release radioactive materials that can be harmful in large concentrations to plant and animal life.

QUESTIONS

29. As the human population density along a shore of a lake increases, the pollution of the lake usually (1) decreases (2) increases (3) remains the same

30. Which graph generally represents the relationship between the quality of river water and the density of human population along the river if sewage treatment facilities are *not* provided?

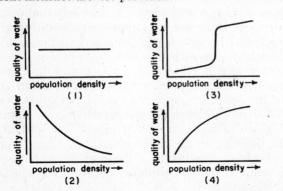

31. A major argument against the construction of nuclear-powered electric generation stations is the claim that they pollute bodies of water by discharging large quantities of (1) noise (2) heat (3) organisms (4) chemicals

32. What is the main reason that a high concentration of aerobic bacteria is harmful to a lake? (1) They release large amounts of oxygen. (2) They use up large amounts of oxygen. (3) They cause excessive cooling of the water. (4) They provide food for predators.

Directions (33–37): Base your answers to questions 33 through 37 on the map below.

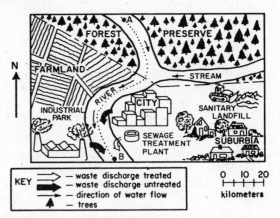

33. Which landscape region has probably been altered *least* by the activities of humans? (1) suburbia (2) sanitary landfill (3) farmland (4) forest preserve

34. Which graph best represents the probable number of bacteria (anaerobic) along line *A-B* in the river?

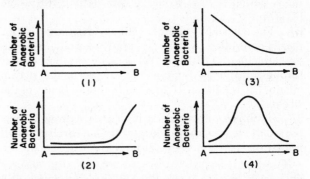

35. If light rains occurred for one hour, which area would most likely experience the greatest amount of surface runoff per square kilometer? (1) farmland (2) suburbia (3) forest preserve (4) city

36. Which diagram best illustrates the probable *air pollution field* of this area at an elevation of 100 meters on a windless spring afternoon?

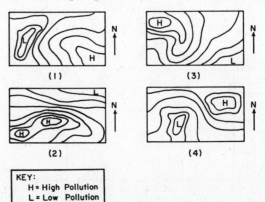

KEY:
H = High Pollution
L = Low Pollution

37. The people of this area defeated legislation that would have allowed the sale of a large section of the public-owned forest preserve for the purpose of a second industrial park. They also passed a bond issue providing funds for an additional sewage-treatment plant for the city. These actions are an indication that a majority of the voters   (1) are opposed to higher taxes for any reason   (2) feel technology can solve all the problems of the environment   (3) are aware of the delicate balance in nature   (4) feel that nature can take care of itself

THE WATER BUDGET

Each locality or region has its own water budget. The **water budget** is a model that accounts for changes in ground water held within the root zone. The root zone is the top several meters of the ground.

A person's financial budget states income (money coming in) and expected expenses (money going out) for a given period of time. In a balanced budget, the money coming in equals the money going out. In a local water budget, precipitation is income and evapotranspiration is an expense.

The water budget of a particular region usually is not balanced. When precipitation exceeds the evapotranspiration of a region, a surplus is said to occur. The result is moist soil in a region that may experience flooding. When evapotranspiration exceeds precipitation in a region, a deficit is said to occur. The result is dry soil in a region that may need irrigation. Thus, the water budget is often used in estimating when crops and other plants have enough water for active growth and when irrigation is likely to be needed. It can also be used to determine when small streams are likely to overflow or run dry.

The text that follows briefly explains the meanings of each of the rows of figures in the water budget for Buffalo, New York. The local water budget represents a continuous cycle in which December precedes January, even though they are on opposite sides of the data table. See Table 8-1. Precipitation and evapotranspiration, as well as other factors in the water budget, are measured in millimeters.

Precipitation (P) is the source of water (rain, snow, hail, etc.), or income, for the water budget.

In Buffalo, the greatest amount of precipitation occurred in January and December (81 mm)—the least amount in April (68 mm).

Potential evapotranspiration (E_p) is the "demand" of the atmosphere for moisture. During evapotranspiration, water is lost (an expense) from the water budget. In Buffalo, the greatest loss of water occurred in July (135 mm). E_p depends upon available energy to support the processes of evaporation and transpiration. For this reason, E_p will reflect changes in air temperature. In the summer, when there is more heat energy, E_p will be the highest. For Buffalo, New York, the highest readings for E_p occur in June, July, and August when the weather is the warmest.

P minus E_p is the difference between the income (P) and the demand (E_p) for water. $P - E_p$ can be negative, positive, or zero. In Buffalo, the demand (E_p) is much greater than the income (P) for water during the months of June, July, and August ($P - E_p = -42$, -62, and -48, respectively).

St is the amount of water in *storage* within the root zone. St is like a savings account at a bank in which water may be deposited or withdrawn. The amount of water in storage has limits. In general, it cannot be less than 0 mm or more than 100 mm. During the summer months, precipitation (P) may be insufficient to meet the great demand (E_p). At this point, water from storage (savings) begins to evaporate (withdrawal). If the demand (E_p) exceeds both the precipitation (P) and the available water in storage (St), a deficit will appear. In Buffalo, a *deficit* (D), or water shortage, occurs in July, August, and September ($D = 4$, 48, and 9, respectively). Note, however, that a water shortage (deficit) did not occur in June because there was enough water in storage (savings) to draw upon. St dropped from 100 mm to 58 mm; this is a difference of 42 mm, which covers $P - E_p$ (-42) in June.

ΔSt is the *change in storage* as water is withdrawn or replaced in the root zone. ΔSt can have a negative, positive, or zero value. A positive ΔSt represents the replacement (*recharge*) of water into storage. It occurs when the soil is not saturated and P is greater than E_p. A negative ΔSt represents the withdrawal (*usage*) of water from storage. It occurs when P is less than E_p and soil storage is greater than zero. A zero for ΔSt indi-

Table 8-1. Monthly Water Budget for Buffalo, New York, Measured in Millimeters

Symbols	J	F	M	A	M	J	J	A	S	O	N	D	Total
P	81	72	71	68	73	69	73	74	75	78	80	81	895
E_p	0	0	0	30	72	111	135	122	84	48	15	0	617
P minus E_p	81	72	71	38	1	−42	−62	−48	−9	30	65	81	—
ΔSt	0	0	0	0	0	−42	−58	0	0	30	65	5	—
St	100	100	100	100	100	58	0	0	0	30	95	100	—
E_a	0	0	0	30	72	111	131	74	75	48	15	0	556
D	0	0	0	0	0	0	4	48	9	0	0	0	61
S	81	72	71	38	1	0	0	0	0	0	0	76	339

cates that no change is taking place in the amount of water in storage. According to the monthly water budget for Buffalo, stored water is withdrawn in June ($\Delta St = -42$) and July ($\Delta St = -58$) for a total withdrawal of -100 mm to meet the demand. Therefore, water in storage drops to zero for the months of July, August, and September. A change in storage (ΔSt) does not occur again until the months of October ($\Delta St = 30$), November ($\Delta St = 65$), and December ($\Delta St = 5$), when storage is again recharged and is filled up to 100 mm.

Actual evapotranspiration is the amount of water that is actually lost to evaporation and transpiration. The actual evapotranspiration (E_a) will be equal to the potential evapotranspiration (E_p) if there was enough water available from precipitation and from the previous month's storage. Only if there is not enough water in storage can E_a be less than E_p. During the months of July, August, and September in Buffalo, storage is empty ($St = 0$); therefore, E_a is less than E_p. Otherwise, E_a equals E_p for all the other months. Note, however, E_a is never greater than E_p.

D represents a water *deficit*. E_a cannot be greater than either E_p or $P + St$. Therefore, when $P + St$ is less than E_p, E_a will also be less than E_p, and a deficit occurs. The amount of deficit equals $E_p - E_a$. For Buffalo, a deficit occurs in July ($E_p - E_a = 135 - 131 = 4$), August ($E_p - E_a = 122 - 74 = 48$), and September ($E_p - E_a = 84 - 75 = 9$).

S represents a water *surplus*. A surplus occurs when the soil is filled to its maximum storage capacity of 100 mm and **P** is greater than E_p. Surplus water becomes runoff or sinks below the water table. A surplus occurs in Buffalo during the months of December to May.

CLIMATE

Unlike weather, the **climate** for a large geographical region is based upon atmospheric con-

ditions measured over a long time period. The average conditions of temperature and precipitation and the annual distribution of these conditions characterize a region's climate.

A water budget, such as the one for Buffalo, New York, in Table 8-1, may be used in analyzing and classifying climates. For example, the total figures of precipitation and potential evapotranspiration are used in classifying a climate as either *humid* (moist) or *arid* (dry). Because its annual precipitation (895 mm) exceeds its potential evapotranspiration (617 mm), Buffalo's climate is classified as humid.

Water-budget data can also be displayed in a graph. Water-budget graphs usually show lines representing the precipitation, potential evapotranspiration, and actual evapotranspiration for each month. Spaces between these lines will show the surplus, deficit, recharge, and usage for each month of the water budget. The graph of a

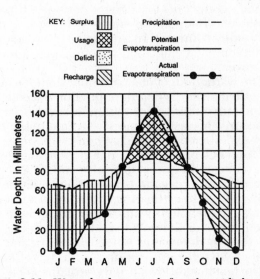

Figure 8-11. Water budget graph for a humid climate. Albany has very little deficit and large surpluses which characterize a humid climate.

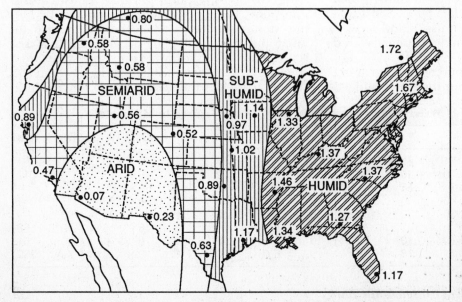

P/E_p Ratio Range	Type of Climate
Over 1.2	Humid
0.8 to 1.2	Subhumid
0.4 to 0.8	Semiarid
Less than 0.4	Arid

Figure 8-12. Climates can be classified as humid or arid based upon the ratio between the total annual precipitation and the total annual potential evapotranspiration.

water budget for Albany, New York indicates a humid climate. See Figure 8-11.

Another system used to classify climates is also based on water-budget data. On the basis of a ratio between precipitation and potential evapotranspiration (P/E_p), a region's climate can be classified into one of four climatic zones of the United States. See Figure 8-12. For example, the water budget data for Buffalo, New York, in Table 8-1 indicates a P/E_p ratio of 1.45 (P/E_p = 895/617 = 1.45). According to the Table in Figure 8-12, the ratio is over 1.2. Therefore, Buffalo's climate is considered humid.

QUESTIONS

38. The main source of moisture for the local water budget is (1) potential evapotranspiration (2) actual evapotranspiration (3) ground water storage (4) precipitation

39. The potential evapotranspiration of an area is most dependent on the (1) insolation from the sun (2) ground water storage (3) amount of runoff (4) pore spaces in the soil

40. As both the duration and the angle of insolation increase, the potential evapotranspiration will generally (1) decrease (2) increase (3) remain the same

41. The potential evapotranspiration (E_p) of an area will be increased if there is an increase in (1) soil porosity (2) temperature (3) storage capacity (4) surface runoff

42. During which month will the potential evapotranspiration usually be the greatest in New York State? (1) January (2) April (3) July (4) October

43. When does a moisture deficit occur in a local water budget? (1) when precipitation is less than potential evapotranspiration and the soil storage is zero (2) when precipitation plus surplus is greater than potential evapotranspiration (3) when precipitation is greater than potential evapotranspiration and the soil is saturated (4) when precipitation is less than potential evapotranspiration

44. Water budget graphs for four cities, A, B, C, and D, are shown below.

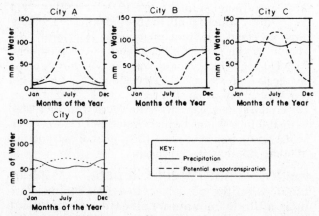

KEY:
—— Precipitation
- - - Potential evapotranspiration

Which city would have the driest climate? (1) A (2) B (3) C (4) D

45. Which graph shows the probable effect in a permeable soil when a rainy season starts following an extremely long dry period until the soil moisture storage reaches a maximum?

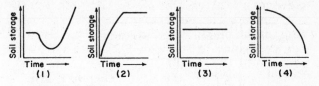

Directions (46–50): Base your answers to questions 46 through 50 on your knowledge of earth science and the water budget table shown below. The table contains part of the data for two consecutive months A and B. All data are in millimeters.

	Month A	Month B
Precipitation (P)	11 mm	18 mm
Potential evapotranspiration (E_p)	43 mm	34 mm
Precipitation minus Potential evapotranspiration ($P - E_p$)	− 32 mm	
Actual evapotranspiration (E_a)	11 mm	
Change in storage (ΔSt)	0 mm	
Storage (St)	0 mm	
Deficit (D)	32 mm	
Surplus (S)	0 mm	

46. For month B, what would be the value for storage (St)? (1) 0 mm (2) 18 mm (3) 26 mm (4) 58 mm

47. What could have caused the zero change in water storage (ΔSt) for this location during month A? (1) There was more actual evapotranspiration than deficit during month A. (2) The actual evapotranspiration was equal to the total precipitation for month A. (3) The storage must equal the change in storage for any month. (4) The potential evapotranspiration had reached a maximum for the year.

48. Which graph best represents the relationship between the data for E_p, D, E_a, and P during month A?

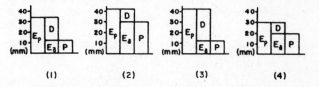

49. During month B, how much moisture must have actually evaporated and transpired? (1) 0 mm (2) 16 mm (3) 18 mm (4) 34 mm

50. The same trend continues for the P and E_p data for a third consecutive month. How would the weather for the third month compare to the weather for months A and B? (1) increasing temperatures and decreasing precipitation (2) increasing temperatures and increasing precipitation (3) decreasing temperatures and decreasing precipitation (4) decreasing temperatures and increasing precipitation

Base your answers to questions 51 through 55 on your knowledge of earth science and the data given.

Moisture, Energy Budgets, Environmental Change

The chart is a record of the monthly average temperature and average precipitation for a locality in New York State. The graph is provided for your use in plotting the given data and to assist you in answering the questions.

Temperature °C	Month	Precipitation cm
−3.1	January	6.0
−2.1	February	6.4
2.7	March	7.5
8.8	April	7.7
14.8	May	8.3
20.1	June	11.0
22.4	July	9.8
21.5	August	8.7
17.9	September	6.8
12.0	October	7.1
5.8	November	10.6
−0.3	December	8.6

KEY TO CLIMATE

Total Yearly
Precipitation

Dry - less than 50 cm

Moderate - 50 cm - 200 cm

Wet - more than 200 cm

FOR STUDENT USE

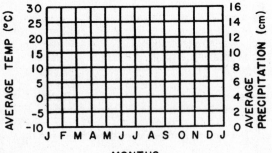

MONTHS

51. During which months does the *least* total amount of precipitation occur in this area? (1) January, February, March (2) April, May, June (3) July, August, September (4) October, November, December

52. Which graph best represents the relationship between the average precipitation and the time of year for this location?

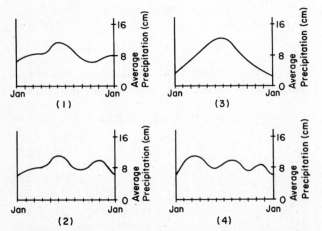

53. The stream discharge in this area is observed to remain relatively low during September, October, and early November, even though the precipitation increased during this time. The best explanation for this observation is that much of the precipitation (1) evaporated because of increased potential evapotranspiration (2) was absorbed by plants due to an increased

air temperature (3) recharged the soil moisture storage that was used during the dry months (4) was used to fill large nearby lakes

54. Which statement best describes the climate of this location during the time that the data in the chart were recorded? (1) constant monthly temperatures with moderate yearly precipitation (2) a cold, dry summer and a warm, wet winter (3) a cold, wet summer and a warm, dry winter (4) warm summer and cool winter temperatures, with a moderate yearly precipitation

55. During which month is the potential evapotranspiration for this location highest? (1) January (2) March (3) July (4) December

Directions (56–60): Base your answers to questions 56 through 60 on the water-budget diagram for Rockford, Illinois, below, and on your knowledge of earth science.

Write the *number* of the word or expression that best completes *each* statement or answers *each* question.

Water Budget Diagram for Rockford, Illinois

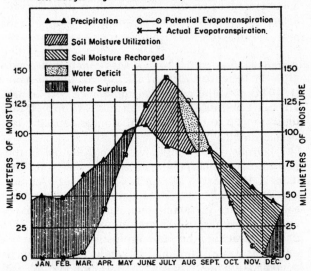

56. A water deficit occurred in Rockford, Illinois, during (1) February (2) June (3) August (4) December

57. During how many months of the year did Rockford have a water surplus? (1) 10 (2) 8 (3) 6 (4) 4

58. During which month did the potential evapotranspiration equal the precipitation in Rockford? (1) March (2) January (3) September (4) November

59. During which month was the soil moisture recharge the greatest? (1) December (2) November (3) October (4) August

60. If the storage capacity of Rockford were increased from 100 to 150 mm., which would *not* change? (1) actual evapotranspiration (2) potential evapotranspiration (3) deficit (4) surplus

Factors That Affect Climate.
Major influences on the climate of a region include latitude, altitude, mountain ranges, oceans and large bodies of water, ocean currents, planetary wind belts, and typical storm tracks.

Latitude. The latitude of a location is an important factor that determines the average local temperatures. As the distance of a location from the equator increases, the average annual temperature of the location generally decreases. Hence, the coldest climates, the polar climates, are found near the poles of the earth. Locations immediately around the equator have tropical climates and are generally warm throughout the year. Between the tropical and polar climate zones, locations have temperate, or middle-latitude, climates. Locations in middle-latitude climates experience large seasonal changes in temperature on a yearly cycle.

Altitude. High-altitude locations have cool climates because of the adiabatic cooling of air as it moves to higher elevations. As the air rises, reduced air pressure causes the air to expand and become cooler. Because of this, high plateaus and mountain peaks have lower temperatures than do places at the same latitude at sea level. Thus, snow is often found at the top of a mountain and blooming flowers at lower elevations. Humidity also decreases as altitude increases, except in the areas of glaciers.

Mountain Ranges. Mountain ranges can modify climate by controlling and changing the surface patterns of atmospheric circulation. For example, warm, moist air from over the Pacific Ocean is often forced to rise along the slope of a mountain barrier, such as the Cascade Mountain range in the Pacific Northwest, and undergo adiabatic cooling. If the air is cooled below the dew point, cloud formation and precipitation will make locations on the *windward* side of the mountains more moist than surrounding lowlands. Once the cooled, drier air rises over the mountain range, it will then descend on the lee (downwind) side of the mountains and the air will be warmed by compression as it moves to lower elevations. This causes the climate on the lee side of the mountains to be warmer and drier than the climate on the windward side. In fact, because the moisture in the air has been depleted, the air warms very quickly as it descends along the leeward side of a mountain range. Temperatures on the *leeward* side will be warmer than temperatures at the same elevation on the windward side. See Figure 8-13.

Oceans and Large Bodies of Water. Because of its specific heat, water heats up and cools down more slowly than land areas. Soil and rock heat up and cool down much more readily than water. For this reason, the climates of locations near the ocean or other large bodies of water are more moderate than inland (*continental*) climates. Seasonal temperature changes are greater at locations far from large lakes and oceans, whereas seasonal temperature changes are smaller for locations along a coastline. Coastal and *marine* cli-

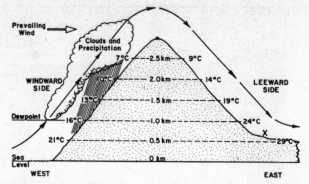

Figure 8-13. Adiabatic temperature changes and condensation cause the climates on windward and leeward sides of a mountain range to differ. As air rises on the windward side, adiabatic expansion causes cooling. Cloud formation (condensation) releases energy to slow the cooling. As the air descends on the leeward side of the mountain range, adiabatic warming is rapid due to the decreased relative humidity.

mates are cooler in the summer and warmer in the winter than are inland climates. The moderating effects of large bodies of water are particularly influential wherever winds blow from the waters onto land. New York's Long Island and the coastal cities of California, for example, enjoy smaller seasonal changes in temperature than nearby areas that are not so close to the oceans.

Ocean Currents. Another factor that influences the climate of a region is its nearness to an ocean current. An ocean current is a riverlike stream of water that circulates through the ocean. Air above an ocean current is affected by the surface temperature of the water. Cool water will cool the air, and warm water will warm the air. If winds consistently blow toward a region's shoreline, a current will have an effect on the region's average temperature for its latitude. For example, palm trees can grow in some parts of southern Great Britain in spite of the fact that these places are much farther from the equator than the colder locations of New England. Warm tropical waters of the Straits of Florida move northward in the form of the Gulf Stream current. Under the influence of the Gulf Stream's moderating effect and the prevailing westerly winds, Great Britain has a remarkably warm and equitable climate for such a high-latitude location. See Figure 8-14. Because of the Alaska current, the coast of Northern California has a cooler climate than might be expected. Winds blowing off the cold ocean water cool the temperatures of the American Pacific Northwest.

Planetary Wind Belts. In Topic 7, the influence of the Coriolis effect on the direction of the prevailing winds of the earth was discussed. Prevailing winds, in turn, influence local climates. Prevailing winds are important in determining the effect of ocean currents on nearby climates. For example, the eastern coast of North America

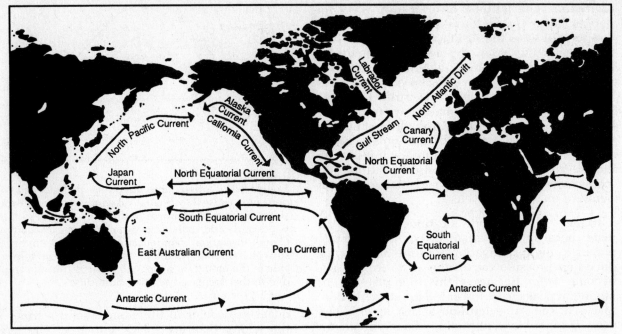

Figure 8-14. Ocean currents.

is seldom influenced by the warm waters of the Gulf Stream because of prevailing winds that come from the west, off the land. Winds from the center of a continent generally bring cold weather in the winter and hot weather in the summer.

Within the different planetary wind belts are various regions of rising air currents (low-pressure systems) and sinking air currents (high-pressure systems). When rising air is cooled by adiabatic expansion, moisture in the air may be released by condensation (cloud formation) and precipitation. Along the equator and in the mid-latitudes where zones of low pressure are com-

mon and cyclonic storms often develop, precipitation is plentiful. Local climates in these regions are humid. But near the poles and in the desert locations, about 20° to 30° on either side of the equator, zones of high pressure mark latitudes at which air sinking within the atmosphere is warmed by adiabatic compression. Local climates in these regions are arid. See Figure 8-15.

Typical Storm Tracks.
Weather systems usually move across the United States from west to east. The weather in Chicago is often the weather that will influence New York about a day later. Another characteristic path for weather systems is the movement of storms from the Gulf states northward along the eastern seaboard. Hurricanes, born in the South Atlantic or in the Caribbean Sea, generally move northward and westward through the Gulf of Mexico and into the United States. The prevailing easterly track of weather systems over North America then carries most hurricanes over the eastern states and back toward the Atlantic Ocean. See Figure 8-16.

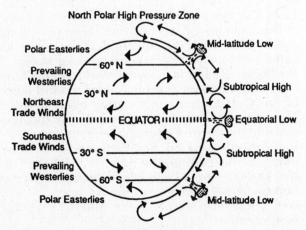

Figure 8-15. Convection cells and prevailing winds of the earth. Convection cells within the atmosphere influence the local climate. Rising air in the equatorial and mid-latitude low-pressure regions causes these locations to have abundant rainfall and moist climates. The subtropical and polar high-pressure zones have very little precipitation.

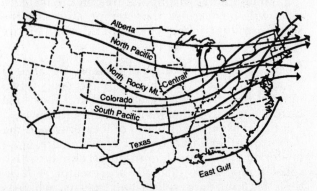

Figure 8-16. Storm tracks in the United States are named according to their regions of origin.

61. What effect does a large body of water usually have on the climate of a nearby landmass? (1) The water causes cooler summers and colder winters. (2) The water causes cooler summers and warmer winters. (3) The water causes hotter summers and warmer winters. (4) The water causes hotter summers and colder winters.

62. Present-day weather predictions are based primarily upon (1) land and sea breezes (2) cloud height (3) ocean currents (4) air mass movements

63. The diagram below represents a map of Western and Central New York State on a day in August. The location of an 18°C isotherm is shown. Why is the 18°C isotherm line farther north over the land than it is over Lake Ontario?

(1) There is a high plateau at the eastern end of Lake Ontario. (2) The air is warmer over the land than over Lake Ontario. (3) Isotherms are the same shape as the latitude lines. (4) The prevailing winds alter the path of the isotherms.

64. The map below indicates four locations *A*, *B*, *C*, and *D* which have the same elevation and latitude. Which location would most likely experience the *smallest* range of annual temperature?

(1) *A* (2) *B* (3) *C* (4) *D*

65. Which variable has the same effect on the temperature patterns of climatic regions as an increase in elevation? (1) increase in latitude (2) increase in insolation (3) decrease in longitude (4) decrease in precipitation

66. New York City and St. Louis, Missouri, are both located at approximately the same latitude. Why does St. Louis experience a greater range of temperatures throughout the year compared to New York City? (1) St. Louis is closer to the equator. (2) St. Louis is at a higher altitude. (3) St. Louis is farther from the ocean coast. (4) St. Louis is on the windward side of mountains.

67. Which single factor generally has the greatest effect on the climate of an area on the earth's surface? (1) the distance from the equator (2) the extent of vegetative cover (3) the degrees of longitude (4) the month of the year

68. How does the average annual surface temperature compare from latitude to latitude? (1) As latitude increases, the average annual surface temperature decreases. (2) As latitude increases, the average annual surface temperature increases. (3) As latitude increases, the average annual surface temperature remains the same.

69. Which will most likely occur in a mid-latitude desert? (1) Precipitation will exceed potential evapotranspiration. (2) Potential evapotranspiration will equal precipitation. (3) Potential evapotranspiration will exceed precipitation. (4) Actual evapotranspiration will exceed potential evapotranspiration.

Directions (70–71): Base your answers to questions 70 and 71 on the diagram below and on your knowledge of earth science.

Points *A*, *B*, and *C* are located on the western portion of a large continent where the prevailing winds are from the west.

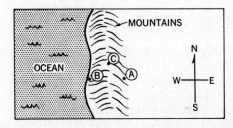

70. The climate of point *A* is probably (1) always moist (2) always dry (3) dry in the summer and wet in the winter (4) wet in the summer and dry in the winter

71. If a person moved from point *B* to point *C*, a region high in the mountains, he would be moving to a climate which would probably be (1) wetter and cooler (2) drier and cooler (3) wetter and warmer (4) drier and warmer

72. In which general direction do low-pressure centers usually travel across New York State? (1) north to south (2) northeast to southwest (3) west to east (4) southeast to northwest

73. England has a milder climate than other land areas of the same latitude because of the influence of the (1) jet stream (2) warm North Sea (3) Gulf Stream (4) southerly airflow

74. Which location in New York State is most likely to have the smallest annual temperature range? (1) Old Forge (2) Elmira (3) the Mohawk River Valley (4) Long Island's south shore

Directions (75–79): Base your answers to questions 75 through 79 on your knowledge of earth science and the sources of data given below. The table gives information about five United States cities and the graph shows the water budget for one of the five cities.

Climate Data for Certain U.S. Cities

City	Total Annual Precipitation (in millimeters) P	Total Annual Potential Evapotranspiration (in millimeters) E_p
R	194	1340
S	291	434
T	708	877
X	825	621
Z	859	1035

Water Budget for a Certain U.S. City having a P/E_p value of 0.14

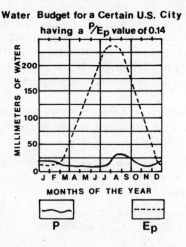

of the same mountain. How would the climate of the city represented by the graph probably compare to the climate of the other city? (1) drier and cooler (2) more humid and warmer (3) drier and warmer (4) more humid and cooler

Directions (80–84): The diagram below is a model representing the general circulation of the earth's atmosphere. Base your answers to questions 80 through 84 on this diagram and on your knowledge of earth science. Write the *number* of the word or expression that best completes the statement or answers the question.

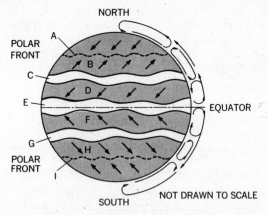

75. Which city probably has the coldest climate? (1) *R* (2) *S* (3) *X* (4) *Z*

76. What is the approximate annual P/E_p ratio at city *T*? (1) 0.24 (2) 0.65 (3) 0.81 (4) 1.21

77. According to the graph, during which month did the potential evapotranspiration equal the precipitation? (1) April (2) June (3) September (4) December

78. Which city's water budget is best represented by the graph? (1) *R* (2) *S* (3) *X* (4) *Z*

79. The city described by the graph is located on the leeward side of a mountain. Another city is located at the same latitude and elevation on the windward side

80. Which letter represents a belt of high pressure? (1) *A* (2) *B* (3) *C* (4) *D*

81. In which belt are daily rains typical? (1) *F* (2) *E* (3) *C* (4) *G*

82. In which belt is New York State located? (1) *G* (2) *B* (3) *E* (4) *D*

83. The diagram represents the location of the pressure and wind belts on September 21. Between September 21 and December 21 belt *E* will migrate into the region presently occupied by belt (1) *I* (2) *F* (3) *C* (4) *D*

84. Which belt has the most variable weather conditions over the course of the year? (1) *F* (2) *B* (3) *C* (4) *D*

TOPIC 9 Weathering and Erosion

WEATHERING AND SOIL

When a rock formed within the earth's crust is uplifted and exposed to the hydrosphere and atmosphere, it may undergo changes in its appearance or composition. The breakdown of rock due to physical or chemical changes is called **weathering**. The end product of weathering is soil.

Physical Weathering.

Physical weathering changes the physical form of a rock—for example, by breaking it into smaller pieces—without changing the rock's chemical composition. **Frost action** is an important form of physical weathering in climates that experience seasonal temperature changes alternately above and below 0°C. In weathering by frost action, water seeps into cracks in rocks. The water expands as it freezes and makes the cracks in the rock a little larger. When the ice melts and the resulting liquid water evaporates, the rock is left more porous than before. Over a period of time, the alternate freezing and melting of the water in the cracks will cause the rock to crumble.

Plant roots that grow in the cracks of rocks and animals that burrow beneath the ground are important agents of physical weathering. As a plant grows, its roots expand in the crevices of a rock and gradually push the rock apart. When animals burrow, they constantly expose new rock surfaces to weathering.

When rock particles are carried along by a stream, they bump and rub against one another and the streambed. Collisions such as these wear down rock particles by a form of physical weathering known as **abrasion**. Wind, moving ice, and gravity are also agents of abrasion.

Some rock minerals are harder than others. Quartz (silicon dioxide) and feldspars (complex aluminum silicates) resist physical weathering. But softer minerals, such as micas (hydrated aluminum silicates), are quickly broken apart by physical weathering.

Chemical Weathering.

Most rocks deep within the earth's crust remain stable under the conditions in which they were formed. However, when these rocks are uplifted to the surface and exposed to the atmosphere and hydrosphere, they often undergo **chemical weathering**. They become unstable and change into new substances. Chemical weathering breaks down rock by changing the rock's chemical composition. For example, when feldspar is uplifted to the earth's surface, it weathers to clay. As chemical weathering occurs, the compounds that make up feldspar react with water and form new substances. The formation of new substances characterizes chemical weathering.

The rusting of a nail is another good example of chemical weathering. When iron rusts in the presence of moisture, iron atoms combine with oxygen atoms to form rust (iron oxide).

Chemical weathering requires heat energy and often water to bring about chemical changes. Thus, chemical weathering takes place more rapidly in warm, moist climates. See Figure 9-1.

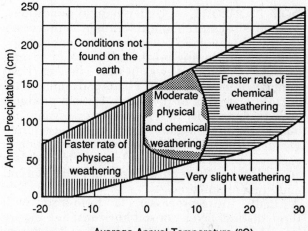

Figure 9-1. Weathering and climate. The type of rock weathering largely depends on the local climate. In general, chemical weathering dominates in warm, moist climates, while cooler climates favor physical weathering (especially frost action).

Chemical weathering occurs at the surface of a rock. When a rock is broken into smaller pieces, its surface area is increased. Therefore, the breaking apart of solid rock usually speeds up the rate of chemical weathering.

Some minerals are more resistant to chemical weathering than others. Quartz, a common mineral in beach sand, is relatively stable and resistant to chemical weathering. However, olivine, a mineral that is common deep within the earth, quickly weathers to clay when it is exposed to the atmosphere and hydrosphere. Limestone is a very hard rock that resists physical weathering until it is decomposed by exposure to acids. For example, rainwater that absorbs carbon dioxide from the atmosphere becomes slightly acidic. The emission of atmospheric pollutants, such as the oxides of sulfur and nitrogen, can make rainwater unnaturally acidic. When acids, such as these in the atmosphere, are released in the form of acid precipitation, they are able to change hard rocks like limestone into a soft residue.

SOIL

Physical and chemical weathering alter the rocks exposed at the surface of the earth. As a result, a layer of weathered rock fragments called **soil** covers much of the earth.

Soil that remains on top of the bedrock from which it formed is called **residual soil**. A residual soil is similar in composition to the parent bedrock. Soil that is carried away from the location of its parent rock to a new location is called **transported soil**. Transported soil may have a different mineral composition from that of the bedrock on which it rests. Agents of erosion, such as running water, moving ice, or wind, along with gravity, the primary driving force of erosion, are responsible for transporting soils from one location to another.

Soil Horizons. Under natural conditions, both physical and chemical weathering processes are usually involved in the development of soils. Physical weathering breaks solid rock into small particles. Chemical weathering changes hard minerals into softer forms. Plants and animals add organic materials in the form of waste products and dead organisms. The decay of organic remains produces organic acids which accelerate chemical weathering. Burrowing animals, such as earthworms, insects, and rodents, help circulate air and water through the soil and mix mineral and organic remains.

Finally, these processes may form a soil with three distinct layers, or **soil horizons**. See Figure 9-2. The upper layer is the A horizon. The top of the A horizon is usually rich in dark-colored organic remains (humus). Water, air, and a variety of living things, such as worms, bacteria, and burrowing animals, are also present. Some important minerals have been **leached** (dissolved) out of the A horizon and carried deeper into the soil as water infiltrates farther into the ground.

The B horizon is poor in organic materials but is enriched by minerals that have been leached out of horizon A.

Horizon C is composed of broken-up bedrock in various stages of decomposition and weathering. It sits upon unweathered, solid bedrock.

As water infiltrates the horizons of a soil, it picks up ions (individual atoms that have lost or gained electrons) from substances formed during the chemical weathering of rocks. After infiltration, a soil solution containing ions is present in the water supply. Plants use the soil solution for growth. Some of the ions likely to be present in a soil solution are potassium, nitrogen, calcium, iron, and phosphate ions.

QUESTIONS

1. The weathering of earth materials is most affected by (1) topography (2) longitude (3) altitude (4) climate

2. Why does one gram of finely ground salt dissolve more rapidly in water than an equal mass of coarsely ground salt? (1) Grinding changes the chemical composition of salt. (2) Finely ground salt is less dense than coarsely ground salt. (3) More surface area is exposed in finely ground salt. (4) The solubility of salt is proportional to the mass of salt.

3. Which is the best example of physical weathering? (1) the cracking of rock caused by the freezing and thawing of water (2) the transportation of sediment in a stream (3) the reaction of limestone with acid rainwater (4) the formation of a sandbar along the side of a stream

4. Which property of water makes frost action a common and effective form of weathering? (1) Water dissolves many earth materials. (2) Water expands when it freezes. (3) Water cools the surroundings when it evaporates. (4) Water loses 80 calories of heat per gram when it freezes.

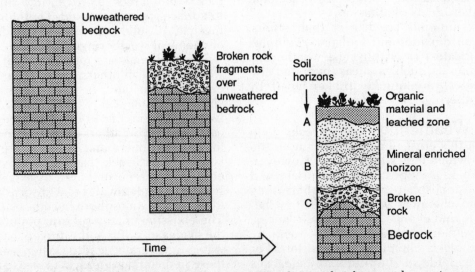

Figure 9-2. The development of soil horizons. Weathering, leaching, and organic processes gradually change exposed bedrock into mature soil with distinct soil horizons.

5. In which climate would chemical weathering occur at the greatest rate? (1) cold and dry (2) cold and humid (3) warm and dry (4) warm and humid

6. For a given mass of rock particles, which graph best represents the relationship between the size of rock particles exposed to weathering and the rate at which weathering occurs?

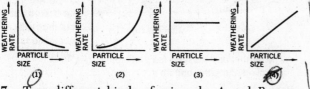

7. Two different kinds of minerals, *A* and *B*, were placed in the same container and shaken for 15 minutes. The diagrams below represent the size and shape of the various pieces of mineral before and after shaking. What caused the resulting differences in shapes and sizes of the minerals?

(1) Mineral *B* was shaken harder. (2) Mineral *B* had a glossy luster. (3) Mineral *A* was more resistant to abrasion. (4) Mineral *A* consisted of smaller pieces before shaking began.

8. At high elevations in New York State, which is the most common form of physical weathering? (1) abrasion of rocks by the wind (2) alternate freezing and melting of water (3) dissolving of minerals into solution (4) oxidation by oxygen in the atmosphere

9. Four samples of the same material with identical composition and mass were cut as shown in the diagrams below. When subjected to the same chemical weathering, which sample will weather the fastest?

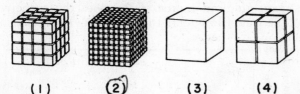

10. Assume that the rate of precipitation throughout the year is a constant. Which graph would most probably represent the chemical weathering of most New York State bedrock?

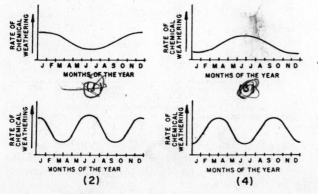

11. Two tombstones, *A* and *B*, each have been standing in a cemetery for 100 years. The same style and size of lettering is clear on *A* but not on *B*. Which is the most probable reason for the difference? (1) *B* was more protected from the atmosphere than *A*. (2) *A*'s minerals are more resistant to weathering than those in *B*. (3) *A* is more porous than *B*. (4) *B* is smaller than *A*.

12. Soil horizons develop as a result of (1) capillary action and solution (2) erosion and ionization (3) leaching and color changes (4) weathering processes and biologic activity

13. The chemical composition of a residual soil in a certain area is determined by the (1) method by which the soil was transported to the area (2) slope of the land and the particle size of the soil (3) length of time since the last crustal movement in the area occurred (4) minerals in the bedrock beneath the soil and the climate of the area

14. Which change would cause the topsoil in New York State to increase in thickness? (1) an increase in slope (2) an increase in biologic activity (3) a decrease in rainfall (4) a decrease in air temperature

Directions (15–17): Base your answers to questions 15 through 17 on your knowledge of earth science and the diagram below which represents the dominant type of weathering for various climatic conditions.

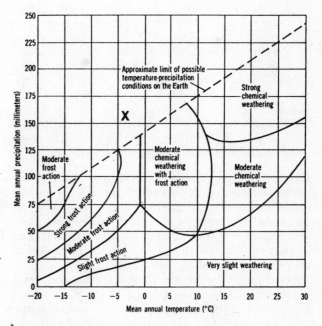

15. Which climatic conditions would produce very slight weathering? (1) a mean annual temperature of 25°C and a mean annual precipitation of 100 mm (2) a mean annual temperature of 15°C and a mean annual precipitation of 25 mm (3) a mean annual temperature of 5°C and a mean annual precipitation of 50 mm (4) a mean annual temperature of −5°C and a mean annual precipitation of 50 mm

16. Why is no frost action shown for locations with a mean annual temperature greater than 13°C? (1) Very little freezing takes place at these locations. (2) Large amounts of evaporation take place at these locations. (3) Very little precipitation falls at these locations. (4) Large amounts of precipitation fall at these locations.

17. There is no particular type of weathering or frost action given for the temperature and precipitation values at the location represented by the letter X. Why is this the case? (1) Only chemical weathering would occur under these conditions. (2) Only frost action would occur under these conditions. (3) These conditions create both strong frost action and strong chemical weathering. (4) These conditions probably do not occur on the earth.

EROSION OF WEATHERED MATERIALS

Rocks that have been broken into fragments, regardless of their size, are called **sediments**. The mineral composition or other characteristics of sediments may be unlike the properties of the underlying bedrock. In such a case, the sediments have been created elsewhere and then transported from their place of origin. **Erosion** involves the transporting of sediments away from their place of origin and the depositing of them elsewhere.

Most forms of erosion are driven by the force of gravity. For example, rock on a cliff that is weakened by weathering is forced by gravity to fall to the bottom of the cliff. The sediments that accumulate at the base of the cliff are called **talus**. Physical and chemical weathering continues to reduce the talus to smaller sediments, which are then moved farther down the slope by agents of erosion (wind, water, or ice) and by gravity. Thus, the breakdown of rock involves both weathering and erosion. In addition, agents of erosion carry away sediments and deposit them elsewhere.

Erosion by Water.
Running water transports sediments in several ways. The smallest particles (ions) are individual atoms that have lost or gained electrons in chemical weathering. Ions are carried in solution. They are so small that they cannot be filtered out of the water. Particles in **suspension** are called colloids. While they can be filtered out, they are small enough that they will not settle out on their own. (A cloud is a mass of tiny water droplets or ice crystals held in suspension in the air.) The largest and heaviest particles are rolled or bounced along the streambed in **traction**. Sediments of low density, particularly organic remains, will be carried along the surface of the water by **flotation**. See Figure 9-3.

The smallest particles, those in suspension and solution, are carried by a stream at the same velocity as the water. However, larger particles carried in traction generally move more slowly than the transporting medium.

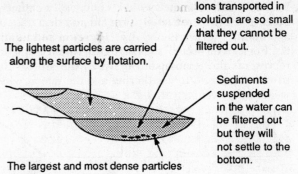

Figure 9-3. Erosion of sedimentary particles by streams.

Running water is the chief agent of erosion in moist areas. Each year, the streams and rivers of the world carry millions of tons of sediment downstream and into the oceans. The relationship of transported particle size to water velocity is shown in Figure 9-4. The graph shows that the water velocity needed to transport particles of sediment is chiefly a function of the size of the particles. Particles in solution and suspension can be carried by slow-moving water. But particles rolled along the bottom of the stream require faster stream velocities. A convenient method to estimate the velocity of a stream is to measure the size of the sedimentary particles that have been carried along the bottom of the stream. Faster streams contain larger particles of sediment. Slow-moving streams can transport only the smaller sedimentary particles.

The Velocity of Streams. The velocity of a stream is controlled by the slope and the amount of **discharge** water flowing in the stream. As the stream gradient increases, so does the velocity of the water flowing in the stream. Velocity is also

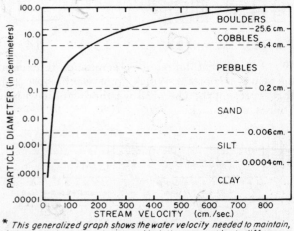

* This generalized graph shows the water velocity needed to maintain, but not start movement. Variations occur due to differences in particle density and shape.

Figure 9-4. There is a direct relationship between the velocity of a stream and the size of the particles it can transport. Large grains of sediment can only be eroded by fast-moving water.

Reviewing Earth Science: Topic 9

increased by an increase in the quantity of water flowing in the stream. Most of the erosion caused by running water takes place when streams are in flood, because of an increase in the quantity of water and because of the velocity of the floodwaters.

The speed of a stream is a balance between the force of gravity pulling the water downhill and the frictional forces slowing the stream. Water usually flows the fastest near the center of the stream away from the stream banks and the streambed. There is even a small amount of friction with the air above the water, so the fastest flow is commonly found at midstream just below the surface. See Figure 9-5.

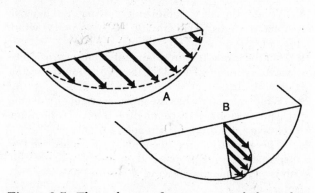

Figure 9-5. The velocity of a stream is a balance between gravity pulling the water downhill and friction with the banks of the stream and the streambed. There is even a small amount of friction with the air above the stream. Therefore, streams have the greatest velocity near the center of the stream, just below the surface. Diagram A shows that the greatest velocity is near the center of the stream, and diagram B shows that the greatest velocity is just below the top surface.

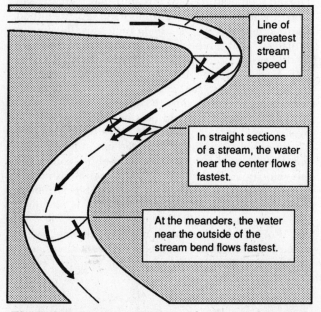

Line of greatest stream speed

In straight sections of a stream, the water near the center flows fastest.

At the meanders, the water near the outside of the stream bend flows fastest.

Figure 9-6. Stream geometry and stream velocity. Although the fastest water is commonly found in the middle of a stream, inertia swings the fastest water to the outside of stream bends (meanders).

Streams with broad, flat valleys often develop S-shaped curves called **meanders**. At the bends in the stream, the fastest-flowing water swings to the outside of the bends, causing erosion along the outer bank of the meanders. See Figure 9-6.

Erosion by Wind and Ice.

Another agent of erosion is wind. It can pick up loose rock materials, like sand, silt, and clay, and carry them away. Wind erosion occurs mainly in dry areas, such as deserts and beaches, where there is little plant life to hold soil in place. Wind also erodes by abrasion. In this process, sand blown by the wind breaks down material on a rock's surface. For example, windblown sand in a desert often grinds rocks into angular shapes called ventifacts. See Figure 9-7. Windblown sand abrasion usually occurs near ground level because sand is not often lifted more than a meter high. This may produce mushroom-shaped rock remnants such as that shown in Figure 9-8.

Characteristics of particles eroded by...

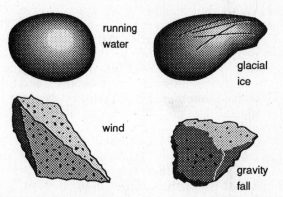

running water

glacial ice

wind

gravity fall

Figure 9-7. Characteristics of particles eroded by different agents. Each agent of erosion produces its own characteristic shape and texture in rocks. Rocks tumbled in running water are round and smooth. Glacial rocks are partly rounded with scratches (striations). Wind-eroded rocks (ventifacts) are smooth and angular with pitted surfaces. Talus rocks (from rock falls) are rough and angular and may show some fresh and some weathered surfaces.

Figure 9-8. Weathering and erosion caused by blowing sand abrade the rocks near ground level. This sometimes leaves mushroom-shaped remnants.

Weathering and Erosion

During the winter, northern regions in the United States receive several meters of snow. If more snow accumulates in the winter than melts in the summer, the snow on the bottom turns to ice. If it becomes thick enough, its weight will cause it to move under the pull of gravity. A **glacier** is a large mass of moving ice. As a glacier moves, it carries, pushes, and drags with it loose rock material. The glacier, with pieces of rock embedded in its ice, acts like a huge abrasion system; it smooths, striates (scratches), and grooves bedrock. When the ice melts, unsorted rocks and boulders are left scattered around on hilltops and the sides of valleys.

A continental glacier deepens and widens valleys parallel to its movement. It grinds down the hills, leaving them polished and rounded. As a valley glacier moves, it scours away the rock to make a U-shaped glacial valley in which the valley walls are nearly vertical. (Valleys eroded by streams are more often V-shaped with narrow valley floors.)

In some ways valley glaciers are like streams and rivers, but glaciers move much slower. The ice may advance less than a meter a day, but, like streams, the ice in a valley glacier moves the fastest near the center of the flowing ice. Unlike water deposits, sediment left by melting glacial ice usually contains clay, sand, cobbles, and boulders mixed together. These unsorted deposits left by glacial ice are often found in ridges and mounds.

Four periods of continental glaciation in the past million years have moved most of the soils of New York from their original locations and deposited them farther to the south. In New York, as elsewhere, transported soils are more common than residual soils. The Pleistocene (500,000 to 2 million years ago) ice sheet that covered mountains, as well as valleys, in New York State has left mountaintops that are rounded off and bedrock that is polished, grooved, and striated.

Effects of Agents of Erosion.

Each agent of erosion causes characteristic changes in the particles that it carries. Sedimentary particles carried by a stream are usually rounded and polished as a result of being tumbled about in the stream's current. Rocks transported by a glacier are usually partially rounded by abrasion and are often scratched (striated) on a flattened face as a result of being dragged along the bottom of the glacier. Rough and angular particles deposited at the base of a cliff usually indicate that gravity alone is responsible for transporting the rock a short distance. In this case, the rock particles often have some freshly exposed surfaces, as well as older surfaces that are more weathered. As different surfaces of a wind-worn rock are exposed to wind erosion, the rock develops smooth, flat surfaces, or facets, with sharp edges. These angular rocks are called ventifacts. Wind-worn rocks are often

pitted where softer minerals have been scoured by the wind. See Figure 9-7.

The Influence of Human Technology in Erosion.

Human technology has contributed to the erosion of the landscape. For example, construction and mining projects have moved great quantities of rock and sediment from their original locations. By destroying plant cover, poor farming and forestry practices have left soil exposed and unprotected. The exposed soil is quickly eroded by running water and wind.

QUESTIONS

18. What is the cause of movement of material in most erosional systems? (1) gravity (2) water (3) wind (4) ice

19. On the earth, the predominant agent of erosion is (1) wave action (2) moving ice (3) running water (4) moving air

20. Which generally has the greatest effect on the rate of stream erosion? (1) stream direction (2) elevation (3) relative humidity (4) stream gradient

21. The primary force responsible for most of the transportation of rock material on the surface of the earth is (1) gravity (2) wind (3) running water (4) glaciers

22. As the slope of a streambed increases, the average velocity of the stream generally (1) decreases (2) increases (3) remains the same

23. Stream A has a steeper slope than stream B. However, the average water velocity of stream B is greater than that of stream A. Which is the most reasonable explanation for this? (1) Stream B has more friction to overcome along its banks. (2) Stream B has a higher average temperature. (3) Stream B has a greater volume of water. (4) Stream B has a curved streambed.

24. As the volume of a stream increases, the amount of material that can be carried by the stream generally (1) decreases (2) increases (3) remains the same

25. As the kinetic energy of a stream increases, the size of the particle that can be moved (1) decreases (2) increases (3) remains the same

26. Which material could best be carried in solution by a stream? (1) clay (2) salt (3) silt (4) sand

27. A pebble is being transported in a stream by rolling. How does the velocity of the pebble compare to the velocity of the stream? (1) The pebble is moving slower than the stream. (2) The pebble is moving faster than the stream. (3) The pebble is moving at the same velocity as the stream.

28. For a given location in a stream channel, which graph best shows the relationship between the changes in the volume of the stream and the resulting stream velocity?

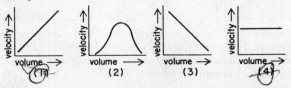

29. Which graph best represents the relationship between the velocity (y) of a stream and the average slope (x) of the streambed?

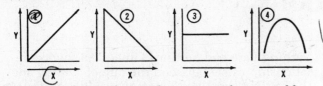

30. According to the *Earth Science Reference Tables*, a stream flowing at a velocity of 100 centimeters per second can transport (1) silt, but not sand, pebbles, or cobbles (2) silt and sand, but not pebbles or cobbles (3) silt, sand, and pebbles, but not cobbles (4) silt, sand, pebbles, and cobbles

31. Which graph best represents the relationship between the speed of a stream and the rate of abrasion of the streambed?

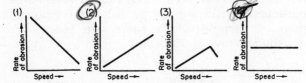

32. Which is the best evidence that erosion has occurred? (1) a soil rich in lime on top of a limestone bedrock (2) a layer of basalt found on the floor of the ocean (3) sediments found in a sandbar of a river (4) a large number of fossils embedded in limestone

33. Which graph best represents the relationship between the maximum particle size that can be carried by a stream and the velocity of the stream?

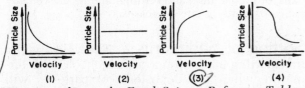

34. According to the *Earth Science Reference Tables*, what is the largest rock particle that can be transported by a stream with a velocity of 250 centimeters per second? (1) silt (2) sand (3) pebbles (4) cobbles

35. The velocity of a stream is 100 centimeters per second. According to the *Earth Science Reference Tables*, what is the largest diameter particle that can be transported? (1) 1.0 cm (2) 0.1 cm (3) 0.01 cm (4) 0.0001 cm

36. According to the *Earth Science Reference Tables*, which is the largest sediment that could be carried by a stream flowing at a velocity of 75 centimeters per second? (1) silt (2) sand (3) pebbles (4) cobbles

37. A contour (topographic) map indicates that a stream is flowing across the landscape. If the stream has a constant volume, where on the map would the stream most likely have the highest velocity? (1) as the stream moves parallel to two contour lines (2) as the stream moves through a large region that has no contour lines (3) as the stream moves across several closely spaced contour lines (4) as the stream moves across several widely spaced contour lines

38. While studying the movement of valley glaciers that are advancing from the north, geologists placed metal stakes extending in a straight line from one val-

ley wall to the other. Which sketch would best illustrate the position of the stakes one year later?

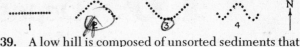

39. A low hill is composed of unsorted sediments that have mixed grain sizes. This hill was probably deposited by (1) a glacier (2) the wind (3) running water (4) wave action

40. Compared to its original shape, a rock that has been transported several kilometers by a stream will normally be more (1) rounded (2) jagged (3) flattened on one side (4) rectangular

41. Which piece of quartz has probably been transported the greatest distance by water?

42. Granite pebbles are found on the surface in a certain area where only sandstone bedrock is exposed. Which is the most likely explanation for the presence of these pebbles? (1) The granite pebbles were transported to the area from a different region. (2) Some of the sandstone has been changed into granite. (3) The granite pebbles were formed by weathering of the exposed sandstone bedrock. (4) Ground water tends to form granite pebbles within layers of sandstone rock.

43. Transported rock materials are more common than residual rock materials in the soils of New York State. Which statement best explains this observation? (1) Solid rock must be transported to break. (2) Weathering changes transported rock materials more easily than residual rock materials. (3) Most rock materials are moved by some agent of erosion at some time in their history. (4) Residual rock material forms only from bedrock that is difficult to change into soil.

Directions (44–46): Base your answers to questions 44 through 46 on your knowledge of earth science and the diagrams below. The diagrams represent the same stream cross section showing the variations in water level and water discharge measured at the *same* location YZ in a river valley at four different times during a certain year.

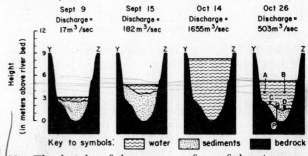

44. The height of the water surface of the river on October 26 was closest to (1) 2.3 m (2) 2.9 m (3) 5.3 m (4) 5.9 m

45. The greatest water velocity in the river was probably recorded on (1) September 9 (2) September 15 (3) October 14 (4) October 26

46. In the diagram for October 26, which location in the river probably experienced the greatest average current velocity? (1) A (2) B (3) C (4) D

TOPIC **10** Deposition

DEPOSITION

When an agent of erosion deposits, or lays down, particles and fragments of earth materials (sediments), the process is called **deposition**. Deposition is also called *sedimentation*. Agents of erosion, such as water, ice, and wind, are also agents of deposition. Most deposition takes place in water.

Rates of Deposition.
The rate at which sediments are deposited depends upon the size, shape, and density of the sediment particles and the speed of the transporting medium.

Particle Size.
The settling rate of particles is affected by particle size. See Figure 10-1. Smaller particles, such as clay and silt, settle more slowly than cobbles and boulders. Very small particles, such as ions and colloidal particles (up to 0.001 mm in size), may remain in solution or suspension indefinitely. Ionic particles of minerals normally do not settle out of a water solution unless the solution becomes *saturated*. For example, in some parts of the Persian Gulf, evaporation leaves the remaining water so rich in salt that the water becomes saturated. It can hold no more salt in solution. If more water evaporates, some of the salt must settle to the bottom of the ocean. The salt crystals that form and settle out of solution are called precipitates, and the process is called precipitation.

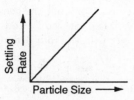

Figure 10-1. Relationship between particle size and settling rate. As particle size increases, settling rate increases.

Particle Shape.
The shape of sedimentary particles also affects how quickly they settle. Friction between water and the surfaces of particles slows down settling. Therefore, flat, angular, and irregular-shaped particles that have more surface area than smooth, rounded ones settle more slowly.

Particle Density.
The density of particles also affects their settling rates. Among particles of the same average size and shape, denser particles settle faster, whereas less dense particles require more time for settling.

Settling Rate and Settling Time.
An inverse relationship exists between the rate of settling and the settling time. Sediments that settle at a faster rate require less time. Thus, as the rate of settling increases, the settling time decreases.

Velocity of a Transporting Medium.
The rate of deposition of sedimentary particles is also affected by the velocity of the transporting medium. For example, the lesser the velocity of a transporting medium, the more rapidly sedimentary particles will settle. See Figure 10-2. Thus, particles in still water are deposited more rapidly than are particles of the same size, shape, and density in moving water.

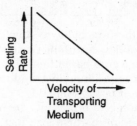

Figure 10-2. Relationship between velocity of the transporting medium and settling rate. As the velocity increases, settling rate decreases.

Sorting of Sediments.
The velocity of a transporting medium plays a major role in determining when the deposition of particles will occur. Deposition is usually initiated by a reduction in the velocity of a transporting medium. For example, when a stream enters a large body of water, such as an ocean, the stream's velocity is reduced as it mixes with the ocean water. Particles of sediment begin to settle out. The largest, roundest, and densest particles are deposited first near the ocean's shoreline, while the smallest, flattest, and least dense particles are carried farthest from shore. The separation of particles, in this case, is called **horizontal sorting**. See Figure 10-3.

When particles sort out from bottom to top in a layer, it is called **vertical sorting**. See Figure 10-4. During vertical sorting, the roundest, largest, and densest particles settle at the bottom of a layer, while the flattest, smallest, and least dense particles settle at the top of a layer. Vertical sorting may occur when a landslide suddenly dumps a variety of particle sizes into still water.

A series of depositional events, such as a succession of underwater landslides in deep water, can cause a type of vertical sorting known as graded bedding. For example, the first landslide causes a large volume of sediments to move

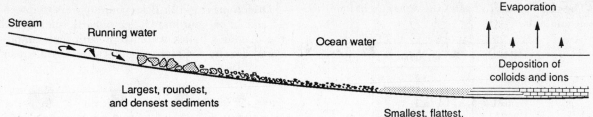

Stream
Running water
Ocean water
Evaporation
Deposition of colloids and ions
Largest, roundest, and densest sediments
Smallest, flattest, and least dense sediments

Figure 10-3. Horizontal sorting at the mouth of a stream. The velocity of the water decreases as it enters a large lake or ocean. The coarsest sediments settle first, near the shore. As distance from the shore increases, sediments become finer. The finest sediments are carried the greatest distance from the shore.

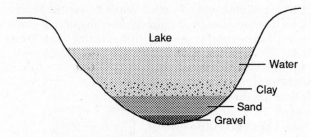

Lake

Water
Clay
Sand
Gravel

Figure 10-4. Vertically sorted sediments in still water. The coarsest particles settle first and the finest settle last.

down an underwater slope. The sediments sort vertically—large particles giving way gradually to smaller and smaller particles from the bottom to the top. This is the first graded bed. Another landslide produces another graded bed. An abrupt change in the particle size—from very fine sediments to a layer of very coarse sediments—separates one graded bed from another. Each graded bed represents a period of deposition or a single, distinct depositional event, such as one landslide. See Figure 10-5.

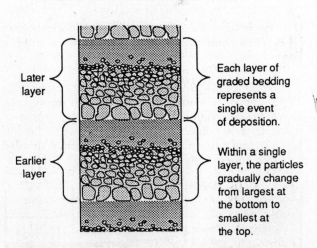

Later layer

Earlier layer

Each layer of graded bedding represents a single event of deposition.

Within a single layer, the particles gradually change from largest at the bottom to smallest at the top.

Figure 10-5. Vertical sorting in graded bedding. Layers of graded bedding represent a series of depositional events.

QUESTIONS

1. The rate at which particles are deposited by a stream is *least* affected by the (1) size and shape of the particles (2) velocity of the stream (3) stream's elevation above sea level (4) density of the particles

2. If all other factors remain constant, as the particle size of sediments increases from fine sand to coarse sand, the time necessary for settling in still water will probably (1) decrease (2) increase (3) remain the same

3. A large glass cylinder containing a mixture of sediments of the same density and water is shaken. Which drawing below best represents the result after settling?

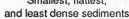

TOP

KEY
Silt
Sand
Coarse Sand
Pebbles

BOTTOM   (1)   (2)   (3)   (4)

4. When the velocity of a stream decreases, there will most likely be an increase in (1) downcutting by the stream (2) deposition by the stream (3) the size of the particles carried in suspension by the stream (4) the amount of material carried in solution by the stream

5. Flat-shaped particles may settle more slowly in a fluid than spherical particles which have the same mass and volume because the flat particles have (1) less weight (2) more potential energy (3) a lower density (4) more resistance due to shape

6. Which graph best represents the general relationship between particle density and settling rate in still water?

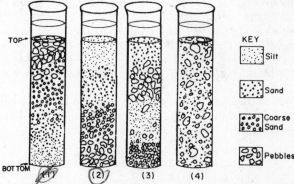

settling rate | density   settling rate | density   settling rate | density   settling rate | density
(1)   (2)   (3)   (4)

7. The chart below indicates the densities of four different minerals.

Mineral	Density (g/cm³)
Calcite	2.8
Diamond	3.5
Hematite	5.3
Quartz	2.7

If spheres 5 millimeters in diameter of these four minerals are dropped at the same time into a large tube filled with water, which would settle to the bottom first? (1) calcite (2) diamond (3) hematite (4) quartz

8. Clay, silt, and sand are added to a jar of water. The jar is shaken and then allowed to stand quietly for a number of hours. The result of this demonstration, which is shown at the right, could be best used as a model to show that
(1) particles with the lowest density settle the fastest (2) particles with the largest diameter settle the fastest (3) water has a higher specific gravity than clay, silt, and sand (4) the bottom layer of a series of sediments is the youngest

9. The particles below, all of equal size, were mixed together in a tube of water

Particle Type	Mass	Volume	Density g/cm³
A	100 g	67 cm³	1.5
B	100 g	33 cm³	3.0
C	100 g	22 cm³	4.5
D	100 g	17 cm³	6.0

Which diagram best represents how the particles will be arranged in the tube of water after all of them have settled?

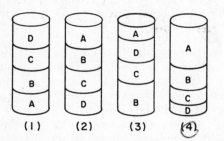

10. Over a period of 5 weeks, the size of particles deposited at one location at the mouth of a river varied from large on the bottom to small on the top. Which graph best represents the relative stream velocity during the deposition of these sediments?

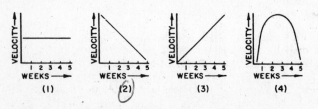

Directions (11–12): Base your answers to questions 11 and 12 on your knowledge of earth science and on the diagrams below which represent four samples of equal-density sediments being carried by a stream.

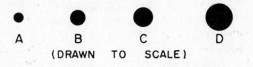

11. Which sample would be deposited first as the stream velocity decreases? (1) A (2) B (3) C (4) D

12. According to the *Earth Science Reference Tables*, which is the *slowest* stream velocity needed to maintain all the particles moving downstream? (1) 50 cm/sec (2) 75 cm/sec (3) 100 cm/sec (4) 125 cm/sec

13. The diagram at the right represents a core sample of a sedimentary deposit found at a particular location. The deposition most likely occurred as a result of (1) dropping directly from a glacier (2) an avalanche on a mountainside (3) a decrease in the velocity of a stream (4) dropping of weathered rock fragments from a cliff

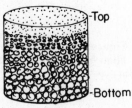

14. The type of deposition in the sketch would most probably occur

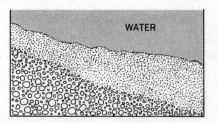

(1) at the bottom of a falls (2) on the midocean bottom (3) in a mountain stream (4) where a stream enters a lake

Directions (15–19): Base your answers to questions 15 through 19 on your knowledge of earth science, the *Earth Science Reference Tables*, and the cross-sectional diagram below. The diagram shows a sediment-laden stream entering the ocean. The ocean is divided into four zones A, B, C, and D.

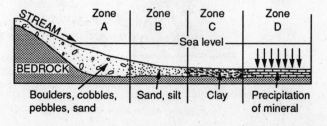

15. In which zone would the stream normally deposit particles of largest size? (1) A (2) B (3) C (4) D

16. Which material would most likely be held in suspension in zone D? (1) cobbles (2) sand (3) silt (4) colloids

17. Which change in the stream system would most likely cause the deposition of larger particles to be farther offshore? (1) a decrease in the stream's gradient (2) a decrease in the quantity of large particles (3) an increase in the stream's velocity (4) an increase in the density of large particles

18. Limestone would most likely form in zone (1) A (2) B (3) C (4) D

19. Which zone would contain particles mostly in the range of 0.05 to 0.10 centimeter in diameter? (1) A (2) B (3) C (4) D

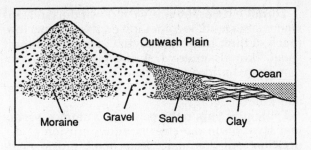

Figure 10-6. Horizontal sorting on an outwash plain. A melting glacier adjacent to the moraine on the left supplied water that carried glacial sediment from the moraine over the outwash plain to the right. Note the decrease in the size of the outwash deposits, from gravel near the moraine to sand and fine clay farther from the source of the sediments.

DEPOSITION BY GLACIERS

Deposition by glaciers occurs when a glacier melts and sediments are released. Glacial deposits are fairly easy to identify. **Glacial erratics** are large rocks that have been transported by glacial ice without being broken into small particles. They are often found high above stream valleys, which shows that they could not have been deposited by running water. Particle rounding and striations (scratches) also indicate transport by glaciers. Erratics commonly differ in composition from the bedrock on which they rest.

Glacial drift consists of deposits of material left by a retreating glacier. *Glacial till* is unsorted drift. It is a mixture of a wide range of sizes of rock particles, from clay and silt to cobbles and boulders.

Stratified drift consists of glacial sediments that were carried away from the foot of a glacier by meltwater and deposited in an outwash plain. The particles of stratified drift may be sorted horizontally, with the coarse sediments closest to the ice front. See Figure 10-6. Rock flour, which consists of very fine particles formed as the glacier

abraded and finely ground up the bedrock, is carried the farthest out on the outwash plain.

EROSIONAL-DEPOSITIONAL SYSTEMS

A river or stream may be thought of as an **erosional-depositional system**. Within a stream system, energy transformations—from potential energy to kinetic energy—are constantly occurring. Overall, the total energy within the system is decreasing. For example, a stream's potential energy is greatest at its place of origin (source). As the stream and its sediments flow downhill, their potential energy is transformed into kinetic energy. The kinetic energy is used to erode rock materials in high places, to transport the resulting sediments to lower places, and to deposit them there. The potential energy of the river reaches zero at its **base level** (the lowest level it can reach). Any remaining kinetic energy at base level is finally lost as the river flows into the sea. As the river slows down, sediments are deposited. See Figure 10-7.

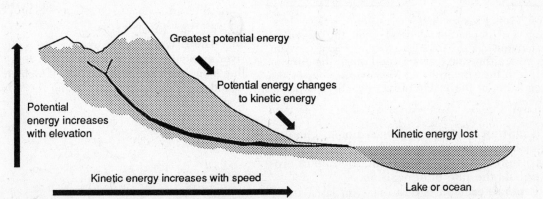

Figure 10-7. As a stream and its sediments move downhill they lose height (potential energy). The stream gains speed (kinetic energy) as it moves faster. As the stream enters calm water, most of its kinetic energy has been used to transport sediments. Through this process there is a net loss of kinetic energy. Some of that kinetic energy is also used to transport weathered sediment that is deposited in the lake or ocean.

Through time, streams wear down the land surface. As the land becomes lower, the streams lose much of their height (potential energy) and their speed (kinetic energy). A subsequent period of mountain building and land uplift may restore the stream to its former levels of high potential and kinetic energy.

Depending upon the conditions along a particular location in the stream, either erosion or deposition will dominate. In general, erosion will dominate in the steeper sections of the stream, and deposition may be more active in the places with less gradient. However, streams that flow over flat, broad valleys may develop meandering courses because of erosion and deposition. Along the outsides of the stream bends, the faster-moving water will erode the banks of the stream, while deposition will occur along the insides of the stream bends where the water is moving slower. See Figure 10-8. The continuing erosion and deposition cause meanders to shift slowly downstream through time.

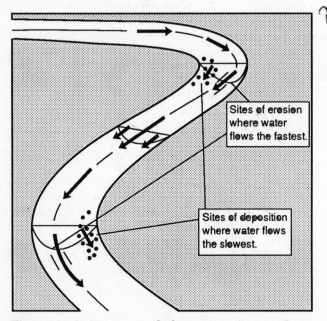

Figure 10-8. Erosion and deposition in meanders. Erosion and deposition depend upon the speed of water moving in a stream. Along the outside of a stream bend, where the water moves the fastest, the current erodes into the stream bank. Meanwhile, the slower moving water at the inside of the meanders deposits sediment.

If a portion of a river appears not to change, then a state of *dynamic equilibrium* exists along that portion. During equilibrium, the rate of erosion equals the rate of deposition.

In general, erosion is dominant on land areas and deposition is dominant in the oceans. The interface between these regions is the shoreline of the oceans. Over the whole earth, erosion and deposition are approximately in balance, or in a state of dynamic equilibrium.

QUESTIONS

20. A hill of unsorted sediments of mixed grain sizes was probably deposited by (1) ice (2) wind (3) water (4) frost action

21. As the kinetic energy of the particles in a river decreases, the rate of deposition generally (1) decreases (2) increases (3) remains the same

22. The diagram below represents a stream profile. At what point is the potential energy of the sediment carried by a stream greatest?

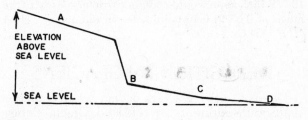

(1) A (2) B (3) C (4) D

23. Which is the most probable description of the energy of a particle in an erosional-depositional system? (1) Particles gain kinetic energy during erosion and lose kinetic energy during deposition. (2) Particles lose kinetic energy during erosion and lose kinetic energy during deposition. (3) Particles gain potential energy during erosion and gain potential energy during deposition. (4) Particles lose potential energy during erosion and gain potential energy during deposition.

24. In the diagram below, those features represented at A, B, C, and D are being formed. At which location is erosion greater than deposition?

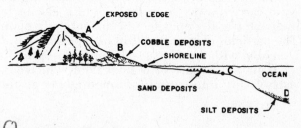

(1) A (2) B (3) C (4) D

25. The diagram below represents a top view of a river emptying into an ocean bay. A-B is a reference line along the bottom of the bay. Which characteristic would most likely decrease along the reference line from A to B?

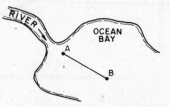

(1) the amount of salt in solution (2) the size of the sediments (3) the density of the water (4) the depth of the water

26. Which diagram of a stream channel showing erosion vectors (arrows to indicate extent of erosion) best represents an area where meanders are well developed?

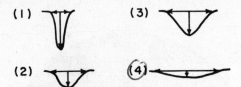

27. The diagram below represents a stream flowing into a lake. Identical particles are at positions A, B, C, and D. At which location do the particles have the *least* amount of combined potential and kinetic energy? (1) A (2) B (3) C (4) D

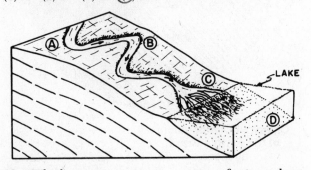

28. Which situation exists in a section of a river where the amount of deposition is the same as the amount of erosion? (1) The water is flowing swiftly in that section. (2) That section of the river is a delta region. (3) Dynamic equilibrium has been reached in that section. (4) Lowest elevation has been reached in that section.

Directions (29–33): Base your answers to questions 29 through 33 on your knowledge of earth science, the Earth Science Reference Tables, and the diagrams below. Diagram I shows the paths of two streams over the earth's surface. Diagram II shows the longitudinal profile of the major stream.

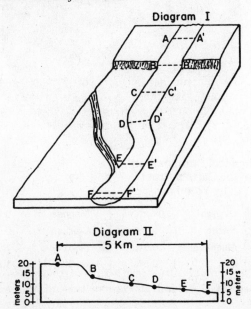

29. At which location would the water in the stream have the greatest potential energy? (1) A (2) B (3) C (4) E

30. What is the approximate average gradient of this stream between points A and F? (1) 1 m/km (2) 15 m/km (3) 3 m/km (4) 20 m/km

31. The greatest volume of water would most likely be moving past which location? (1) F—F' (2) B—B' (3) C—C' (4) D—D'

32. Which cross section best represents the shape of the stream at D—D'?

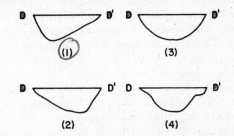

33. The diagram below shows the cross section of the stream at C—C'. At which position in the stream channel would the velocity of the water be greatest? (1) 1 (2) 2 (3) 3 (4) 4

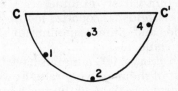

TOPIC 11 The Formation of Rocks

ROCK-FORMING MINERALS

The solid part of the earth is composed of substances collectively known as **rock**. Most rocks are composed of one or more naturally occurring inorganic crystalline substances called **minerals**. Some minerals, like sulfur and graphite (carbon), are pure elements. Others, like quartz (SiO_2) and calcite ($CaCO_3$), are chemical compounds. Many minerals, like plagioclase feldspar, are mixtures for which there is no exact chemical formula. But each mineral has relatively uniform properties and a well-defined range of chemical composition. Although plagioclase feldspar varies somewhat in composition, fresh samples are always very hard and split along perpendicular surfaces.

Some rocks, like limestone, are composed primarily of a single mineral—in this case, calcite. These rocks are called **monomineralic**. Others, like granite, are **polymineralic** because they are composed of a variety of minerals. Granite usually contains feldspar, quartz, biotite mica, and hornblende, and minor amounts of other minerals. See Table 11-1.

Although about 2,000 minerals have been identified, most of them are very rare. Fewer than 10 minerals form over 90% of the rocks found at the earth's surface. A few common minerals, like quartz and feldspar, make up a large portion of many rocks.

Table 11-1. Common Rocks and Minerals of the Earth's Crust

	Rock Name	Mineral Composition
Monomineralic rocks	quartzite	quartz
	limestone	calcite
	shale	clay
	rock salt	halite
Polymineralic rocks	granite	feldspar, quartz, biotite mica, hornblende
	basalt	feldspar, augite, olivine, etc.
	sandstone	quartz, feldspar, etc.
	gneiss	feldspar, quartz, hornblende, mica, pyroxene, etc.

Silicate Minerals. By mass, the two most common elements found in the earth's crust are oxygen (46%) and silicon (28%). However, when measured by volume, oxygen makes up 94% of the earth's crust. See Figure 11-1.

The most common group of minerals is the **silicates**, which are composed of oxygen, silicon,

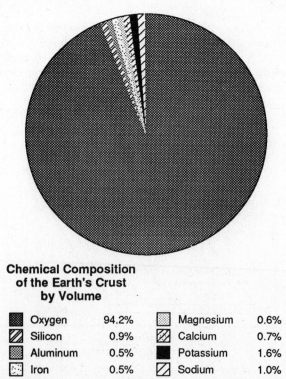

Chemical Composition of the Earth's Crust by Mass

■ Oxygen	46.4%		▨ Calcium	2.4%
▨ Silicon	28.2%		■ Potassium	2.3%
▨ Aluminum	8.2%		▨ Sodium	2.1%
⠿ Iron	5.6%		⊞ Others	0.6%
▨ Magnesium	4.2%			

Chemical Composition of the Earth's Crust by Volume

■ Oxygen	94.2%		▨ Magnesium	0.6%
▨ Silicon	0.9%		▨ Calcium	0.7%
▨ Aluminum	0.5%		■ Potassium	1.6%
⠿ Iron	0.5%		▨ Sodium	1.0%

Figure 11-1. Chemical composition of the earth's crust.

and a variety of other elements. The structural unit of any silicate is the **silica tetrahedron**, which consists of four oxygen atoms bonded to one silicon atom. In all silicates, the oxygen atoms pack together around the silicon atom in a four-sided shape known as a tetrahedron. See Figure 11-2.

Silicate Bonding. Although they all contain oxygen and silicon, the silicates display a variety of physical properties. This is mainly due to the way the tetrahedra are attached to one another. An oxygen atom can be shared by two tetrahedra to form chains, sheets, and networks of tetrahedra. See Figure 11-3.

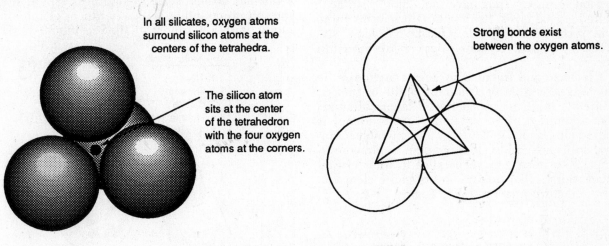

Figure 11-2. The silica tetrahedron.

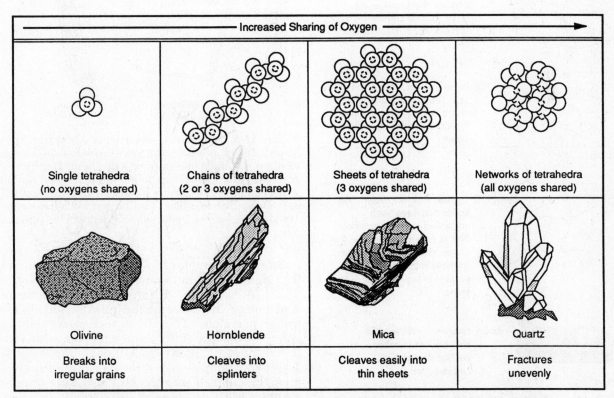

Figure 11-3. The physical properties of minerals are often determined by the bonding of their atoms. Weak bonds split easily. Strong bonds make a hard mineral that does not break easily in any direction. In some minerals, like hornblende and mica, weak metallic bonds exist between layers of silicon-oxygen sheets. Thus, silicate minerals with this structure tend to cleave into thin layers or sheets containing stronger silicon-oxygen bonds within the sheets—a property characteristic of the micas.

The Formation of Rocks

Physical and Chemical Properties of Minerals.

Each mineral substance can be identified on the basis of specific physical and chemical properties or a definite range of properties. (Be sure to use fresh, unweathered surfaces to observe these properties.)

The arrangement and bonding of the atoms of a mineral determine its solid geometric shape, or **crystal** form. Crystals have flat, smooth surfaces called crystal faces. Rock salt (halite) forms cubic and rectangular crystals. Quartz has long, six-sided (hexagonal) crystals. Mica crystals form thin sheets.

Cleavage and **fracture** are terms that describe the way a sample of a mineral splits or breaks. Minerals tend to split between layers of atoms that are joined by weak bonds. This tendency is called cleavage. The surfaces along which a mineral splits are called cleavage planes. Many minerals, like mica, cleave parallel to their crystal faces. Some, like quartz, do not show cleavage. They fracture unevenly. See Figure 11-4.

Crystal Form, Fracture, and Cleavage
As Keys to Mineral Identification

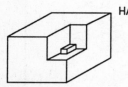

QUARTZ forms six-sided (hexagonal) crystals that break along wavy, curved surfaces. This is called concoidal fracture.

HALITE is the primary mineral in rock salt. The crystals are cubic. Halite breaks (cleaves) into tiny cubes and rectangular solids.

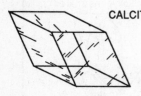

CALCITE crystals look like rectangular solids that have been squashed over to one side. This is called a rhombohedral shape. Calcite crystals split (cleave) in three directions parallel to their crystal faces.

MICA crystals cleave into thin sheets. This is called perfect cleavage in one direction.

ASBESTOS fractures into tiny fibers.

Figure 11-4.

Some minerals are readily identified by their *color*. While color is easy to observe, care must be taken with light-colored minerals, such as quartz. Small amounts of impurities can make quartz almost any color. Quartz can be clear and colorless, or it can be white, pink, green, brown, or even dark gray to black.

Hardness is a mineral's resistance to being scratched. Mohs' scale of hardness ranges from the soft mineral talc, with a hardness of 1, to diamond, with a hardness of 10. See Figure 11-5.

Mohs' Scale of Hardness

1. Talc	6. Feldspar
2. Gypsum	7. Quartz
3. Calcite	8. Topaz
4. Fluorite	9. Corundum
5. Apatite	10. Diamond

Fingernail 2.5   Penny 3

Window glass 5.5   Steel file 6.5

Figure 11-5. Mohs' scale of hardness. Mohs' scale provides a list of minerals of known hardness. Other convenient materials are shown to the right. Hardness is tested by rubbing a sharp corner of the mineral sample across a surface of known hardness. The mineral will scratch a substance that is softer, but not a harder material. The harder material will scratch the mineral sample.

Streak is the color of the powder of a mineral. It is determined by scratching a hard, white porcelain streak plate with the mineral in question and noting the color of the powder left on the white porcelain. The streak test works only on minerals that are softer than porcelain, which has a hardness of nearly 7. Although the color of a mineral sample may differ because of impurities, the color of the streak of a specific mineral rarely varies. In general, all metals and most minerals showing metallic luster show the same color whether in the solid or powdered form. Nonmetallic minerals generally leave streaks that are lighter in color than the sample. See Figure 11-6.

Reviewing Earth Science: Topic 11

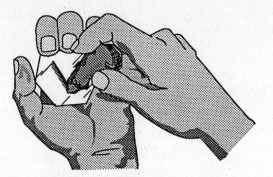

Figure 11-6. The streak test is used to find the color of the powder of a mineral with a metallic luster. A corner of the sample is rubbed across an unglazed porcelain streak plate.

Luster is the way that a surface reflects light. Minerals with a metallic luster look shiny, as if they were made of polished metal. This is because light is unable to penetrate the surface. A glassy luster is also shiny, but it differs from a metallic luster because some of the light is transmitted into and through the mineral. Other terms used to describe nonmetallic lusters include waxy, pearly, and earthy.

A mineral's **transparency** is determined by how it interacts with light. Transparent minerals allow light to pass through, and objects can be seen clearly through them. Translucent minerals allow some light to pass through, but objects cannot be seen through them clearly. No light passes through opaque minerals.

Specific gravity, or relative density, is the ratio of a mineral's density to that of water. The density of water is 1 g/cm³. Therefore, a mineral with a density of 4 g/cm³ would have a specific gravity of 4.

A substance with a specific gravity greater than 1 would sink in water. A substance that floats in water has a specific gravity less than 1.

Minerals can also be chemically analyzed, although special equipment is usually needed. A simple test that can be performed is the *acid test.* For example, a few drops of cold dilute hydrochloric acid applied to calcite will produce bubbles of carbon dioxide gas.

QUESTIONS

1. All rocks contain (1) minerals (2) intergrown crystals (3) sediments (4) fossils
2. Which element comprises most of the earth's crust both by weight and by volume? (1) nitrogen (2) hydrogen (3) oxygen (4) silicon
3. The silica tetrahedron model is most directly useful in explaining the properties of the materials in the (1) hydrosphere (2) earth's crust (3) atmosphere (4) earth's core

4. Which two elements listed below are most abundant by weight in the earth's crust? (1) silicon and oxygen (2) hydrogen and iron (3) oxygen and magnesium (4) hydrogen and calcium
5. Which object is the best model of the shape of a silicon-oxygen structural unit?

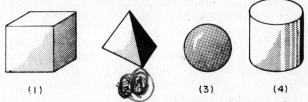

(1)   (2)   (3)   (4)

6. Silicate minerals that form by the joining together of silicon-oxygen tetrahedra into chains will most likely break apart when struck by a hammer into (1) splinters (2) pyramids (3) sheets (4) cubes
7. Which is the best explanation for the cleavage of mica into thin layers? (1) the high density of mica (2) the arrangement of the mica molecules (3) the softness of mica (4) the impurities found in mica
8. The diagram below represents a single silicon-oxygen tetrahedron unit. Two different minerals have these same units arranged in different patterns. How will the minerals differ?

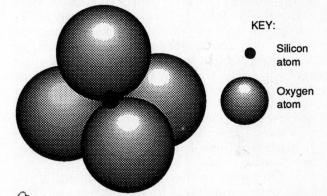

KEY:

● Silicon atom

● Oxygen atom

(1) One mineral will have some physical properties different from the other. (2) One mineral will be more radioactive than the other. (3) One mineral will have the silicon atom outside the tetrahedron while the other will have it inside the tetrahedron. (4) One mineral will have larger silicon atoms than the other.
9. The physical properties of a mineral are largely due to its (1) volume (2) organic composition (3) internal arrangement of atoms (4) melting point
10. When dilute hydrochloric acid is placed on the sedimentary rock limestone and the nonsedimentary rock marble, a bubbling reaction occurs with both. What would this indicate? (1) The minerals of these two rocks have similar chemical compositions. (2) The molecular structures of these two rocks have been changed by heat and pressure. (3) The physical properties of these two rocks are identical. (4) The two rocks originated at the same location.
11. When various minerals are split by a wedge, some break evenly along a flat surface while others fracture unevenly. Which property of a mineral is responsible for the way in which it splits? (1) softness (2) density (3) atomic arrangement (4) chemical composition

12. The crystal characteristics of quartz shown in the accompanying diagram are the result of the

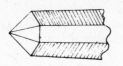

(1) internal arrangement of the elements from which quartz is formed (2) shape of the other rock crystals in the area where the quartz was formed   (3) amount of weathering that the quartz has been exposed to   (4) age of the quartz crystal

HOW ROCKS FORM

Rocks are classified according to their origin. **Sedimentary rock** can originate from particles of rock, from remains of plants and animals, or from newly formed mineral crystals that are transported by agents of erosion and then deposited in new locations on land or underwater.

Fragmental Sedimentary Rocks.

Most sedimentary rocks are composed primarily of the weathered remains of other rocks. Fragmental sedimentary rocks contain layers of particles, or fragments, formed from the breakdown of other rocks. Particles may be worn and rounded or pointed and angular. Particles within a rock can vary in size; but particles of one size, as in sand or clay, often predominate throughout the layers of a rock. Layering in sedimentary rocks is particularly helpful in distinguishing them from nonsedimentary rocks.

Unlike loose sediments, sedimentary rocks have been **compressed** by the pressure of overlying sediments and rocks and are often held together by a hard matrix of crystalline **cement**. With finer grained sediments, such as clay and silt, compaction alone will hold the sediment particles together. Coarser or larger sediment particles are also compacted, but to form sedimentary rock they must be cemented together by minerals dissolved in water. Calcite, the mineral that makes up limestone, is a common rock-forming cement. Silica, a form of quartz, may also serve as a natural cement.

Most sedimentary rocks are classified on the basis of their texture, or the size of the **grains** of sediment they contain. *Shale* is composed of clay particles so small that the individual particles cannot be seen without magnification. *Sandstone* grains are easily visible on close inspection, and they feel gritty. **Conglomerate** is made of pebbles, cobbles, or boulders held together by a natural cement. The sedimentary rocks chart in the *Earth Science Reference Tables* tells the ranges of particle sizes in these sedimentary rocks. See Figure 11-7.

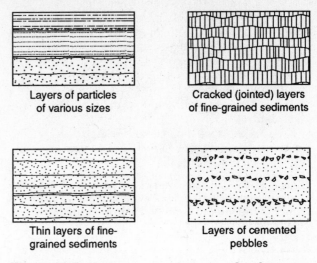

Figure 11-7. Four common textures of sedimentary rocks.

Layers of particles of various sizes

Cracked (jointed) layers of fine-grained sediments

Thin layers of fine-grained sediments

Layers of cemented pebbles

Organic Sedimentary Rocks.

Organic sedimentary rocks are formed by the accumulation of plant or animal remains. For example, to form coal, plant remains from tropical swamps and marshes accumulate in layers. As these layers are compressed, volatile materials in the plants escape as gases or dissolve in groundwater. What remains is black carbon, sometimes full of plant impressions. Limestone is often created by the accumulation of seashells and other animal skeletons. Sometimes these animal remains are ground into fragments by wave action or by currents. Sometimes they remain whole.

Chemical Sedimentary Rock.

A third group of sedimentary rocks is the chemical *evaporites* and *precipitates*, which start out as minerals dissolved in water. Evaporites, like limestone and rock salt, are formed from minerals that were once dissolved in water. During evaporation, the minerals crystallized. Evaporites are common in large inland lakes or seas, such as the Great Salt Lake in Utah and the Dead Sea between Israel and Jordan.

Crystals can also precipitate out of solution without evaporation. Sometimes ions combine chemically to form insoluble compounds, which settle on the lake or seabed to form sedimentary rocks. Dolomite (calcium magnesium carbonate) forms in this way.

Although most sedimentary rocks are a mixture of different minerals and even different rocks, all chemical sedimentary rocks are monomineralic. Limestone, a monomineralic rock composed primarily of calcite, can form in a variety of ways. Coquina is an organic limestone made from cemented animal shells. Fragmental limestone results from the compaction and cementing of calcite sand deposits. Some limestone is precipitated from solution in tropical seawater.

The presence of **fossils**, the remains of prehistoric life, is usually interpreted as evidence that a rock is of sedimentary origin. Sedimentary rocks originated as sediments on the earth's surface, where most organisms live. When these organisms died, sediments would often cover their remains, which would later become part of the sedimentary rock.

Fossils are rare in **nonsedimentary** rocks because the remains of the organisms are usually too fragile to survive the extreme heat and pressure that form nonsedimentary rock.

QUESTIONS

13. What kind of rock is formed when rock fragments are deposited and cemented together? (1) igneous (2) metamorphic (3) plutonic (4) sedimentary

14. According to the *Earth Science Reference Tables*, sedimentary rocks formed by compaction and cementation of land-derived sediments are classified on the basis of (1) composition (2) type of cement (3) particle size (4) rate of formation

15. According to the *Earth Science Reference Tables*, compaction and cementation of pebble-sized particles would form the sedimentary rock known as (1) shale (2) conglomerate (3) sandstone (4) siltstone

16. According to the *Earth Science Reference Tables*, some sedimentary rocks form as the direct result of the (1) solidification of molten magma (2) recrystallization of material (3) melting of minerals (4) cementation of rock fragments

17. Which process would form a sedimentary rock? (1) cooling of molten magma within the earth's crust (2) recrystallization of unmelted material within the earth's crust (3) cooling of a lava flow on the earth's surface (4) precipitation of minerals as seawater evaporates

18. According to the *Earth Science Reference Tables*, dolostone is formed by the (1) local metamorphism of marble (2) biological deposition of skeletons and shells (3) chemical replacement of limestone (4) mechanical deposition of silts

19. According to the *Earth Science Reference Tables*, which is a sedimentary rock that forms as a result of precipitation from seawater? (1) conglomerate (2) gypsum (3) basalt (4) shale

20. According to the *Earth Science Reference Tables*, which type of sedimentary rock contains the greatest range of particle sizes? (1) conglomerate (2) sandstone (3) shale (4) siltstone

21. Which property best describes a rock which has formed from sediments? (1) crystalline structure (2) distorted structure (3) banding or zoning of minerals (4) fragmental particles arranged in layers

22. Which property is common to both sedimentary rocks and sediments? (1) fragmental particles (2) distortion of structure (3) crystal alignment (4) crystalline structure

23. According to the *Earth Science Reference Tables*, which sedimentary rock could form as a result of evaporation? (1) conglomerate (2) sandstone (3) shale (4) limestone

24. A massive sedimentary rock layer composed of uniformly small particles probably formed from the (1) precipitation of material from seawater (2) cooling of a lava flow (3) cooling of magma (4) cementation of glacial material

25. Large rock salt deposits in the Syracuse area indicate that the area once had (1) large forests (2) a range of volcanic mountains (3) many terrestrial animals (4) a warm, shallow sea

Igneous Rocks.

Igneous rocks are formed directly from the cooling of magma beneath the surface of the earth. Most minerals melt at a temperature of about 1,000°C near the earth's surface. When liquid rock cools, it changes to a solid made of intergrown crystals. This process is called **crystallization**.

Igneous rocks are classified on the basis of their *texture* and *composition*. The **texture** of an igneous rock describes the size, shape, and arrangement of the mineral crystals of which it is made. See Figure 11-8. The size of the crystals formed depends upon the rate of cooling. Slow cooling gives the atoms time to line up to form large crystals. Fine crystals in an igneous rock result from rapid cooling.

Large, intergrown crystals of one or more minerals formed by slow cooling.

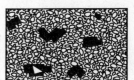
A few large crystals in a fine-grained matrix of other minerals made by slow cooling followed by rapid cooling.

A mass of small intergrown crystals of one or more minerals formed by rapid cooling.

A shiny mass of volcanic glass containing tiny crystals or none, made by very rapid cooling.

Figure 11-8. Characteristic textures of igneous rocks.

Extrusion occurs when molten rock flows out of the earth (lava) and cools quickly at the surface to form very fine crystals. See Figure 11-9. Rocks formed this way have a fine-grained texture, for example, rhyolite and basalt. (See *Earth Science Reference Tables*.) Sometimes the molten rock cools so quickly that it does not have time to form

The Formation of Rocks

111

crystals. The resulting rock appears glassy. Obsidian, sometimes called volcanic glass, is an example of a glassy igneous rock.

Rocks with a coarse-grained texture cooled slowly, usually deep within the earth, when the molten rock may have flowed upward into the more solid part of the crust. This process is called **intrusion**. Gabbro and granite are coarse-grained, intrusive igneous rocks. (See *Earth Science Reference Tables*.)

Most igneous rocks of the continental crust are rich in the aluminum silicate minerals. They are light in color, **felsic** abundant in quartz and feldspar), and relatively low in density. Igneous rocks of the ocean basins are usually abundant in the **mafic** (iron and magnesium) minerals, which are darker and slightly more dense.

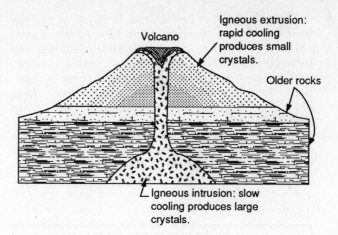

Figure 11-9. Extrusive and intrusive igneous rocks.

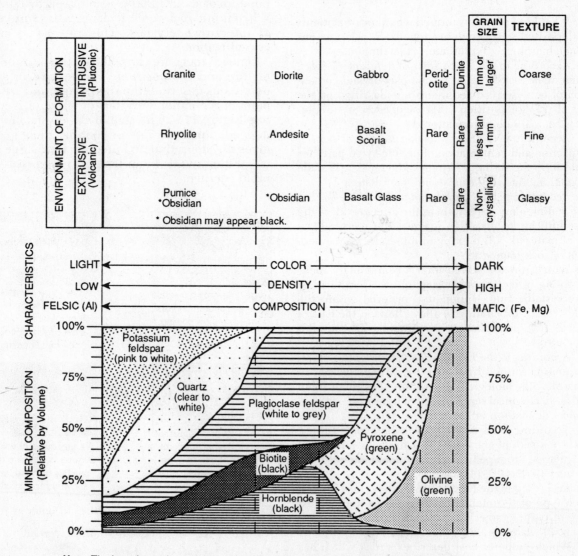

Note: The intrusive rocks can also occur as exceptionally coarse-grained rock, Pegmatite.

Figure 11-10. Scheme for igneous rock identification.

The *Scheme for Igneous Rock Identification* shown in Figure 11-10 uses composition, texture and environment of formation to describe common igneous rocks (including granite, rhyolite, gabbro, and basalt). To identify an igneous rock sample, compare it with the characteristics of rocks given in the chart. The upper portion of the chart deals with the density, color, and grain size of the rocks. The lower portion shows the mineral composition of the rocks (in percentage by volume). For example, granite to the left of the chart fits into the category of felsic rocks. These rocks are light in color, rich in the elements silicon (Si) and aluminum (Al) and are less dense than mafic rocks to the right of the chart. Mafic rocks, like gabbro, are dark in color, rich in the elements iron (Fe) and magnesium (Mg), and are denser than felsic rocks.

The graph can also be used in interpreting the texture of igneous rocks. For example, granite is a coarse-grained igneous rock containing mainly potassium feldspar and quartz, while rhyolite is fine-grained with the same composition as granite.

QUESTIONS

26. Which is most likely a nonsedimentary rock: (1) a rock containing fossil shells (2) a rock showing ripple marks and mud cracks (3) a rock composed of layers of gravel cemented together (4) a rock consisting of large intergrown crystals

27. In general, the size of the crystals in igneous rocks depends chiefly on the (1) amount of iron present as the magma cools (2) amount of silicate (SiO₄) present as the magma cools (3) dissolved gases present as the magma cools (4) rate at which the magma cools

Directions: Base your answer to question 28 on your knowledge of earth science and on the accompanying diagram, which represents a cross-sectional view of a volcanic island which has not erupted during recorded history.

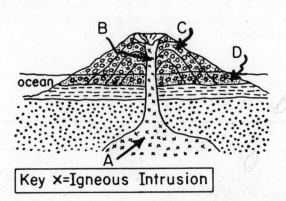

Key X=Igneous Intrusion

28. Where would rocks containing the largest mineral crystals most likely be found? (1) deep in the interior (A) (2) near the surface of the cooled lava (B) (3) in the cinders forming the cone (C) (4) in the solidified lava flow in the ocean (D)

29. Which would most likely cause molten rock material to become glassy igneous rock? (1) cooling over a long period of time (2) cooling under high pressure (3) cooling on the surface (4) cooling at a great depth

30. Which would most likely occur during the formation of igneous rock? (1) compression and cementation of sediments (2) recrystallization of unmelted material (3) solidification of molten materials (4) evaporation and precipitation of sediments

31. A certain igneous rock is composed of large mineral grains. This suggests that the rock formed (1) on the surface, under high pressure, and at a rapid rate of cooling (2) on the surface, at high temperature, and at a slow rate of cooling (3) under high pressure, at high temperature, and at a rapid rate of cooling (4) under high pressure, at high temperature, and at a slow rate of cooling

32. According to the *Earth Science Reference Tables*, generally, as the percentage of felsic minerals in a rock increases, the rock's color will become (1) darker and its density will decrease (2) lighter and its density will increase (3) darker and its density will increase (4) lighter and its density will decrease

33. A fine-grained rock has the following mineral composition: 50 percent potassium feldspar, 26 percent quartz, 13 percent plagioclase, 8 percent biotite, and 3 percent hornblende. The rock would most likely be (1) granite (2) rhyolite (3) gabbro (4) basalt

34. Which observation about an igneous rock would support the inference that the rock cooled slowly underground? (1) The rock has well-defined layers. (2) The rock has large crystals. (3) The rock is about 50 percent plagioclase feldspar. (4) The rock is light in color and low in density.

35. According to the *Earth Science Reference Tables*, which is a fine-grained igneous rock made up primarily of pyroxene and plagioclase feldspar? (1) gabbro (2) basalt (3) granite (4) rhyolite

36. A coarse-grained igneous rock contains plagioclase feldspars and pyroxenes, but no quartz. According to the *Earth Science Reference Tables*, this rock is most likely (1) basalt (2) rhyolite (3) granite (4) gabbro

37. Which graph best shows the relationship between the size of the crystals in an igneous rock and the length of time it has taken the rock to solidify?

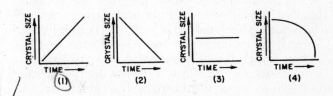

38. According to the *Earth Science Reference Tables*, which rock is of felsic composition, low in density, light in color, and coarse-grained? (1) rhyolite (2) basalt (3) granite (4) gabbro

39. According to the *Earth Science Reference Tables*, which minerals could both be contained in the rocks gabbro and granite? (1) quartz and pyroxene (2) biotite and hornblende (3) potassium feldspar and olivine (4) plagioclase and olivine

The Formation of Rocks

40. Extremely small crystal grains in an igneous rock are an indication that the crystals formed (1) under high pressure (2) over a short period of time (3) from an iron-rich magma (4) deep below the surface of the earth

41. The diagrams below represent magnifications of rocks. Which is most likely a diagram of a *nonsedimentary* rock?

KEY

Quartz   Hornblende   Feldspar

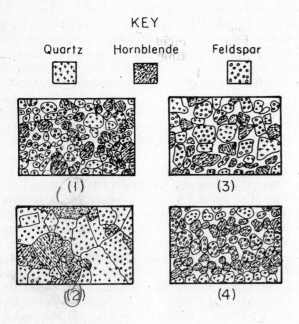

(1)   (3)

(2)   (4)

found in areas where mountains are or have once been.

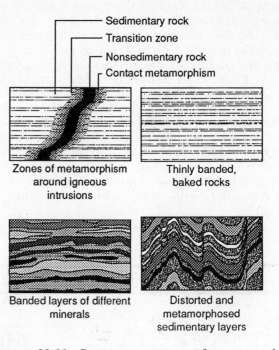

Figure 11-11. Common textures of metamorphic rocks.

Metamorphic Rocks.

A **metamorphic rock** is one whose original form has been changed by heat, pressure, or chemically active fluids. This alteration is called *recrystallization*. These changes are not caused by melting. (If the rock melted and cooled, it would be an igneous rock.)

The changes caused by recrystallization may include the creation of new minerals and the growth of mineral crystals. Metamorphism can also compress rock (making it more dense), and **distort** (bend) or destroy original structures such as layers of sediment or fossils. The growth of new minerals may cause the rock to appear **banded**, with layers of light and dark minerals (foliation). This banding is particularly helpful in identifying metamorphic rock. See Figure 11-11.

Any kind of rock—sedimentary, igneous, or even metamorphic—can undergo recrystallization to form metamorphic rock. The metamorphic rock marble is formed from limestone, slate from shale, and quartzite from sandstone.

Regional metamorphism occurs when large masses of rock are changed by deep burial within the earth. In general, the deeper the burial, the greater will be the changes in the original rock.

The extreme pressure and temperature required for regional metamorphism are usually associated with the earth processes that build mountains. Thus, metamorphic rock is often

Contact metamorphism can be found next to igneous intrusions. Heat from liquid rock (magma) alters the surrounding rocks and causes mineral changes. These changes are the greatest at the interface between the magma and the surrounding rock and become less intense away from the source of heat.

The transition from unchanged rock to metamorphic is gradual, and it may be difficult to determine where the original rock type becomes a metamorphic rock. Rocks that show a gradual increase in metamorphic character lie within the **transition zone**. See Figure 11-11.

QUESTIONS

42. As the depth within the earth's crust increases, the amount of sedimentary rock, compared to the amount of nonsedimentary rock, will generally (1) decrease (2) increase (3) remain the same

43. Which characteristic of rocks tends to increase as the rocks are metamorphosed? (1) density (2) volume (3) permeability (4) number of fossils present

44. What is the main difference between metamorphic rocks and most other rocks? (1) Many metamorphic rocks contain only one mineral. (2) Many metamorphic rocks have an organic composition. (3) Many metamorphic rocks exhibit banding and distortion of structure. (4) Many metamorphic rocks contain a high amount of oxygen-silicon tetrahedra.

Base your answers to questions 45 and 46 on the diagram below which represents a cross-sectional view of a portion of the earth's crust with specific points A, B, C, and D within the cross section.

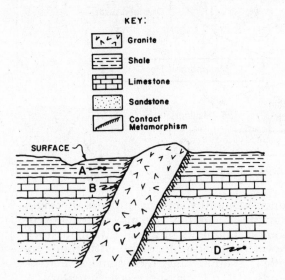

45. In which region would rock be found which shows a gradual transition from sedimentary to metamorphic rock? (1) A (2) B (3) C (4) D

46. At which point would rock be found which consists of intergrown mineral crystals of feldspar and quartz? (1) A (2) B (3) C (4) D

GEOGRAPHIC DISTRIBUTION OF ROCK TYPES

Most of the land areas of the earth are covered by a thin layer of sedimentary rocks. Igneous rocks are common within and around volcanoes, and where rock, once buried and melted deep within the earth, has been pushed up and exposed at the surface by erosion. Metamorphic rocks are found in transition zones between igneous and sedimentary rocks, as well as in mountainous areas where rock has been pushed up from deep within the earth. See Figure 11-12.

THE ROCK CYCLE

The earth has a limited supply of solid rock material that is constantly changing from one form to another. The **rock cycle** provides a useful model of these changes. See Figure 11-13.

This diagram distinguishes between those processes that take place primarily at the surface of the earth (external processes) and those that take place within the earth (internal processes). Internal processes, such as compression and heating, require the conditions of high temperature and pressure that occur deep underground.

The rock cycle illustrates several important facts of geology. Nearly all rocks are formed from other rocks. (Coal and other sedimentary rocks of organic origin are notable exceptions.) Through the processes shown along the outside of the circle, rocks of one type are changed to rocks of another type. For example, sedimentary rock can be weathered, eroded, deposited, and cemented to form new sedimentary rock. It can be changed into metamorphic rock by heating, crystal growth, and the formation of new minerals. Sedimentary rock can also be melted and crystallized to form igneous rock. There is more than one path through the rock cycle. The arrows within the circle show that igneous rock can not only undergo weathering, erosion, and deposition to make sediment, but it can also be changed by heating, crystal growth, and the formation of new minerals to make a metamorphic rock. Alternately, it can be remelted to make molten rock (known as magma within the earth or lava at the surface of the earth). Metamorphic rock can be melted and crystallized to become igneous rock, or weathered, eroded, and cemented into sedimentary rock. It can also be further altered by heat and pressure into new metamorphic rock.

Rocks are classified by their origin. The name applied to a rock depends upon how the rock formed. For example, any rock formed by the crystallization or solidification of molten rock is

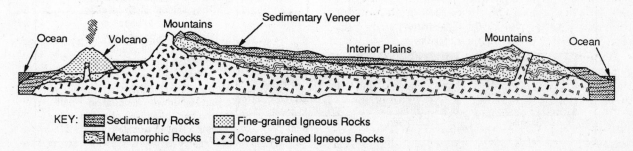

Figure 11-12. Typical distribution of rocks in a continent.

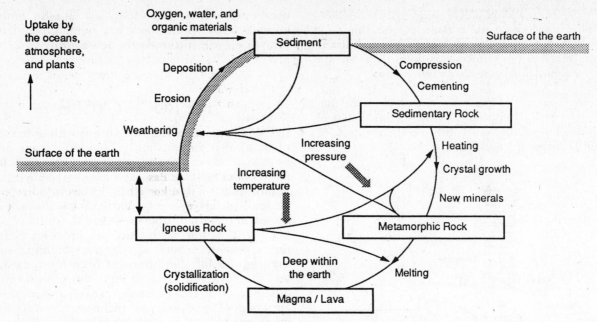

Figure 11-13. The rock cycle.

an igneous rock. No other rock type forms in this way. See Figure 11-14.

Each rock type can remain relatively stable for long periods of time. Changes from one rock type to another may require thousands or even millions of years. Sometimes a rock may show evidence of more than one process or origin. For example, a conglomerate may be composed of cemented fragments of granite (igneous rock) and gneiss (metamorphic rock). Although conglomerate is a sedimentary rock, some of the rock fragments within it may be nonsedimentary.

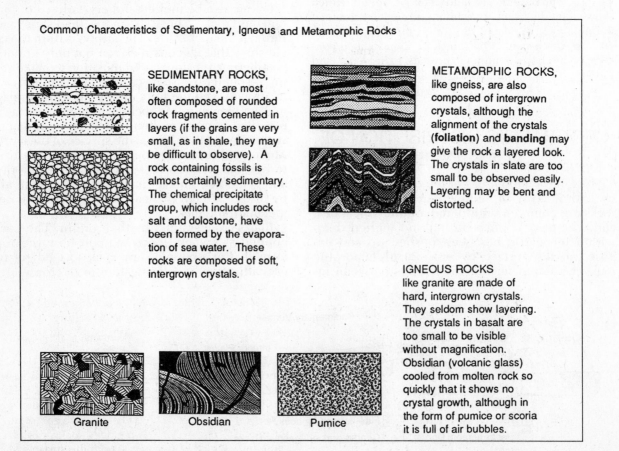

Figure 11-14. Common characteristics of sedimentary, igneous, and metamorphic rocks.

47. Which statement correctly describes the distribution of sedimentary rocks on the earth? (1) Sedimentary rock layers are thickest in the middle of the oceans. (2) Sedimentary rocks extend down into the earth's crust as far as the inner core. (3) Sedimentary rocks are usually located in volcanic regions. (4) Sedimentary rocks usually form a thin layer over large areas of the continents.

48. Why is the conglomerate rock shown below good evidence that rocks form from other rocks?

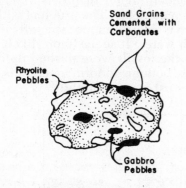

Sand Grains Cemented with Carbonates

Rhyolite Pebbles

Gabbro Pebbles

(1) The conglomerate contains some nonsedimentary rock fragments. (2) The conglomerate was formed from material that was buried deep underground. (3) The conglomerate's pebbles are all weathering at the same rate. (4) The conglomerate was formed by the cooling of molten rock material.

49. Which statement is supported by information in the Rock Cycle diagram in the *Earth Science Reference Tables*? (1) Metamorphic rock results directly from melting and crystallization. (2) Sedimentary rock can only be formed from igneous rock. (3) Igneous rock always results from melting and solidification. (4) All sediments turn directly into sedimentary rock.

50. Which characteristic provides the best evidence about the environment in which a rock was formed? (1) the color of the rock (2) the size of the rock (3) the texture of the rock (4) the thickness of the rock

Directions (51–55): Questions 51 through 55 are based on the accompanying sketches, which show four

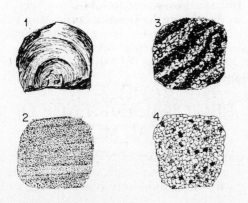

hand *specimens* of rocks. Write the *number* of the sketch that best answers *each* question.

51. Which sketch represents a sedimentary rock?
52. Which sketch represents a metamorphic rock?
53. Which sketch represents a rock that was formed at great depth?
54. Which sketch represents a rock originating in a lava flow?
55. Which sketch represents a rock that formed in the shortest time interval?

Directions (56–60): Base your answers to questions 56 through 60 on your knowledge of earth science, the *Earth Science Reference Tables*, and the following two graphs.

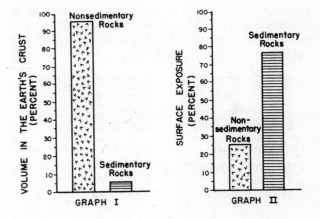

GRAPH I GRAPH II

Graph I represents the percentage of sedimentary and nonsedimentary rock which makes up the earth's crust by volume. Graph II represents, of those rocks that are exposed at the surface (outcrops), the percentage that are sedimentary rocks and nonsedimentary rocks.

56. Approximately what percentage of the earth's crust is composed of sedimentary rock? (1) 5% (2) 25% (3) 75% (4) 95%

57. Which is the most abundant element present in the rocks shown in graph I? (1) nitrogen (2) oxygen (3) silicon (4) hydrogen

58. All of the rocks represented in graph I must contain (1) fossils (2) intergrown crystals (3) sediments (4) minerals

59. Most sedimentary rock has been formed by which two processes? (1) uplifting and melting (2) extrusion and intrusion (3) compaction and cementation (4) faulting and folding

60. Which statement is best supported by the data shown in the graphs? (1) The crust of the earth is composed mostly of sedimentary rocks. (2) Rock outcrops on the earth's surface are chiefly of the nonsedimentary type. (3) Most nonsedimentary rocks are composed of the melted remains of sedimentary rocks. (4) Most sedimentary rock is found at or near the surface of the earth.

TOPIC 12 Dynamics of the Earth

LOCAL EVIDENCE OF CRUSTAL MOTIONS

As erosion wears down the earth's crust, other processes within the earth create new mountains. Most of these processes are too slow to observe from day to day, but over millions of years, they have dramatically changed our planet.

For example, sedimentary beds are deposited as horizontal layers, or **strata**. But sometimes these layers appear to have been moved from their original position. *Tilted*, *folded*, and *faulted* (offset) strata are evidence of motions within the earth's crust. See Figure 12-1.

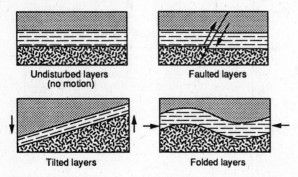

Undisturbed layers (no motion) **Faulted layers**

Tilted layers **Folded layers**

Figure 12-1. Evidence of crustal motion. Faulted, tilted, and folded strata provide evidence of motions of the earth's crust since these layers were first deposited as flat, horizontal layers.

We usually do not observe the movements that cause rock strata to fold or to form faults. (A **fault** is a break in the rock of the earth's crust along which there has been movement.) Following an earthquake, however, changes may be observed in the local landscape, including fault lines and uplifted land. Thus, earthquakes provide direct evidence of crustal movement.

Careful mapping surveys have established the elevations of specific points on the land surface throughout the United States. Many of these places are marked with small brass disks known as **bench marks**. A record of the exact positions and elevations of the bench marks is kept by the United States Geological Survey.

Repeated surveys have remeasured the bench marks and recorded any changes in elevation. These surveys found that some bench marks were higher, while others were lower than previously measured. Most of the movements that produced these changes were too slow to be felt directly, but their effects could be measured over time. In the mountainous western part of the United States, some bench marks have risen as much as half a meter or more per century. Changes in the

elevation of bench marks are evidence that the land is either rising or sinking. See Figure 12-2.

Marine fossils are the remains of plants and animals that once lived in the oceans. In some locations, these fossils are found in mountains thousands of meters above sea level. Such findings could be interpreted as evidence that the sea level was much higher than it is now, covering even these mountains. The problem with this interpretation is that we cannot account for a source of so much water. It seems more likely that the rocks with the fossils were pushed up from previous ocean bottoms to form mountains. The rising of the crust is called **uplift**.

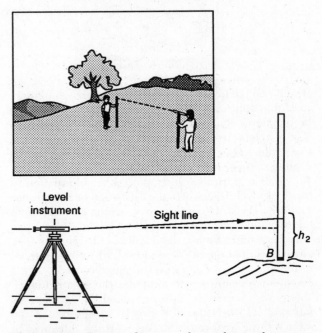

Level instrument **Sight line** h_2 B

Figure 12-2. Repeated surveys have shown that some locations are changing in elevation through time.

Most marine organisms live in shallow waters where sunlight can penetrate to the ocean bottom. But shallow-water fossils have been found at great depths in the oceans, indicating that the ocean bottom in these locations has sunk to a deeper level since the fossil organisms were alive. The sinking of the crust is called **subsidence**.

REGIONAL EVIDENCE OF CRUSTAL MOTIONS

Ocean waves sometimes erode flat areas along the shore. In some places, a series of flat areas that go up from the shoreline like steps can be

Figure 12-3. Marine terraces are created at sea level by the breaking waves. When we see these flat terraces elevated above sea level, we may infer that the land has been pushed up above sea level.

found. See Figure 12-3. These **marine terraces** are often well above the current elevation of the breaking waves, even at high tide. Thus, they show the changing height of the land over time.

If these terraces were found at the same elevations throughout the world, they might indicate that the oceans were once higher than they are today. However, from place to place these terraces do differ in their elevations above sea level. Such observations indicate that in these places the land has been pushed up from below. Each time the land is pushed up, a new step is formed as the sea erodes the shore.

QUESTIONS

1. Which diagram indicates the *least* amount of crustal activity?

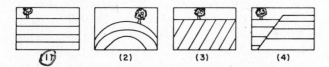

2. Which best explains why fossil remains of sharks have been found in the sedimentary rocks of Wyoming? (1) Sharks used to live in freshwater basins. (2) Sharks were once land animals. (3) The teeth were carried to Wyoming by streams from another area. (4) The area was once covered by the sea.

3. A sandstone layer is found tilted at an angle of 75° from the horizontal. What probably caused this 75° tilt? (1) The sediments that formed this sandstone layer were originally deposited at a 75° tilt. (2) This sandstone layer has changed position due to crustal movement. (3) This sandstone layer has recrystallized due to contact metamorphism. (4) Nearly all sandstone layers are formed from wind-deposited sands.

4. An observer discovers shallow-water marine fossils in rock strata at an elevation of 5000 meters. What is the best explanation for this observation? (1) The level of the ocean was once 5000 meters higher. (2) Violent earthquakes caused crustal subsidence. (3) Marine organisms have evolved into land organisms. (4) Crustal uplift has occurred in this area.

5. In 1915, an elevation marker was placed on the highest point of Baker Pass, California (elevation 1158 m above sea level). In 1965, the elevation of the marker was 1164 m. Assuming no erosion has occurred, what is the approximate rate of uplift per century? (1) 0.12 m (2) 12 m (3) 120 m (4) 1.2 m

6. Two geologic surveys of the same area, made 50 years apart, showed that the area had been uplifted 5 centimeters during the interval. If the rate of uplift remains constant, how many years will it take for this area to be uplifted a total of 70 centimeters? (1) 250 years (2) 350 years (3) 500 years (4) 700 years

7. Which is the best evidence of crustal movement? (1) molten rock in the earth's outer core (2) tilted sedimentary rock layers (3) residual sediments on top of bedrock (4) marine fossils found below sea level

8. Which is the best evidence that the earth's crust has been uplifted? (1) younger fossils above the older fossils in layers of rock (2) shallow-water fossils found at great ocean depths (3) marine fossils found at high elevations above sea level (4) marine fossils found in horizontal sedimentary layers

9. Shallow-water fossils are found in rock layers that are deep beneath the ocean floor. This suggests that (1) shallow-water organisms always migrate to the deeper waters to die (2) parts of the ocean floor have been uplifted (3) parts of the ocean floor have subsided (4) the surface water cooled off, killing the organisms

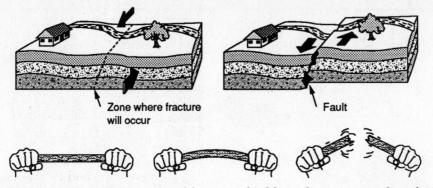

Figure 12-4. Earthquakes are caused by stress building along a zone of weakness. Sudden shifting along the fault releases the energy that you can feel as an earthquake.

EARTHQUAKES

An **earthquake** is any vibrating, shaking, or rapid motion of the earth's crust. Some earthquakes are caused by the movement of magma inside volcanoes, but most result from a process known as faulting. Faulting is the movement of rock along a surface where the rocks are broken.

Slow movement of the crust over long periods of time builds stress within the rocks. Sometimes the pressure is so great that the rock strata break and move past each other, creating a fault. The stress caused by such movements of the crust is usually released by a rapid movement along an existing fault, where the crust is already weak. Many of the most destructive earthquakes occur this way.

When the faulting occurs, energy radiates through the earth as **seismic waves** that cause the ground to vibrate. Seismic waves travel outward from the break in all directions, much as sound radiates from an explosion. See Figure 12-4.

Measuring Earthquakes.

Scientists use two types of scales to measure the strength of earthquakes. The Modified Mercalli scale is a relative scale based upon the observations of people who experienced the earthquake and upon the damage it caused. See Table 12-1. This scale measures the **intensity** of the earthquake, from 1 to 12.

More often, scientists use the more precise Richter scale. The Richter scale uses an instrument called a **seismograph** to determine the earthquake's **magnitude**. Magnitude is the total energy released by an earthquake.

The Richter scale uses a numerical scale from 1 to 10 to measure the amount of energy released. See Table 12-2. Each of the numerical steps in the scale represents a tenfold increase in the amount of energy released. For example, a 3.0 quake indicates the release of 10 times more energy than a 2.0 quake. And a 6.0 quake indicates the release of 1,000 (10 times 10 times 10) times more energy than a 3.0 quake on the Richter scale. Earthquakes of magnitude 1 or 2 are too small to be felt or to cause significant damage.

Table 12-1. The Mercalli Scale

Mercalli	Mercalli Characteristics
I	Detectable only by seismographs
II	Feeble: noticed only by some people at rest
III	Slight: similar to vibrations of a passing truck
IV	Moderate: felt indoors; parked cars rock
V	Rather strong: felt generally; sleepers wake
VI	Strong: trees sway; furniture moves; some damage
VII	Very strong: general alarm; walls crack
VIII	Destructive: weak structures damaged; walls fall
IX	Ruinous: some houses collapse as ground cracks
X	Disastrous: many buildings destroyed; rails bend
XI	Very disastrous: few buildings survive; landslides
XII	Catastrophic: total destruction; ground forms waves

Table 12-2. The Richter Scale

Richter Number	Increase in Magnitude
9	100,000,000
8	10,000,000
7	1,000,000
6	100,000
5	10,000
4	1,000
3	100
2	10
1	1

The most destructive earthquakes recorded in modern times had magnitudes between 8 and 9 on the Richter scale.

The place underground where the break, or fault, occurs is the **focus** of the earthquake. The **epicenter** is the location along the surface of the earth just above the focus where the earthquake is usually felt most strongly. Earthquakes release several types of energy waves, but the most im-

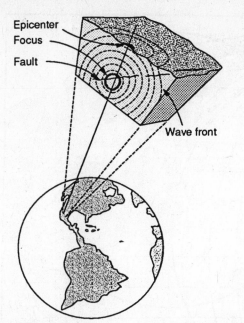

Figure 12-5. Earthquakes occur when the rocks break and shift within the earth. The location of the break is called the focus. Above this point, at the earth's surface, is the epicenter. The epicenter is generally where the earthquake is felt the most strongly.

portant ones are the primary (P) waves and the secondary (S) waves. See Figure 12-5.

Primary (P) waves travel faster than secondary waves and are therefore the first to be recorded by a seismograph. As P-waves move forward, they cause the ground to vibrate forward and back parallel to the direction of travel. Because of this push-pull action, P-waves are also known as *compressional waves.* P-waves can travel through both solids and fluids. (Liquids and gases are fluids.)

Secondary (S) waves, or *shear waves,* are slower than P-waves. S-wave vibrations occur perpendicular to the direction of travel. This includes up-and-down as well as side-to-side motion. Unlike P-waves, S-waves *cannot* travel through a fluid. See Figure 12-6. Both S- and P-waves travel faster through denser material.

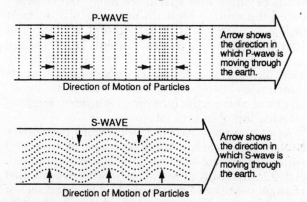

Figure 12-6. P-waves cause the ground to vibrate forward and back, parallel to the direction of travel. S-waves vibrate side to side, perpendicular to the direction of travel.

Finding the Epicenter.

The seismograph records the magnitude of an earthquake and the time when the seismic waves arrive. Using the time difference between the arrival of primary and secondary waves, you can determine the distance from an earthquake to the recording station. To do this, you will need a chart such as the *Earthquake S-Wave & P-Wave Time Travel Graph* in the *Earth Science Reference Tables.* On the graph, note that as the distance from the epicenter increases, so does the difference in travel times between P- and S-waves.

Finding Your Distance From an Earthquake Epicenter. See Figure 12-7. To calculate your distance from an earthquake epicenter, proceed as follows:

1. Subtract the arrival time of the P-waves from the arrival time of the S-waves. (This can be expressed in minutes and seconds, such as 06:40.)

2. On the clean edge of a sheet of paper, mark that interval along the travel-time scale on the vertical axis of the *Time Travel Graph.*

3. Slide the marks on the edge of your paper along the P- and S-curves of the travel-time scale until the marks coincide with both curves. See Figure 12-7.

4. Follow the marked edge of your paper down to the horizontal axis to find the distance to the epicenter.

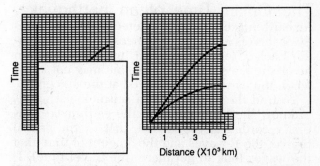

Figure 12-7. The distance to the epicenter of an earthquake can be determined if we know the time difference between the arrival of P-waves and S-waves.

This procedure has not yet located the epicenter, but it has established the distance from the recording station to the epicenter. If a circle with a radius equal to that distance is drawn around the recording station, the epicenter should be located somewhere along that circle. To find the exact location, follow the procedure above to find the distance from the epicenter to three seismic recording stations. Draw circles around each of these stations at the proper distances. The epicenter is the point at which the *three* circles intersect. See Figure 12-8. (In practice, the circles seldom intersect at a single point. More often, they make a small triangle. The epicenter's location is at the center of that triangle.)

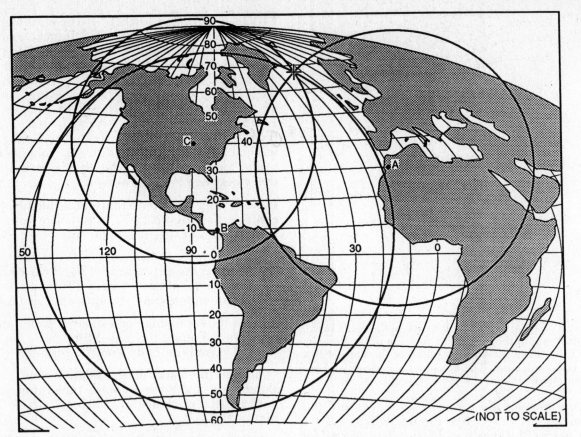

Figure 12-8. The location of an epicenter can be determined if we know the distances from three seismic recording stations.

The Origin Time of an Earthquake.

An earthquake's waves are detected at later times by observers at greater distances from its epicenter. Each observer may know immediately when he or she feels the vibrations, but may not know when the earthquake occurred at the epicenter.

To find the **origin time**, a seismologist needs to know the time at which the earthquake was first recorded at the station, that is, the arrival time of the P-waves and the amount of time that the waves took to get there (the travel time). If we know the distance to the epicenter (as determined in the section above), the travel time can be determined from the *Earthquake S-Wave & P-Wave Time Travel Graph* in the *Earth Science Reference Tables*. For example, if the epicenter is 4000 kilometers away, the travel time for P-waves is 7 minutes. Thus, if the earthquake was recorded at a station at 14:25 (2:25 in the afternoon) and the P-waves took 7 minutes to get there (travel time), then the earthquake must have actually happened 7 minutes earlier, at 14:18.

THE LAYERS OF THE EARTH

The Crust.   The **crust**, the outermost layer of our planet, varies from about 5 kilometers of thickness under the oceans to a maximum of about 60 kilometers under some mountain ranges on the continents. The composition of the crust is reasonably well known from observations at the surface and from mines and bore holes. In most places a thin layer of sedimentary rocks covers the mostly granitelike (**granitic**) rocks of the **continental crust**. The **oceanic crust**, under the layers of marine sediments, is composed mostly of darker and denser rocks similar to basalt (**basaltic**).

The Mantle.   Although we have explored the whole surface of the earth and have traveled thousands of miles into space, we have barely penetrated the ground beneath our feet. The deepest drill holes are about 10 kilometers, a mere $\frac{1}{10}$ of 1% of the earth's diameter. The solid layers of the earth and increasing heat and pressure within the earth have prevented direct observations of its interior. By using observations within the upper layers of the earth, however, we have inferred information about its interior.

As earthquake waves travel toward the earth's center, they reach a layer in which their speed suddenly increases. The Yugoslavian geophysicist Andrija Mohorovicic, who discovered this change, postulated that it marked an interface, or boundary, between the rocks of the crust and a denser layer. This interface is called the **Moho**, or the Mohorovicic discontinuity. The layer below the Moho is the earth's **mantle**.

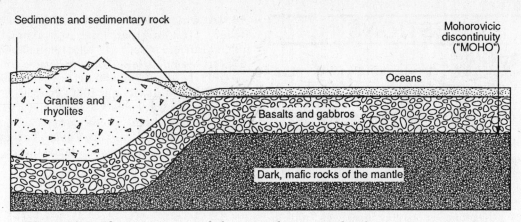

Figure 12-9. The continents and the ocean basins. Under the granitic rocks of the continents and the basaltic rocks of the ocean basins is the earth's mantle layer. The mantle is probably composed of mafic minerals rich in iron and magnesium.

The mantle, extending to a depth of about 2900 kilometers, includes most of the earth's volume. Scientists have inferred its composition from a variety of observations:

• In Topic 3, we learned how Eratosthenes determined the circumference of the earth. From this we can readily calculate the volume of our planet. The mass of the earth has been determined from measurements of gravitational attraction. From these figures, scientists have calculated the average density of the earth to be about $5\frac{1}{2}$ times the density of water. That's about twice the density of most rocks found at the earth's surface.
• Earthquake waves travel faster in the mantle than they do in the crust.
• The composition of magmas from deep within the earth includes a high proportion of the dense, mafic minerals.
• A large portion of the **meteorites** that fall to the earth are composed of the mafic minerals on the far right side of the *Scheme for Igneous Rock Identification* in the *Earth Science Reference Tables*. Scientists believe that these meteorites are the remains of the material from which the earth formed billions of years ago. If they are, they should show an overall composition similar to that of the earth.

All these observations suggest that the mantle is composed mostly of the dense, dark mafic minerals olivine and pyroxene. See Figure 12-9.

The Core.

The deepest layers of the earth are known as the *outer* and *inner cores*. The composition of these layers is thought to be a mixture of iron and nickel. These elements are abundant in some meteorites, and they are relatively dense. It is logical that these densest materials would sink into the earth's center.

The **outer core** is thought to be a liquid because S-waves are unable to pass through the outer core. The **inner core** seems to be a solid. Although the outer core and the inner core are both composed of iron and nickel, the higher pressures at the center of the earth cause the inner portion of the core to be a solid. The solid state of the inner core is inferred from the speed of P-waves, which travel relatively fast through it.

Earthquake Shadow Zones.

When a major earthquake occurs, both P-waves and S-waves are received over most of the earth. The part of the earth opposite to the side where the earthquake occurs receives P-waves, but no S-waves. This is because S-waves cannot penetrate the liquid outer core. Surrounding this "P-wave only" zone is a region where neither P- nor S-waves are received. Refraction (bending) of the waves at the mantle-core boundary causes this ring-shaped region known as the *shadow zone*. It extends from 102° to 143° from the epicenter. See Figure 12-10.

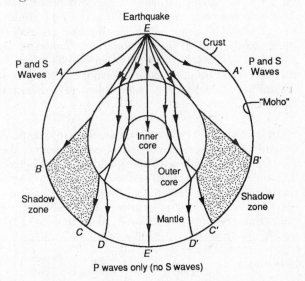

Figure 12-10. The layers of the earth have been defined based upon the passage of earthquake energy waves. The core and the mantle allow both P- and S-waves to pass. The outer core, being a liquid, will not pass S-waves. Refraction (bending) of the waves at the mantle-core boundary causes a shadow zone where neither P- nor S-waves are received.

QUESTIONS

10. Where are earthquakes most likely to take place? (1) along the core-mantle interface (2) where the composition of the earth tends to be uniform (3) near the earth's equator (4) near a fault zone

11. The immediate result of a sudden slippage of rocks within the earth's crust will be (1) isostasy (2) an earthquake (3) erosion (4) the formation of convection currents

12. Which graph best represents the relationship between the differences in arrival times of *P*-waves and *S*-waves for locations at varying distances from an earthquake?

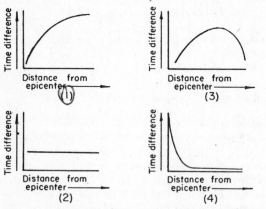

13. The distance between an earthquake epicenter and the location of a seismograph can be calculated because (1) seismographs are sensitive to directions (2) earthquake waves decay at known rates (3) shear waves will not pass through liquids (4) shear waves and compression waves travel at different speeds

14. A seismograph station records a difference in arrival time between the *S*- and *P*-waves of 4 minutes. About how far away is the earthquake epicenter? (Refer to the *Earth Science Reference Tables*.) (1) 1000 km (2) 1900 km (3) 2600 km (4) 5200 km

15. The most frequent cause of major earthquakes is (1) faulting (2) folding (3) landslides (4) submarine currents

Directions (16–17): Base your answers to questions 16 and 17 on your knowledge of earth science, the *Earth Science Reference Tables*, and the chart below. This chart provides partial seismic data from an earthquake which was detected at two different seismographic stations. The earthquake occurred at 10hr:00min:00sec A.M. eastern standard time (e.s.t.).

	P-wave Arrival Time (e.s.t.)	*S*-wave Arrival Time (e.s.t.)	Distance From Epicenter (km)
Triville	10hr:07min:00sec a.m.		
Endburg			9,000

16. At what time (e.s.t.) did the *S*-wave arrive at Triville? (1) 10hr:01min:45sec (2) 10hr:04min:00sec (3) 10hr:07min:00sec (4) 10hr:12min:30sec

17. At what time (e.s.t.) did the *P*-wave arrive at Endburg? (1) 10hr:07min:00sec (2) 10hr:09min:00sec (3) 10hr:12min:10sec (4) 10hr:22min:15sec

18. The seismogram below shows the arrival times of *P*- and *S*-waves from a single earthquake. According to the *Earth Science Reference Tables*, how far from the earthquake epicenter was the station that recorded this seismogram?

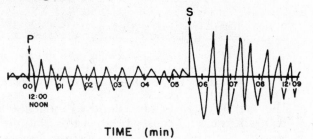

TIME (min)

(1) 1.5×10^3 km (2) 2.5×10^3 km (3) 3.0×10^3 km (4) 4.0×10^3 km

Directions (19–20): The illustration below represents a seismogram recording of an earthquake which shows the arrival of the *P*- and *S*-waves. Answer questions 19 and 20 based on the seismogram and on your knowledge of earth science.

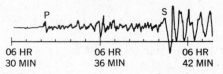

19. Which statement is true regarding the speed of *P*- and *S*-seismic waves? (1) *S*-waves travel faster than *P*-waves. (2) *P*-waves travel faster than *S*-waves. (3) They both travel at the same speed. (4) It is impossible to determine which wave travels faster.

20. A second seismic station records the same earthquake and detects a 3-minute difference between the arrival times of the *P*- and *S*-waves. Compared to the first seismic station, how far is the second station from the earthquake? (1) The second seismic station is the same distance from the earthquake as the first. (2) The second seismic station is nearer to the earthquake than the first. (3) The second seismic station is farther from the earthquake than the first. (4) It is impossible to determine from the data given which station is closer.

21. Four seismograph stations receive data from the same earthquake. The table below shows the differences in travel times for the *P*- and *S*-waves recorded at each station. Which station is the closest to the epicenter of the earthquake?

Station	Travel-Time Difference
A	4 min 32 sec
B	3 min 52 sec
C	3 min 10 sec
D	4 min 17 sec

(1) A (2) B (3) C (4) D

22. The time that an earthquake occurs can be inferred by knowing the (1) arrival time of the *P*-waves (2) distances between seismograph stations (3) travel time of the *S*-waves (4) epicenter distance and arrival time of the *P*-waves

23. At which location would seismic measurements indicate that the earth's crust is thickest? (1) Mississippi valley (2) Gulf of Mexico (3) Rocky Mountains (4) Lake Erie

24. Which statement best describes the continental and oceanic crusts? (1) The continental crust is thicker and less dense than the oceanic crust. (2) The continental crust is thicker and more dense than the oceanic crust. (3) The continental crust is thinner and less dense than the oceanic crust. (4) The continental crust is thinner and more dense than the oceanic crust.

25. The oceanic crust is thought to be composed mainly of (1) granite (2) sandstone (3) basalt (4) rhyolite

26. The Mohorovicic discontinuity (Moho) represents a transitional interface between the (1) lithosphere and hydrosphere (2) core and mantle (3) mantle and crust (4) inner core and outer core

27. The "shadow zone" observations made by seismologists are used as evidence for the existence of the (1) crust (2) mantle (3) outer core (4) Moho

28. As one travels from an ocean shore to the interior of a continent, the thickness of the earth's crust generally (1) decreases (2) increases (3) remains the same

29. According to the *Earth Science Reference Tables*, when compared to the granitic continental crust, the basaltic oceanic crust is (1) denser (2) thicker (3) composed of lighter colored rocks (4) composed of coarser grained rocks

30. Seismic studies of the moon have helped scientists to make inferences about (1) water erosion on the moon (2) weathering on the moon's surface (3) radioactivity of the moon's surface rocks (4) the moon's interior

31. According to the *Earth Science Reference Tables*, which zone of the earth has the greatest density? (1) crust (2) mantle (3) outer core (4) inner core

32. Which evidence best supports the inference that the earth's outer core possesses liquid characteristics? (1) The velocities of both primary and shear waves increase through the outer core. (2) The primary wave velocity decreases, while the shear wave velocity increases in the outer core. (3) Primary waves pass through the outer core but shear waves do not. (4) Both primary waves and shear waves pass through the outer core.

33. According to the *Earth Science Reference Tables*, what is the temperature of rock located 2000 kilometers below the earth's surface? (1) 800°C (2) 2400°C (3) 4100°C (4) 5000°C

34. Which evidence has led to the inference that solid zones and a liquid zone exist within the earth? (1) analysis of seismic wave data (2) the earth's rotational speed during the different seasons (3) direct temperature measurements of the earth's interior (4) gravitational measurements made at the earth's surface

35. The composition of the earth's core is thought to be the same as the composition of (1) certain meteorites (2) most basalts (3) most granites (4) volcanic ash

36. According to the *Earth Science Reference Tables*, as the depth within the earth's interior increases, the (1) density, temperature, and pressure increase (2) density, temperature, and pressure decrease (3) density and temperature increase, but pressure decreases (4) density increases, but temperature and pressure decrease

37. Why do geologists infer that the earth's outer core is a liquid? (1) *S*-waves travel faster than *P*-waves in the outer core. (2) *S*-waves do not pass through the outer core of the earth. (3) Instruments indicate that the earth's temperature increases with depth. (4) *P*-waves can travel through the core of the earth.

38. According to the *Earth Science Reference Tables*, the *rate* of temperature increase below the earth's surface is greatest between depths of (1) 0 and 250 km (2) 1500 and 2500 km (3) 2500 and 3500 km (4) 3500 and 4000 km

39. The composition of some meteorites supports the inference that the earth's core is composed of (1) aluminum and calcium (2) iron and nickel (3) silicon and oxygen (4) magnesium and potassium

Directions (40–43): Base your answers to questions 40 through 43 on your knowledge of earth science, the *Earth Science Reference Tables*, and the diagram below. The diagram represents a cross section of the earth showing the paths of earthquake waves from a single earthquake source. Seismograph stations are located on the earth's surface at points *A* through *F*, and they are all located in the same time zone.

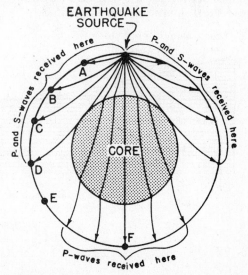

40. At which station is the difference in time between the arrival of *P*- and *S*-waves the greatest? (1) *A* (2) *B* (3) *C* (4) *D*

41. Station *E* did *not* receive any *P*-waves or *S*-waves from this earthquake because the *P*-waves and *S*-waves (1) cancel each other out (2) are bent, causing shadow zones (3) are changed to sound energy (4) are converted to heat energy

42. Seismograph station *D* is 7700 kilometers from the epicenter. If the *P*-wave arrived at this station at 2:15 P.M., at approximately what time did the earthquake occur? (1) 1:56 P.M. (2) 2:00 P.M. (3) 2:04 P.M. (4) 2:08 P.M.

43. Seismograph station *B* recorded the arrival of *P*-waves at 2:10 P.M. and the arrival of *S*-waves at 2:15 P.M. Approximately how far is station *B* from the earthquake epicenter? (1) 1400 km (2) 2400 km (3) 3400 km (4) 4400 km

ISOSTASY, GEOSYNCLINES, AND THE GROWTH OF CONTINENTS

Isostasy is the theory that the earth's crust floats on the denser rock beneath it in a state of equilibrium. Mountains float on the upper mantle as blocks of wood float on water. If wood blocks of equal density that have different volumes are placed in water, the largest block floats the highest and extends the deepest into the water. Likewise, the higher the mountain, the deeper material of similar density extends into the earth. See Figure 12-11.

Erosion constantly removes rock particles from the continents and transports them downhill toward the oceans. When rivers reach the calmer waters of the oceans, they deposit most of these particles as sediments near the shore. In this way, the continents grow at their margins.

This movement of sediments causes a decrease in the weight of the crust where erosion occurs and an increase in weight where sediments are deposited. The crust responds by rising where rock and sediments are carried away and sinking where these materials are deposited.

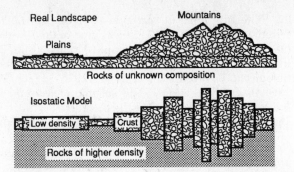

Figure 12-11. Isostasy as a model for the formation of mountains. Isostasy is the theory that the crust of the earth floats in equilibrium on the denser rocks of the mantle. Mountains are places where the relatively light crust extends deeper into the mantle and, therefore, rises above the surrounding parts of the crust.

A geosyncline is a shallow-water basin at the edge of a continent that is sinking as it constantly collects sediments. Continued erosion from the source area may cause uplift to maintain the erosion, while ongoing deposition in the geosyncline keeps the crust sinking to accept more deposition. Most of this sinking, or subsidence, occurs at the basin's center. The Gulf of Mexico is a modern example of an active geosyncline.

New York's Catskill Mountains are composed of horizontal layers of sedimentary rock that are thousands of feet deep. Fossils collected from these layers show that despite their total thickness, they were all laid down in relatively shallow water. The Catskills are considered an ancient geosyncline that has been pushed high above sea level and deeply eroded by fast-moving streams. See Figure 12-12.

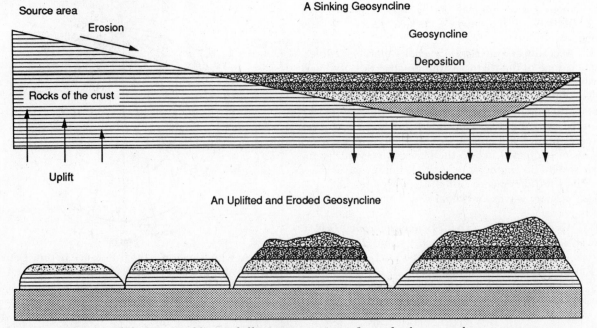

Figure 12-12. New York's Catskill Mountains were formed when a sinking geosyncline collected thousands of meters of shallow water sediments. Uplift and stream erosion have produced the mountains that we see today.

The theory of isostasy, with geosynclinal subsidence and uplift, explains only the vertical movements involved in coastal mountain-building. But it does not adequately explain horizontal movements that are evident in layers of sedimentary rock in mountains of geosynclinal origin. A unifying theory that accounts for this horizontal movement will be explained later in this chapter.

QUESTIONS

44. The term *isostasy* refers to a (1) line of equal air pressure (2) series of anticlines (3) deflection of winds on the earth caused by rotation (4) condition of balance between segments of the earth's crust

45. In some geosynclinal areas of the United States, the sedimentary rock layers are as much as 13,000 meters thick. Geologists believe that these rock layers were deposited in regions where (1) sedimentary rock had been uplifted by earth processes (2) sediments were deposited in basins that were originally 13,000 meters deep (3) sediments accumulated in basins that were being filled as they were sinking (4) sedimentary rock formed at the same time that the earth's crust formed

46. A sequence of very thickly bedded rocks containing shallow-water marine fossils was most likely formed in (1) an ocean trench (2) a meandering stream (3) a geosyncline (4) a glacial lake

47. As the thickness of sediment in a geosyncline increases, the pressure on the lower layers will (1) decrease (2) increase (3) remain the same

48. Major mountain systems are believed to have developed on the sites of (1) geosynclines (2) major ocean basins (3) continental shelves (4) thin sediments

49. Which is the best indication that central New York State was a geosyncline? (1) the presence of both igneous and metamorphic rocks (2) the presence of shallow water fossils found in sedimentary layers at great depths (3) signs of surface glaciation (4) the lack of Mesozoic rocks in western New York

50. The great thickness of geosynclinal deposits, many with shallow water characteristics, may be explained by (1) a very deep trench (2) lower sea level (3) the continuous sinking of a shallow trough (4) igneous activity

THE ORIGIN OF CONTINENTAL DRIFT

In 1912, the theory of **continental drift** was published by Alfred Wegener, a German meteorologist and astronomer. Wegener proposed that the earth's continents have separated and collided as they have moved over the surface of the earth for millions of years. Wegener cited the following evidence for his theory:

1. If South America and North America were moved across the Atlantic Ocean, they would fit remarkably well, shoreline to shoreline, with Africa and Europe. If the edges of the continents were defined by the edges of the continental shelves, where the deep parts of the oceans begin, the fit is even better.

2. Some fossil species have been found on widely separated parts of the earth without apparent connection from place to place. However, if the continents are moved together so that their shorelines match, these fossil locations often come into close contact.

3. If the Americas were moved next to Africa and Europe, there would be a remarkable match of ancient continental rocks and **tectonic** (fault and fold) structures.

4. Evidence of ancient climates, such as coal beds resulting from the accumulation of plants in tropical swamps, fossil coral reefs that have grown in tropical waters, glacial polish, striations (scratches), and till deposits left by glaciers, have been found in areas where the climate is now very different from when they formed. This could indicate that the earth's climate has changed, but a more likely explanation is that the continents have moved. When Wegener reassembled the continents to fit this evidence, they formed a great ancient continent that he called **Pangaea**. See Figures 12-13 and 12-14.

Thus, Wegener brought together widely dispersed evidence and fitted it into a logical pattern to support his theory of continental drift. One weakness of his theory, however, was that it did not explain how the continents, considered part of a solid continuous crust, could move about the earth.

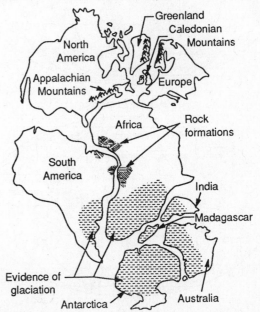

Figure 12-13. When the continents are reassembled to form the ancient continent of Pangaea, glacial features, rock formations, and mountain ranges come into contact from both sides of the Atlantic Ocean.

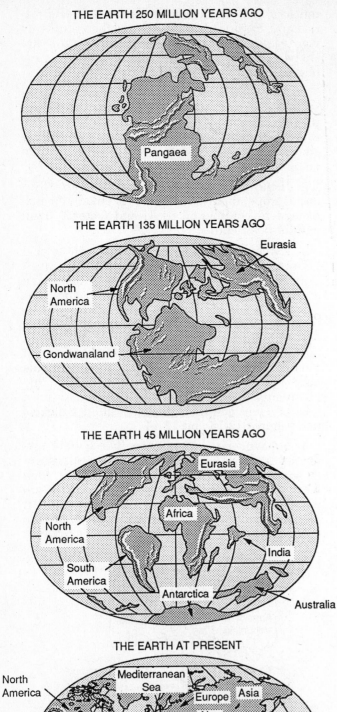

THE EARTH 250 MILLION YEARS AGO

Pangaea

THE EARTH 135 MILLION YEARS AGO

Eurasia

North
America

Gondwanaland

THE EARTH 45 MILLION YEARS AGO

Eurasia

Africa

North
America

India

South
America

Antarctica

Australia

THE EARTH AT PRESENT

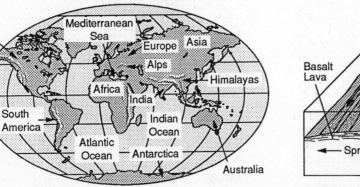

North
America

Mediterranean
Sea

Europe   Asia

Alps

Himalayas

Africa

India

Indian
Ocean

South
America

Atlantic
Ocean   Antarctica

Australia

Figure 12-14. The Atlantic Ocean was born when the great continent of Pangaea began to split apart approximately 200 million years ago. While this was happening, Australia and India were moving north from the south polar region to their present positions.

Ocean-Floor Spreading.

For 50 years, most scientists rejected Wegener's model of continental drift. But oceanographic research in the 1950s and 1960s lent further support to a dynamic model of horizontal movements of the earth's crust.

5. Mapping of the ocean floors showed a system of submerged mountain ranges, called **mid-ocean ridges**, that encircle the earth, somewhat like the pattern of seams on a baseball.

Investigations of the ocean bottoms led geologists to infer that oceanic crust is created at the mid-ocean ridges. Upwelling material from deep within the earth comes to the surface at the ocean ridges, where it spreads apart to make new oceanic crust. The theory of **ocean-floor spreading** was supported by the following evidence.

6. Ships towing instruments sensitive to changes in the magnetic field showed parallel bands of normal and reversed magnetism in the igneous rocks of the ocean floor on either side of the mid-Atlantic ridge and other ocean ridges. These patterns of magnetic polarity resulted from molten rock, or magma, coming to the surface at the ridges. While the rock was still molten, the iron particles in it aligned with the magnetic poles of the earth. When the rock hardened, it kept that alignment, forming a permanent record of the magnetic field of the earth at the time when the new oceanic crust was formed.

Igneous rocks near the ridges today are aligned with the present magnetic field. Rocks found farther from the ridges, on both sides, have a **reversed magnetic polarity** because these older parts of the crust formed thousands of years ago when the magnetic field of the earth was reversed. Parallel stripes of magnetism on both sides of the ridges preserve a record of many reversals of the earth's magnetic field in the geologic past. See Figure 12-15.

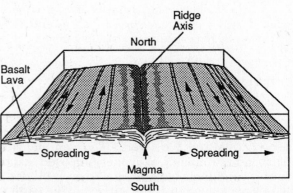

Ridge
Axis

North

Basalt
Lava

← Spreading ←   → Spreading →

Magma

South

Figure 12-15. Upwelling magma at the mid-ocean ridges cools to make a permanent record of the earth's magnetic field. Parallel bands of normal and reversed polarity help geologists to establish the rate at which new crust spreads outward from the ridges.

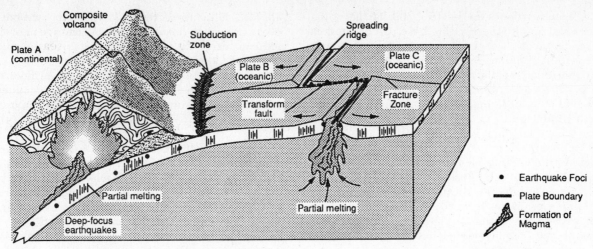

Figure 12-16. As material from deep within the earth rises at the ocean ridges, new crust is created. This crust spreads outward from the ridges toward the trenches where it is consumed as it sinks back into the earth.

7. Investigations of sediments from the ocean bottoms have shown that the dark, dense igneous rocks of the crust near the ocean ridges are covered by a thin layer of recent sediments. Geologists have interpreted this as evidence that the earth's crust is very young near the ridges. Farther from the ridges, on both sides, older sediments are found in contact with the igneous crust, and the accumulation of sediments is thicker.

The oldest portions of the ocean floors are only about 200 million years old. The oldest parts of the oceanic crust are found far from the ocean ridges, near the continents.

8. Scientists have found that the greatest heat flow comes from the earth's crust along the ocean ridges. This supports the idea that hot material from deep within the earth is constantly moving toward the surface at the ridges, where it makes new oceanic crust.

9. Scientists have also discovered very deep parts of the ocean floor, called **ocean trenches**, where heat flow is the lowest. They have theorized that as the ocean floor spreads out from the ridges, it places stress on the older crust, which eventually buckles to form the trenches. The old crustal material is then drawn downward toward the mantle, of which it eventually becomes a part. See Figure 12-16.

Further Investigations on the Continents.
Evidence of sea floor spreading added to the credibility of crustal movements but did not explain continental movements. However, land-based observations provided further evidence for global movements of the earth's crust.

10. Analysis of igneous rocks has shown that the earth's magnetic poles have wandered over millions of years. If we try to trace these movements, we get conflicting positions on the different continents. However, if we reconstruct the positions

of the continents based upon our interpretations of their past movements, the inferred positions of the magnetic poles come together for any given time in the geologic past.

QUESTIONS

51. In the past 100,000 years the distance between South America and Africa has (1) decreased (2) increased (3) remained the same

52. According to the Inferred Position of Earth Landmasses information shown in the *Earth Science Reference Tables*, on what other landmass would you most likely find fossil remains of the late Paleozoic reptile called Mesosaurus shown below?

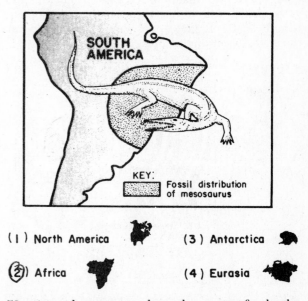

(1) North America (3) Antarctica

(2) Africa (4) Eurasia

53. As evidence accumulates, the support for the theory that the present continents were at one time a single, large landmass (1) decreases (2) increases (3) remains the same

54. Which evidence does *not* support the theory that Africa and South America were once part of the same large continent? (1) correlation of rocks on opposite sides of the Atlantic Ocean (2) correlation of fossils on opposite sides of the Atlantic Ocean (3) correlation of coastlines on opposite sides of the Atlantic Ocean (4) correlation of living animals on opposite sides of the Atlantic Ocean

55. Which statement best supports the theory that all the continents were once a single landmass? (1) Rocks of the ocean ridges are older than those of the adjacent sea floor. (2) Rock and fossil correlation can be made where the continents appear to fit together. (3) Marine fossils can be found at high elevations above sea level on all continents. (4) Great thicknesses of shallow-water sediments are found at interior locations on some continents.

56. Igneous materials found along oceanic ridges contain magnetic iron particles that show reversal of magnetic orientation. This is evidence that (1) volcanic activity has occurred constantly throughout history (2) the earth's magnetic poles have exchanged their positions (3) igneous materials are always formed beneath oceans (4) the earth's crust does not move

57. Which is the best evidence supporting the concept of ocean floor spreading? (1) Earthquakes occur at greater depths beneath continents than beneath oceans. (2) Sandstones and limestones can be found both in North America and Europe. (3) Volcanoes appear at random within the oceanic crust. (4) Igneous rocks along the mid-oceanic ridges are younger than those farther from the ridges.

Directions (58–61): Base your answers to questions 58 through 61 on your knowledge of earth science and on the diagram below. The diagram shows an enlargement of the mid-Atlantic ridge and surrounding area in its position with respect to the continents. Magnetic polarity bands of igneous rock parallel to the ridge are illustrated according to the key.

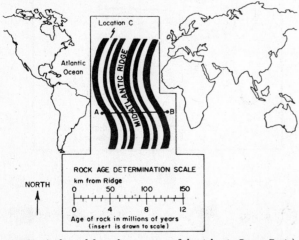

58. Ocean floor rock found 20 kilometers west of the ocean ridge would have an approximate age of (1) 1.6 million years (2) 2.0 million years (3) 15 million years (4) 30 million years

59. What are two characteristics of ocean floor rock found at location *C*? (1) normal polarity, continental composition (2) normal polarity, oceanic composition (3) reverse polarity, continental composition (4) reverse polarity, oceanic composition

60. Along the line from position *A* to position *B*, the comparative age of the rock (1) continuously decreases from *A* to *B* (2) continuously increases from *A* to *B* (3) decreases from *A* to the mid-Atlantic ridge and then increases to *B* (4) increases from *A* to the mid-Atlantic ridge and then decreases to *B*

61. Which of the cross-sectional diagrams below best represents a model for the movement of rock material below the crust along the mid-Atlantic ridge?

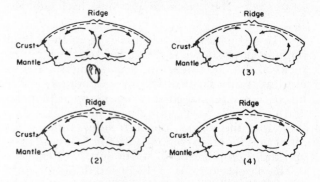

PLATE TECTONICS PROVIDES A GLOBAL SYSTEM

Continuing observations on the continents and under the oceans have been integrated into a unified theory of **plate tectonics**. According to this theory, the surface of the earth is composed of about a dozen major, rigid, moving crustal plates and several smaller plates. Some plates contain areas of light continental rocks and other areas of denser oceanic rocks. For example, the western Atlantic Ocean and the North American continent occupy a single plate. Some plates contain no continent, while others may contain more than one. See Figure 12-17.

Precision instruments, some using terrestrial satellites and laser beams, have measured recent movements of the plates. They have recorded movements (a few centimeters per year) that match the rates of movement inferred from the magnetic and geological studies discussed earlier.

These crustal plates move because they are driven by convection cells circulating within the mantle. See Figure 12-18. The rigid portion of the plates includes the crust of the earth as well as a small part of the upper mantle. This rigid layer is known as the lithosphere. The plates float on a partially molten portion of the mantle called the asthenosphere. These convection cells bring material to the surface at the ocean ridges and pull

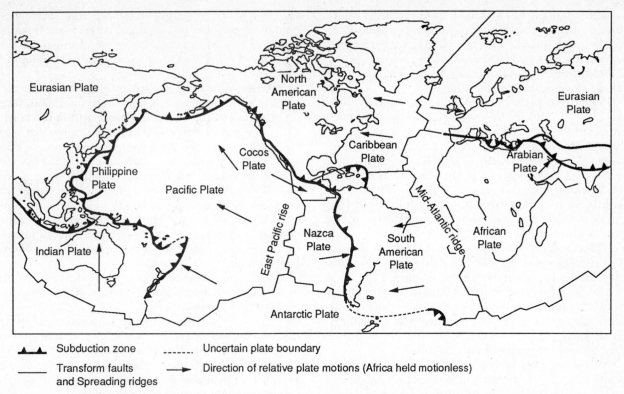

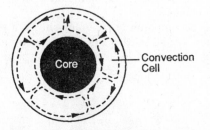

Figure 12-17. The surface of the earth is composed of about a dozen major plates. Their relative motions are shown by the arrows along the plate boundaries.

Figure 12-18. Convection cells within the mantle of the earth.

it back into the earth at the trenches. An area where crust is being pulled down into the mantle is called a **subduction zone**. In general, the direction of movement of the plate is away from the ocean ridges and toward the trenches.

Scientists have mapped **zones** (or belts) **of crustal activity** around the earth that support the theory of plate tectonics. Most volcanoes and earthquake epicenters are located in or near ocean ridges and continental mountain ranges. This pattern indicates that mountain building, volcanoes, and earthquakes are related events. The **Ring of Fire** that surrounds the Pacific Ocean is a belt of frequent earthquake activity, active volcanoes, and mountain building. See Figure 12-19.

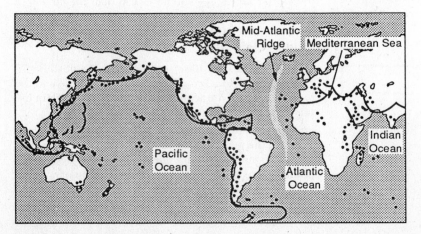

Figure 12-19. Earthquakes, active volcanoes, and regions of mountain building generally occupy distinct linear zones of crustal activity. These zones often follow the boundaries of the earth's plates. One such zone is the "Ring of Fire" that surrounds the Pacific Ocean.

Dynamics of the Earth

These zones of crustal activity actually mark the boundaries of the plates because as the plates move and meet, crustal changes (volcanoes, earthquakes, and mountain building) occur. Sometimes the plates collide; sometimes they move or slide past each other.

When two plates collide, one generally bends and buckles while the other sinks into the earth at a subduction zone. The oceanic crust, composed mainly of dense rocks like basalt, is consumed as it sinks into the asthenosphere. The continental portions of the plates are composed of lighter rocks like granite. These rocks resist subduction as they are folded and deformed. This process often results in mountain building along the continental side of a subduction zone.

The eruption of volcanoes adds to the mountain-building process. As the lithosphere is drawn into the earth, it becomes hotter. Some of the rock melts, which makes it lighter than the surrounding rock. This molten rock (**magma**) pushes up through cracks in the earth to erupt as volcanoes. In this way, volcanoes add to the mountain-building process in areas of subduction.

Measurements of temperature changes within the earth also support the convection model of plate motions. Heat from within the earth flows toward the surface by conduction and by convection. The ocean ridges are places where up-welling pushes heated material toward the earth's surface. Heat flow and heat loss are the greatest near the ocean ridges. At the subduction zones, cool material of the lithosphere is being drawn down into the earth where the heat flow is relatively low. Heat flow is also reduced by the thickening of the crust at the subduction zones. The folded and thickened crust acts like a blanket to reduce heat loss. Thus, measurements of the heat escaping from the earth's interior support the convection model of plate motions.

Of course, as the plates collide and slide past each other, pressure and stress build up in the surrounding crust. This stress can be relieved by earthquakes, as discussed earlier.

The theory of plate tectonics has given earth scientists important insights into the formation of continents and ocean basins, the distribution of earthquakes, volcanoes, and mountain ranges, the creation of valuable mineral deposits, and the history of life on our planet.

QUESTIONS

62. Which graph best represents the relationship between volcanic and earthquake activity in an area?

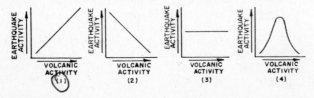

63. Where have earthquakes occurred most frequently during the last one hundred years? (1) in the polar regions (2) in the interior of continental areas (3) along the Pacific Ocean coastlines (4) along the Atlantic Ocean coastlines

64. Where do most earthquakes originate? (1) at the mantle-core boundary (2) randomly at the surface (3) in the core (4) in specific zones within the crust

65. Continental drift might be an indication that (1) the earth is cooling (2) the core of the earth is iron and nickel (3) convection currents exist in the mantle (4) the temperature of the earth is increasing

66. Which best describes a major characteristic of both volcanoes and earthquakes? (1) They are centered at the poles. (2) They are located in the same geographic areas. (3) They are related to the formation of glaciers. (4) They are restricted to the Southern Hemisphere.

67. Earthquakes generally occur (1) in belts (2) uniformly over the earth (3) only under the oceans (4) mostly in North America

68. Which is suggested by the occurrence of higher than average temperature below the surface of the earth in the area of the mid-Atlantic ridge? (1) the existence of convection cells in the mantle (2) the presence of heat due to orographic effect (3) a high concentration of magnetism in the mantle (4) the existence of a thinner crust under mountains

69. A large belt of mountain ranges and volcanoes surrounds the Pacific Ocean. Which events are most closely associated with these mountains and volcanoes? (1) hurricanes (2) sandstorms (3) tornadoes (4) earthquakes

70. The accompanying diagram shows a cross-sectional view of the earth's interior. The motion represented by the arrows indicates that the earth's mantle

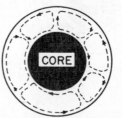

(1) has properties of a fluid (2) is composed of solid metamorphic rocks (3) is not affected by the heat from the earth's core (4) is more dense than the core

71. Which is the chief cause of earthquakes in California? (1) cavern collapse (2) volcanic activity (3) folding (4) faulting

Directions (72–76): Base your answers to questions 72 through 76 on your knowledge of earth science and the two diagrams given which are used to help explain the theory of continental drift.

Diagram I represents a map of a portion of the earth showing the relative position of the mid-Atlantic ridge. Points *A* through *D* are locations in the ocean and points *X* and *Y* are locations on the continents.

Diagram II represents a portion of the earth's interior with a model of probable convection cells. Locations 1 through 4 are at the earth's surface.

DIAGRAM I

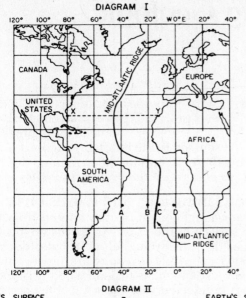

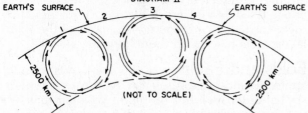

DIAGRAM II

(NOT TO SCALE)

the eastern coast of the United States and the southern coast of Africa   (2) central Canada and central Europe   (3) the eastern coast of South America and the western coast of Africa   (4) the central United States and central South America

73. A ship obtains a sample of igneous bedrock from each of the positions $A, B, C,$ and D. Which rock sample would probably be the oldest?   (1) A (2) B (3) C (4) D

74. Which location in Diagram II would correspond to the position of the mid-Atlantic ridge in Diagram I? (1) location 1   (2) location 2   (3) location 3   (4) location 4

75. Diagram II refers to convection cells which probably exist in the   (1) crust   (2) mantle   (3) outer core (4) inner core

76. Which graph best represents the most likely pattern of heat flow along line XY?

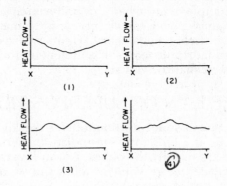

72. According to the theory of continental drift, which locations in Diagram I would most likely have the best correlation of rock, mineral, and fossil evidence?   (1)

TOPIC 13 Interpreting Geologic History

THE PRINCIPLE OF UNIFORMITY

Our planet has existed for about four and a half billion years. The rocks of the crust preserve clues to the earth's rich history, its changing features, and the development of life. One of the primary roles of a geologist is to locate, observe, and interpret these clues.

By looking at features of rocks and rock outcrops, geologists can infer events of the past. In their investigations, they assume that forces that acted upon the earth's crust in the past are the same as those that are active today. This is called the principle of uniformity, or **uniformitarianism**. For example, you can observe ripple marks in shallow stream beds today. Geologists assume that similar ripple marks in sedimentary rock also formed in shallow water.

THE LAW OF SUPERPOSITION

The **law of superposition** tells us that the rock layers on the bottom of an undisturbed rock exposure are usually the oldest. Lower layers must be in place before younger rocks can be deposited on top of them. Therefore, geologists can date the relative ages of the strata, from bottom to top (oldest to youngest).

The Law of Superposition does have exceptions. Various processes can cause younger layers to be below older layers. Some of these processes will be discussed in the following sections. While studying these exceptions, keep in mind that *rock is always older than the process that changed it.*

Igneous Intrusions and Extrusions.
An *extrusion* is igneous rock that formed from lava at the surface of the crust. An extrusion must be younger than the strata below it, but older than any layers above. *Intrusions* are created when molten rock, known as magma when it is underground, is injected into older rock layers in the crust. It cools and crystallizes to form igneous rock. Intrusions are younger than all of the rock layers in contact with them. See Figure 13-1.

Folds and Faults.
Folds are bends in rock strata. Sometimes folding can overturn rock strata so that older rock lies on top of younger rock.

You recall from Topic 12 that *faults* are cracks in rock strata along which there has been movement. Faults produce offset layers.

Rock strata must be older than the folds and faults that have changed them. Figure 13-2 illustrates some of the processes that can change the order of rock strata from their original positions.

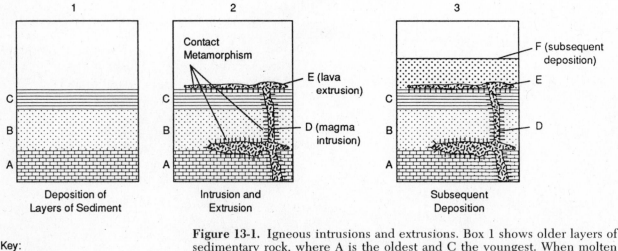

Figure 13-1. Igneous intrusions and extrusions. Box 1 shows older layers of sedimentary rock, where A is the oldest and C the youngest. When molten rock comes into contact with such rock, the heat escaping from magma or lava bakes the rock layers along the interface. This is what has happened in Box 2, where molten rock (design with x's) has intruded into the three layers as magma (D) and extruded to the surface as lava (E). The baked area next to an intrusion or extrusion is called a *contact metamorphism* zone (designated by perpendicular lines). An intrusion will cause contact metamorphism in the strata above and below it. An extrusion will show contact metamorphism only in the layer below. In Box 3, notice that a new layer of rock (F) has been deposited above the extrusion (E); therefore, no contact metamorphism exists between E and F.

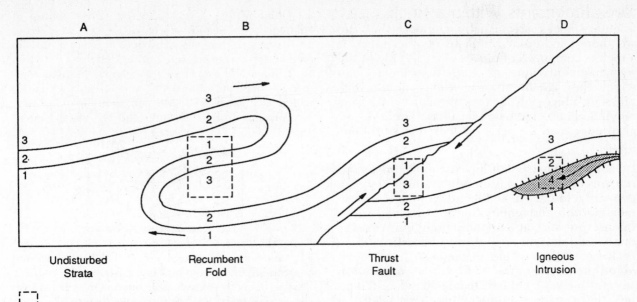

Undisturbed
Strata

Recumbent
Fold

Thrust
Fault

Igneous
Intrusion

The dotted boxes show where superposition does not apply.

Figure 13-2. In some situations the law of superposition does not apply. Normally, the oldest layers in a geological cross section are at the bottom. However, folding, faulting, or intrusion can cause exceptions to this rule. Section A shows three layers in their original sequence with the oldest layer (1) on the bottom. The tight fold in section B has created a reverse order of layers within the dashed box where layers 3 and 2 are below layer 1. (The sequences both above and below the box are normal.) Section C shows a thrust fault that has pushed an older layer (1) above a younger layer (3). In the final section, D, an intrusion of magma has caused a younger igneous rock to form below layer 2, which is older.

Joints, Veins, and Natural Cement.

Joints, veins, and natural cement are features created after rock or sediment has been deposited. See Figure 13-3.

Joints are cracks in the rock along which there has not been movement. Joints are caused by shrinkage or compression, which occurs when rocks are cooling or being bent or folded.

Veins form in several ways. After molten rock is injected into cracks, it cools to form a vein (an intrusion of igneous rock). Other veins result from a portion of the rock melting in place. Some-

times groundwater deposits minerals from solution into cracks in the rock. The minerals harden to form solid veins.

Natural cement is usually deposited by groundwater percolating through layers of sediment. Minerals dissolved in the water are deposited in the pores between the grains of sediment. Calcium carbonate (the mineral calcite, which makes up limestone) and clay are common rock-forming cements. Natural cement helps to transform soft layers of sedimentary particles into hard layers of sedimentary rock.

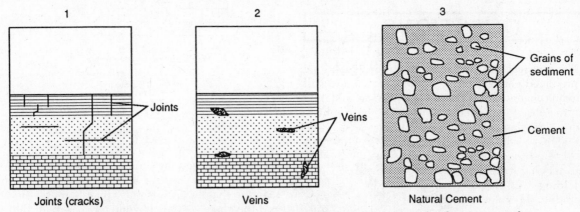

Joints (cracks)

Veins

Natural Cement

Figure 13-3. Joints, veins, and natural cement. Box 1 shows layers of sedimentary rock with joints, or cracks, within them. The joints are younger than the sedimentary rock that contains them. Box 2 shows veins within the older sedimentary layers. Box 3 shows grains of sediment being held together by natural cement. The grains are older than the natural cement that binds them.

Interpreting Geologic History

135

Rock Fragments Within a Rock.
Sedimentary rocks are usually composed of the weathered and eroded remains of other rocks. If a rock is composed of pieces of former rocks, the rock fragments must be older than the rock in which they are found. Sometimes molten rock picks up pieces of the rock through which it is moving. These inclusions, called xenoliths, are also older than the igneous rock that surrounds them.

Fossils.
Fossils are any naturally preserved remains or impressions of living things. They are generally found in sedimentary rock, because metamorphic and igneous rocks are formed under intense pressure at extremely high temperatures that would deform or destroy any fossils.

Occasionally, whole organisms have been found preserved in the earth. Insects encased in amber (tree sap), animals that have fallen into tar pits, and ice-age mammoths that have been frozen or encased in mud are all fossils that have been almost totally preserved.

More often, only the hard parts, like bones, teeth, and shells, are preserved. Some limestone formations are composed almost entirely of whole and broken marine shells. Because of their hardness, the bones and teeth are the most common remains preserved of higher animals.

If the hard parts have been replaced by minerals washed in by groundwater, they are said to be petrified. An impression in mud can be preserved as a mold and the material filling it forms a cast that duplicates the shape of the organism forming it. Dinosaur footprints have been found in many locations. Even the fossilized excretions of animals have helped scientists understand the eating habits of extinct animals.

Fossils also give us information about the ancient environment in which the organisms that formed them lived. For example, coral grows only in warm, tropical waters. Fossilized woolly mammoths indicate a cold, continental environment.

QUESTIONS

1. The physical and chemical conditions which long ago produced changes on the earth's surface are still producing changes. This statement is one way of stating the principle of (1) catastrophism (2) diastrophism (3) uniformitarianism (4) isostasy

2. Which earth movement is best represented by the drawing at the right? (1) folding (2) faulting (3) jointing (4) vulcanism

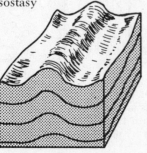

3. Older layers of rock may be found on top of younger layers of rock as a result of (1) weathering processes (2) igneous extrusions (3) joints in the rock layers (4) overturning of rock layers

4. If the vertical cross section, shown on the accompanying diagram, represents sedimentary rock layers which have *not* been overturned, then the oldest rock layer is most probably indicated by which letter?

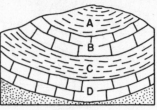

(1) A (2) B (3) C (4) D

5. Unless a series of sedimentary rock layers has been overturned, the bottom rock layer usually (1) contains fossils (2) is the oldest (3) contains the greatest variety of minerals (4) has the finest texture

6. The diagram at the right represents a core drilling in a region consisting of only four sedimentary rock layers, A, B, C, and D. Which geologic event could explain the order of the rock layers in the core drilling? (1) Volcanic activity caused rapid deposition of the sedimentary layers. (2) Large-scale erosion caused a gap in the time record. (3) Extensive folding caused the rock layers to overturn. (4) Intrusion of igneous material occurred sometime between the deposition of layer A and layer D.

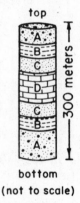

7. In the diagram below which shows a portion of the earth's crust, what is the relative age of the igneous rock?

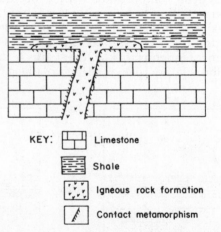

KEY:
Limestone
Shale
Igneous rock formation
Contact metamorphism

(1) It is older than the limestone but younger than the shale. (2) It is younger than the limestone but older than the shale. (3) It is older than both the limestone and the shale. (4) It is younger than both the limestone and the shale.

8. In which rock type are fossils usually found? (1) igneous (2) volcanic (3) sedimentary (4) metamorphic

9. The diagram below is a cross-sectional area of part of the earth's crust.

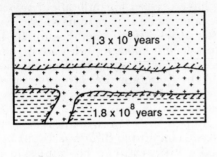

KEY:

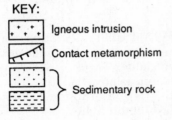

Igneous intrusion

Contact metamorphism

Sedimentary rock

A possible age of the igneous intrusion is   (1) 1.0 × 10^8 years   (2) 1.5 × 10^8 years   (3) 1.8 × 10^8 years   (4) 2.0 × 10^8 years

10. The geologic cross section below represents a portion of the earth's crust. Which rock is the oldest?

(1) rock A   (2) rock B   (3) rock C   (4) rock E

11. Which is the youngest rock shown in the diagram below?

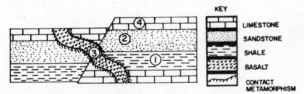

(1) 1   (2) 2   (3) 3   (4) 4

12. Which feature in a rock layer is older than the rock layer?   (1) igneous intrusions   (2) mineral veins   (3) rock fragments   (4) faults

Directions: Base your answer to question 13 on the diagram below which shows a geologic cross section and landscape profile of a section of the earth's crust.

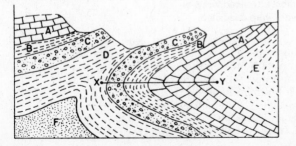

13. Which graph best represents the age of the rocks along line XY?

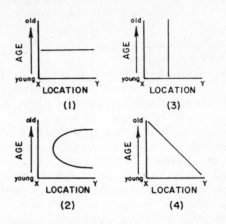

Directions (14–18): Base your answers to questions 14 through 18 on your knowledge of earth science, the *Earth Science Reference Tables*, and the diagram below. The diagram represents a geologic cross section consisting of various sedimentary and nonsedimentary rocks which have not been overturned.

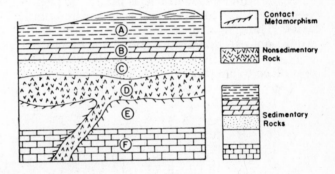

14. Fossils would *least* likely be found in rock layer   (1) A   (2) B   (3) C   (4) D

15. What can be inferred about the relative age of the various rocks?   (1) Rock D is older than rock C, but younger than rock E.   (2) Rock D is older than rocks C, E, and F.   (3) Rock C is older than rock E.   (4) Rock C is older than rock D, but younger than rocks A and B.

16. Rock layer A could have formed by the   (1) metamorphism of slate   (2) rapid cooling of molten material   (3) deposition of clay   (4) recrystallization of basalt

17. Rock layer E is composed of nonuniform particle sizes ranging in diameter from 0.9 to 2.3 centimeters. According to the *Earth Science Reference Tables*, this rock layer should be represented by which symbol?

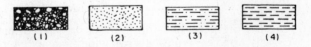

18. Rock layer D is classified as nonsedimentary because it was formed by   (1) the compression and cementing of particles   (2) the evaporation of seawater   (3) biologic processes   (4) the cooling of molten material

CORRELATION OF ROCK STRATA

Geologists try to match similar rock strata in different locations to see if they formed at the same time or under similar conditions. This is called **correlation**. There are several ways to correlate rock formations.

At an exposed outcrop, it is often possible to follow a rock layer by walking from one end of the exposure to the other. This "**walking the outcrop**" is *correlation by continuity*.

We can match the rock strata in one location with the strata in a more distant location by comparing the properties of the rocks, such as color, texture, or composition. However, the same rock types are not necessarily the same age. It is more helpful to match the sequence of rock layers, for example, limestone, sandstone, shale. Even if the sequence of rock layers in two locations is the same, the layers may not have formed at the same time.

Time correlation requires other methods. One way to do this is to compare **index fossils** contained in the strata. The best index fossils are of organisms that existed for a very brief time (geologically speaking, this could be as long as 20 million years) but were found over a large portion of the earth. Thus, in a rock outcrop, an index fossil would not extend very far above or below vertically but would be widespread horizontally from one place to another.

It is likely that, millions of years from now, humans will be an excellent index fossil. Modern humans have existed for only about two million years, yet our remains and signs of our existence can be found worldwide. See Figure 13-4.

If layers lack a specific index fossil, they can still often be tentatively correlated by the kinds of fossils they contain. For example, we could match layers containing fossils of organisms that we know existed in a cold climate, or on land in a warm climate, or in warm shallow seas. A layer of sandstone containing dinosaur fossils could be correlated with sandstone containing fossils of plants that existed at the same time as the dinosaurs.

Volcanic Ash Falls.

Another way of correlating layers by time is through **volcanic ash falls**. Some volcanoes erupt explosively, leaving a layer of volcanic ash over a large area. A recent example of this is the eruption of Mount Saint Helens in Washington State.

In terms of geologic time, these ash falls are very rapid events. A single layer of volcanic ash that can be found over a large area allows geologists to make a remarkably exact time correlation from one location to another at the position of a common ash fall. Geologists can do this even though different kinds of rock layers may have been deposited above or below the ash fall at different locations.

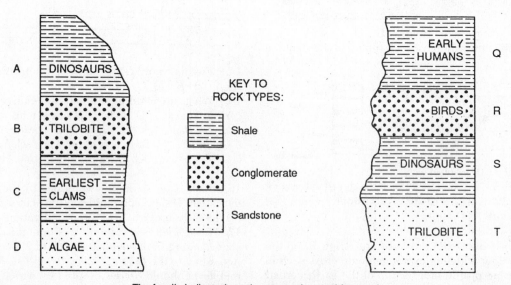

The fossils indicated are the most advanced forms of life alive at the time the layers were deposited.

Figure 13-4. Rock layers may be correlated by rock types or by age. The diagram above represents two widely separated rock outcrops. The sequence of rock types on the left side of this diagram exactly matches the sequence on the right. However, the fossils show that the time correlation is not the same. The two top layers on the left (B and A) contain the same fossils as the two bottom layers on the right (T and S). Only these layers correlate in time. Therefore, layer B, which is conglomerate, was actually deposited at about the same time as layer T, which is sandstone. Within both outcrops, D and C are the oldest layers, while Q and R are the youngest.

GEOLOGIC TIME SCALE

In the late 18th and early 19th centuries, geologists in Europe noticed that rock **formations** could often be identified by the fossils they contained. They also found that certain formations were consistently located above or below other formations. From these observations, they established a relative time scale with a sequence of fossil groups from oldest to youngest. Each of these groups was named for a location where its characteristic fossils could be observed in the rocks. For example, fossils characteristic of Devon, in the south of England, were named *Devonian*.

Over the years, further observations from around the world established a geologic time scale based on rock formations containing these characteristic fossil groups. Refer to the *Geologic time scale showing major events in geological history* in the *Earth Science Reference Tables*. The scale is divided into eras, periods, and epochs. Note, however, that they do not represent exact units of measure for time, like the hour. For example, no two eras span the same amount of time on the scale. You should use the geologic time scale when studying major events in New York State's geologic history, as shown in the map of *Generalized Bedrock Geology of New York State* in the reference tables.

Note that the most recent portion of the geologic time scale has been expanded on the right side of this diagram. An **orogeny** is the process of mountain building. The center of the diagram shows the major orogenies in New York's geologic history. For example, the Taconic Orogeny occurred during the Ordovician Period.

EVOLUTION OF LIFE

Early geologists noticed that the oldest rocks found in Europe lacked fossils. They inferred that life began with the life forms whose fossils characterized the early Cambrian Period, 570 million years ago.

Today, scientists are not yet sure how life began, but they know that it began before the Cambrian Period, sometime during the billions of years of the Precambrian Era. Fossils of simple marine organisms, like algae that left calcite reefs, have been found in rocks over three billion years old. Geologists believe that many other forms of life may have existed in the Precambrian Era, but they had no hard parts and, therefore, left no fossils. Precambrian fossils are very rare, not only because the life that existed then was probably difficult to preserve, but also because these oldest rock formations are more likely to have been altered by erosion and metamorphism, which would destroy the fossils. In the Cambrian Period, a great variety of more complex life forms developed, many with skeletons and shells that left a good fossil record.

As geologists studied the fossil record, they found that more and more complex organisms developed as time went on. Some organisms disappeared from the fossil record, that is, they became extinct. Scientists sought an explanation for these changes. They found that within each **species** there are individual variations in size, shape, and other traits. The **theory of organic evolution**, proposed by Charles Darwin, postulates that individuals possessing traits that better adapt them to their environment would survive longer and have more offspring to whom they would pass on these desirable traits. Eventually, more and more individuals of a species would possess the desirable traits, while those lacking them would become fewer and fewer. This process, called natural selection, leads to the extinction of some species and the formation of new ones.

The fossil record shows evidence of many of these variations in traits. Paleontologists (geologists who study fossils) have found remains of a wide variety of plants and animals that lived in many different environments. Some of these organisms still exist. Most have become extinct.

Because most individual organisms decompose or are consumed by other organisms after they die, few leave any fossil remains. As a result, many forms of life will never be known.

Humans are probably the most complex life form to have evolved. Fossils found in Africa indicate that we evolved from apelike creatures in the past four million years. This is only about $\frac{1}{10}$ of 1% of the earth's age. Thus, humankind is a very recent form of life.

QUESTIONS

19. Which distribution of fossils is most useful in determining the relative age of rock formations of different areas? (1) widespread horizontally and limited vertically (2) limited horizontally and widespread vertically (3) widespread horizontally and widespread vertically (4) limited horizontally and limited vertically

20. Geologists have subdivided geologic time into units based on (1) rock type (2) fossil evidence (3) erosion rates (4) landscape development

21. For which segment of the earth's geologic history are fossils rarely found? (1) Cenozoic (2) Mesozoic (3) Paleozoic (4) Precambrian

22. If a 24-hour clock were scaled to the age of the earth and the geological events were plotted on the clock, the duration of man's existence on the clock would most nearly be (1) 20 seconds (2) 30 minutes (3) 6 hours (4) 12 hours

23. The climate that existed in an area during the early Paleozoic Era can best be determined by studying (1) the present climate of the area (2) recorded climate data of the area since 1700 (3) present landscape surface features found in the area (4) the sedimentary rocks deposited in the area during the Cambrian and Ordovician Periods

24. Which evidence best supports the idea that the Great Plains area of the United States was once covered by a vast inland sea? (1) Considerable erosion has occurred there. (2) Extensive igneous intrusions are presently exposed there. (3) Extensive sedimentary rock layers have been formed there. (4) Numerous earthquakes occur there.

25. Why are fossils rarely found in Precambrian rock layers? (1) Few Precambrian rock layers have been discovered. (2) Nearly all fossils from this era have been destroyed by glaciers. (3) Few rock layers were formed during the Precambrian Era. (4) Life that would produce fossils was not abundant during the Precambrian Era.

Directions (26–27): Base your answers to questions 26 and 27 on the block diagram below of a portion of the earth where the rock layers have not been overturned.

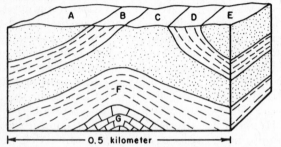

26. The evidence present in the diagram supports the inference that (1) rock *B* is the same age as rock *F* (2) rock *B* is the same age as rock *D* (3) rock *C* is older than rock *G* (4) rock *D* is younger than rock *A*

27. Rock layers *A* and *C* are sandstones that have the same texture. Layer *A* contains quartz grains, but layer *C* does not. This information suggests that layers *A* and *C* probably (1) are part of the same formation (2) have different types of cementing material (3) have undergone different amounts of metamorphism (4) were formed by sediments originating from different sources

28. According to the *Earth Science Reference Tables*, a rock formation containing fossils of many fishes and the earliest amphibians was probably formed during which period? (1) Carboniferous (2) Cambrian (3) Devonian (4) Ordovician

29. The fossil record indicates that most of the plants and animals that lived on the earth in the past (1) appeared during the Cambrian Period (2) became index fossils (3) have become extinct (4) lived on land

30. A time line is made on a strip of paper to illustrate the earth's history. A length of 1.0 centimeter is used to represent 10 million years. According to the *Earth Science Reference Tables*, what distance should be used to represent the length of the Mesozoic Era? (1) 0.16 cm (2) 1.6 cm (3) 16 cm (4) 160 cm

31. Which era covers the shortest length of geologic time? (1) Cenozoic (2) Mesozoic (3) Paleozoic (4) Precambrian

32. According to the *Earth Science Reference Tables*, during which era did the mammoth live? (1) Precambrian (2) Paleozoic (3) Mesozoic (4) Cenozoic

33. Which line is the best representation of the relative duration of each of the geologic time intervals?

(1) PRECAMBRIAN | PALEOZOIC | MESOZOIC | CENOZOIC

(2) PRECAMBRIAN | PALEOZOIC | MESOZOIC | CENOZOIC

(3) PRECAMBRIAN | PALEOZOIC | MESOZOIC | CENOZOIC

(4) PRECAMBRIAN | CENOZOIC MESOZOIC PALEOZOIC

34. What is one possible explanation why very few fossils are found in Precambrian rocks? (1) No life existed during the Precambrian Era. (2) Most primitive fossils have been destroyed through time. (3) Most forms of life became extinct during the Precambrian Era. (4) No new forms of life evolved after the Precambrian Era.

35. Which fact provides the best evidence for the scientific theory of the evolutionary development of life on the earth? (1) Fossils are found almost exclusively in sedimentary rocks. (2) Characteristics of simpler forms of life can be found in more complex forms of life. (3) Only a small percentage of living things have been preserved as fossils. (4) Most species of life on earth have become extinct.

36. According to the Geologic Time Scale in the *Earth Science Reference Tables*, what is the estimated age of the earth as a planet in millions of years? (1) 570 (2) 4,000 (3) 4,500 (4) 5,000

37. Which statement about dinosaurs is supported by information provided in the *Earth Science Reference Tables*? (1) Dinosaur fossils first appeared in rocks of the Paleozoic Era. (2) The number of dinosaurs increased before dinosaurs became extinct. (3) Dinosaur fossils and trilobite fossils may be found in the same rocks. (4) Dinosaurs lived only on land.

38. Index fossils have usually formed from organisms which had a (1) wide geographic distribution and existed for only a short time (2) narrow geographic distribution and existed for only a short time (3) wide geographic distribution and existed for a long time (4) narrow geographic distribution and existed for a long time

39. The geologic columns *A, B,* and *C* in the diagrams below represent widely spaced outcrops of sedimentary rocks. Symbols are used to indicate fossils found within each rock layer. Each rock layer represents the fossil record of a different geologic time period.

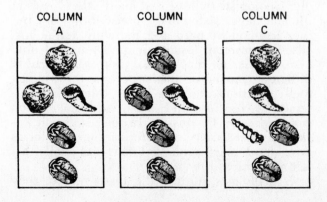

COLUMN A   COLUMN B   COLUMN C

According to the diagrams for all three columns, which would be the best index fossil?

(1) (2) (3) (4)

40. Which is the best method of determining the relative ages of a layer of sandstone in western New York State and a layer of sandstone in eastern New York State? (1) Compare the thickness of the two layers. (2) Compare the colors of the two layers. (3) Compare the size of sand particles of the two layers. (4) Compare the index fossils in the two layers.

41. Why can layers of volcanic ash found between other rock layers often serve as good geologic time markers? (1) Volcanic ash usually occurs in narrow bands around volcanoes. (2) Volcanic ash usually contains index fossils. (3) Volcanic ash usually contains the radioactive isotope carbon-14. (4) Volcanic ash usually is rapidly deposited over a large area.

42. What is indicated by the presence of trilobite fossils in many layers of the Devonian-age rocks in New York State? (1) Trilobites lived in terrestrial environments during the Devonian Period. (2) The trilobites became extinct during the Devonian Period. (3) The surface of New York State was greatly eroded during the Devonian Period. (4) Areas of New York State were under seas during the Devonian Period.

43. What characteristics of fossils are most useful in correlating sedimentary rock layers? (1) limited geographic distribution but found in many rock formations (2) limited geographic distribution and limited to a particular rock formation (3) wide geographic distribution but limited to a particular rock formation (4) wide geographic distribution and found in many rock formations

44. For which geologic period are no fossils found in New York State? (1) Ordovician (2) Silurian (3) Devonian (4) Permian

45. The most complete fossil record of past invertebrate life in New York State can be found in rocks of which era? (1) Cenozoic (2) Mesozoic (3) Precambrian (4) Paleozoic

Directions (46–50): Base your answers to questions 46 through 50 on the *Earth Science Reference Tables* and *Geologic Map* and on your knowledge of earth science. Write the *number* of the word or expression that best completes *each* statement or answers *each* question.

46. Where in New York State would you find rocks of Triassic age? (1) north central (2) extreme southwest (3) southeast (4) northeast

47. In which section of New York State would you be most likely to find fossils of the earliest amphibians? (1) southeast of Lake Erie (2) in the Adirondacks (3) on Long Island (4) along the shores of Lake Ontario

48. The Tug Hill plateau is located approximately 40 kilometers due east of Lake Ontario. What geologic age bedrock would you expect to find there? (1) Cretaceous (2) Devonian (3) Triassic (4) Ordovician

49. During which geologic period were rocks deposited in New York State that are now 400 million years old? (1) Triassic (2) Silurian (3) Cambrian (4) Cretaceous

50. According to the *Earth Science Reference Tables*, near which community in New York State would you be least likely to find fossils? (1) Old Forge (2) Albany (3) Elmira (4) Watertown

51. According to the *Earth Science Reference Tables*, approximately how many years ago did the Palisades Sill form? (1) 195 million (2) 2 million (3) 570 million (4) 1,650 million

52. According to the *Earth Science Reference Tables*, sediments containing which fossil remains would probably have been most recently deposited? (1) armored fish fin (2) mammoth (3) trilobite (4) dinosaur

53. A rock formation in New York State contains fossils of many trilobites but of no fish. According to the *Earth Science Reference Tables*, in which general area is this rock formation probably located? (1) Long Island (2) south of Lake Ontario (3) southwestern New York State (4) northeastern New York State

54. According to the *Generalized Geologic Map of New York State*, the Finger Lakes are located on bedrock that was formed during which period? (1) Precambrian (2) Ordovician (3) Devonian (4) Silurian

55. According to the *Earth Science Reference Tables*, the most complete rock record found in New York State is represented by which geologic period? (1) Devonian (2) Triassic (3) Cretaceous (4) Tertiary

56. According to the *Earth Science Reference Tables*, the earliest terrestrial plant fossils are most likely to be found in bedrock closest to which city? (1) Watertown (2) Jamestown (3) Syracuse (4) New York City

57. According to the *Generalized Geologic Map of New York State*, what is the geologic age of the bedrock found at the surface at 43° 30′ N. latitude by 75° 00′ W. longitude? (1) Devonian (2) Cambrian (3) Early Ordovician (4) Middle Proterozoic

58. According to the *Earth Science Reference Tables*, which event occurred at the time of the Alleghenian Orogeny? (1) the extinction of many kinds of marine animals (2) the extinction of many kinds of land animals (3) the development of primitive aquatic plants (4) the development of birds and mammals

59. According to the *Earth Science Reference Tables*, most of the surface bedrock in New York State south of latitude 43° N. and west of longitude 75° W. was formed during which period? (1) Silurian (2) Devonian (3) Cambrian (4) Ordovician

60. According to the geologic map of New York State in the *Earth Science Reference Tables*, Triassic bedrock is found in New York State at approximately (1) 41° 05′ N., 74° 00′ W. (2) 44° 05′ N., 74° 00′ W. (3) 74° 00′ N., 41° 05′ W. (4) 74° 00′ N., 44° 05′ W.

Directions (61–64): Base your answers to questions 61 through 64 on your knowledge of earth science, the *Earth Science Reference Tables*, and the map given which represents the generalized bedrock geology of a section of the southern United States.

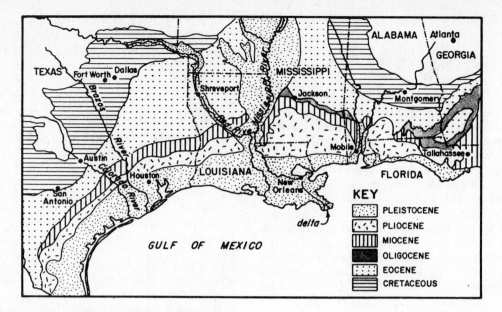

KEY
- PLEISTOCENE
- PLIOCENE
- MIOCENE
- OLIGOCENE
- EOCENE
- CRETACEOUS

61. Which of the following cities is built on the youngest rock material? (1) Dallas, Texas (2) Houston, Texas (3) Montgomery, Alabama (4) Tallahassee, Florida

62. During which geologic epoch was the bedrock around Tallahassee, Florida, formed? (1) Pleistocene (2) Pliocene (3) Miocene (4) Eocene

63. Why do some of the Pleistocene layers extend far upstream along the Red and the Mississippi Rivers? (1) Pleistocene layers are generally very resistant to erosion. (2) Waters from the Gulf of Mexico have washed the Pleistocene layers inland. (3) Pleistocene layers were deposited along the rivers on top of older sedimentary layers. (4) Downcutting by the rivers has exposed the Pleistocene layers which are below the Eocene layers.

64. Which area in New York State was forming at the time the sediment was being deposited in Louisiana? (1) Adirondack Mountains (2) Taconic Mountains (3) Palisades Sill (4) Long Island

Directions (65–69): Base your answers to questions 65 through 69 on your knowledge of earth science and the information in the chart and diagram.

The chart shows the time periods when several species of organisms lived and the type of environment, either ocean or land, in which each species lived.

The diagram shows the fossils of these organisms that are found in the rock layers (*A* through *H*) of two separate outcrops that are 25 kilometers apart. Each rock layer contains a complete fossil record of the organisms that existed in the depositional environment during the time of deposition. If a fossil symbol is not shown in a rock layer, the species either lived in the other environment or did not exist at the time that the rock formed.

65. According to the chart, when did dinosaurs live on the earth? (1) between 65 and 2 million years ago (2) between 225 and 65 million years ago (3) between 395 and 280 million years ago (4) between 570 and 435 million years ago

DIAGRAM

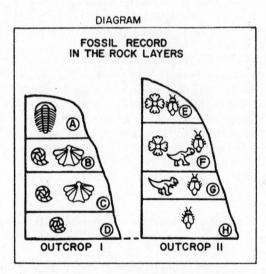

FOSSIL RECORD IN THE ROCK LAYERS

OUTCROP I OUTCROP II

CHART

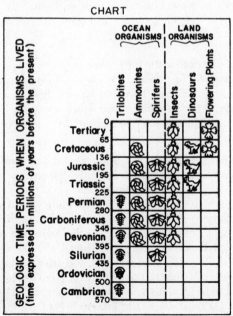

66. The extinction of spirifers occurred at most nearly the same time as the (1) extinction of the insects (2) beginning of trilobites (3) beginning of flowering plants (4) extinction of dinosaurs

67. Which rock layer in outcrop I could be the same age as layer *F* in outcrop II? (1) *A* (2) *B* (3) *C* (4) *D*

68. Which statement best explains the differences between the types of fossils found in outcrop I and those found in outcrop II? (1) Different types of rocks are found at outcrop I than are found at outcrop II. (2) The rocks in each outcrop were deposited in different types of environments. (3) Faulting has removed from outcrop I those fossils found in outcrop II. (4) Erosion has removed from outcrop II those fossils found in outcrop I.

69. Based on fossil evidence, during which time period was rock layer *E* most likely deposited? (1) Tertiary (2) Triassic (3) Permian (4) Ordovician

GEOLOGIC EVENTS OF THE PAST

No single location shows a complete record of the geologic past. If an area was above sea level for a while, it is likely that sediments are not deposited and that older sediments or rocks were destroyed by erosion. Thus, erosion causes gaps in the geologic record. When a new layer of rock is laid down on a surface left by erosion, it forms a buried erosion surface, or an **unconformity**.

When a rock outcrop shows an unconformity, it indicates that the area, at some time in the past, was uplifted above water level and then eroded. Later the area subsided below water level and new layers of sediment were deposited on top of the eroded surface. Often the uplifting is accompanied by folding or faulting, which deforms the original horizontality of the lower strata. Thus, the new layers on top of the unconformity may not parallel the older, lower layers. Sometimes, however, the older layers are parallel to the layers above the unconformity, and the gap in the geologic record is indicated in some other way, for example, by gaps in the fossil record in the strata. See Figure 13-5.

Many rock outcrops show evidence of a variety of geologic events. The original rock layers were created by deposition of sediments or the solidification of molten magma or lava. But folding can bend the layers and faulting can cause them to be offset. Intrusion of magma can result in veins of igneous rock and metamorphism. In turn, metamorphism can form new minerals and distort or destroy layering and other structures. Weathering and erosion can destroy rock strata.

Using the principles outlined in the beginning of this chapter, a geologist can study a rock outcrop to determine its geologic history, that is, the sequence of events that made it what it is today. If fossils are present, they will aid the geologist in dating the layers of rock and the events that occurred in them. See Figure 13-6.

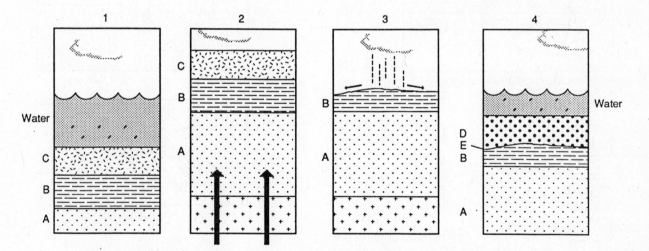

Figure 13-5. How an unconformity, or buried erosion surface, forms. In Box 1, sediments settle in calm water, first layer A, then B, then C (deposition). In Box 2, the layers are pushed above the water from below (uplift), exposing layer C to surface erosion (wind action, rain, etc.). In Box 3, the top layers (C and part of B) are worn away (erosion). In Box 4, the layers sink, or subside, below water level. A new layer (D) is deposited onto the erosion surface (E) above B (subsidence, then new deposition). The line E between B and D marks the unconformity, or buried erosion surface.

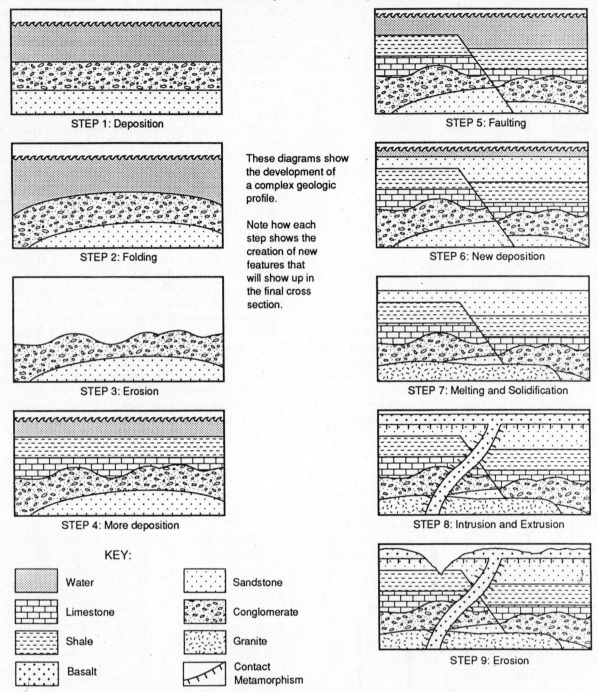

These diagrams show the development of a complex geologic profile.

Note how each step shows the creation of new features that will show up in the final cross section.

STEP 1: Deposition

STEP 2: Folding

STEP 3: Erosion

STEP 4: More deposition

STEP 5: Faulting

STEP 6: New deposition

STEP 7: Melting and Solidification

STEP 8: Intrusion and Extrusion

STEP 9: Erosion

KEY:

Water

Limestone

Shale

Basalt

Sandstone

Conglomerate

Granite

Contact Metamorphism

Figure 13-6. Development of a complex geological profile. Each successive box shows one change needed to produce the final profile in step 9. *Step 1.* Sediments which will form sandstone and conglomerate are deposited under water. *Step 2.* The layers are folded by a bending of the layers. *Step 3.* Exposed to weathering, part of the conglomerate layer is eroded away. *Step 4.* After submergence, new layers are deposited to form limestone and shale. *Step 5.* Faulting is caused by the subsidence of strata on the right. *Step 6.* New deposition results in the formation of a layer of sandstone. *Step 7.* Heat from below has melted the rock on the bottom, which later crystallizes to make the igneous rock granite. *Step 8.* The intrusion and extrusion of a dark-colored magma produces a body of basalt. *Step 9.* Erosion destroys part of the basalt and the sandstone layer below to form the final profile.

70. Which sequence of events will produce a gap in the time record between two sedimentary layers? (1) deposition, uplift, extensive erosion, submergence, and deposition (2) continuous sedimentation in a deep basin over a long period (3) deposition of gravel, followed by the deposition of sand and silt (4) a period of extensive volcanism followed by another period of extensive volcanism

71. The diagram below represents various sedimentary rock layers and the geologic periods during which they formed. According to the *Earth Science Reference Tables*, between which rock layers does a geologic time gap exist?

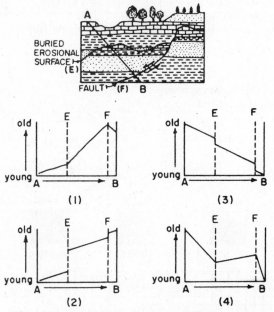

(1) A and B (2) B and C (3) C and D (4) D and E

72. Which graph most accurately indicates the relative age of the rocks along line *AB* in the geologic cross section below if no overturning has occurred?

73. The diagram below shows a geologic cross section of a region where no faulting has occurred.

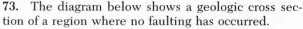
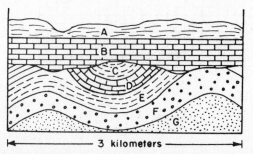

Which statement about the geologic history of the area is best supported by the evidence in the diagram? (1) The rocks at A formed before those at B. (2) The rocks at D folded after the deposition of rock layer B. (3) A long period of erosion took place before the deposition of rock layer B. (4) The major agent of erosion acting on the present surface is ice.

Directions (74–77): Base your answers to questions 74 through 77 on the *Earth Science Reference Tables* and the diagram below. The diagram represents a cross section of the earth's crust showing several rock layers containing marine fossils. Overturning has not occurred. [Diagram is not to scale.]

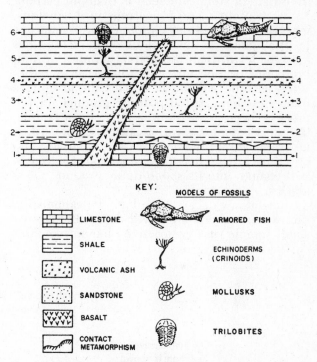

74. Why is layer 4 likely to be a good time marker? (1) Volcanic ash is usually a unique gray color. (2) Volcanic ash is usually rapidly deposited over a large area. (3) Volcanic ash can usually be dated with carbon-14. (4) Volcanic ash usually contains index fossils.

75. Which best describes the order of events for the formation of this section of the earth's crust? (1) intrusion of basalt; deposition of rock layers 1, 2, 3, 4, 5, and 6 (2) deposition of rock layers 1, 2, 3; intrusion of basalt; deposition of rock layers 4, 5, and 6 (3) deposition of rock layers 1, 2, 3, 4, and 5; intrusion of basalt; deposition of rock layer 6 (4) deposition of rock layers 1, 2, 3, 4, 5, and 6; intrusion of basalt

76. Which is the best explanation for the irregular surface between layers 1 and 2? (1) Layer 1 was folded after 2 was deposited. (2) Volcanic actions pushed layer 1 up before 2 was deposited. (3) Pressure from the layers above pushed layer 2 into layer 1. (4) Layer 1 was partially eroded before 2 was deposited.

77. Which rock was formed by the compaction and cementation of particles 0.07 centimeter in diameter? (1) limestone (2) sandstone (3) shale (4) basalt

Interpreting Geologic History   **145**

RADIOACTIVE DATING

Through fossil evidence, geologists established the geologic time scale discussed earlier in this chapter. This was only a relative time scale, however, an inferred order of events. Fossils could not tell geologists how long ago, in years, the organisms lived or the rock strata formed. Measurements of natural radioactivity in the rocks have allowed the geologic time scale to become an absolute time scale, one that gives the **absolute age** of an object (measured in years).

Chemical elements often have several forms, called **isotopes**, that differ in the number of neutrons in their atomic nuclei. For example, carbon-12 has 6 protons and 6 neutrons in its nucleus, whereas carbon-14 has 6 protons and 8 neutrons in its nucleus. If the nucleus of an isotope has more or fewer than the normal number of neutrons, the isotope may be radioactive. A radioactive isotope will break down naturally into a lighter element called a **decay product**. In the process, it gives off radioactivity. For example, the most common form of carbon, carbon-12, is not radioactive; but carbon-14, with two extra neutrons in its nucleus, is unstable. Carbon-14 will change into its stable decay product, nitrogen-14.

Since atoms decay at random, we cannot predict when a single atom will decay. But even a small sample of a radioactive element contains millions of atoms, from which we can predict a rate of decay.

Half-Life.
The rate of decay of a radioactive element is measured by its half-life. Different radioactive elements have different half-lives. A **half-life** is the time required for half of an element's atoms in a sample to change to the decay product. At the end of one half-life, a sample contains equal amounts of the radioactive element and its decay product. In each succeeding half-life, half of the remaining atoms decay (no matter how large the sample).

As the element decays, fewer radioactive atoms remain in the sample, and more and more decay product accumulates. Therefore, the higher the ratio of decay product to radioactive element, the older the sample.

The Decay-Product Ratio.
The ratio between the mass of a radioactive element and its decay product in a sample is the **decay-product ratio**. After we determine this ratio, we can calculate how many half-lives have gone by since the sample was formed, and, in turn, determine its age. See Figure 13-7.

For example, if a sedimentary rock contains equal amounts of carbon-14 and its decay product, nitrogen-14, the rock must have gone through one half-life, which for carbon-14 is 5.7×10^3 years. The half-lives of commonly used radioisotopes are printed in the *Earth Science Reference*

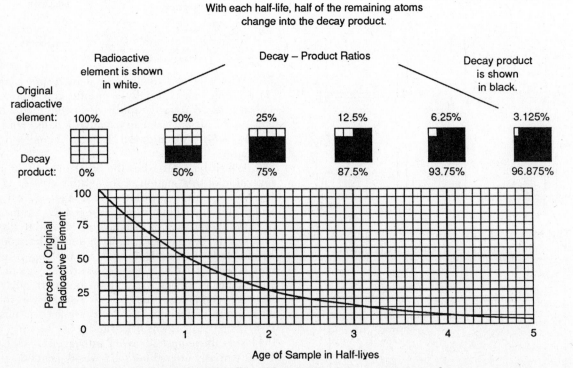

Figure 13-7. With each half-life that passes, half of the remaining radioactive atoms will change to the decay product. Through time, the original radioactive isotope changes into the decay product.

Table 13-1. Radioactive Decay Data

Radioactive Element	Disintegration	Half-Life
Carbon-14	$C^{14} \rightarrow N^{14}$	5.7×10^3 years
Potassium-40	$K^{40} \rightarrow Ar^{40}$	1.3×10^9 years
Uranium-238	$U^{238} \rightarrow Pb^{206}$	4.5×10^9 years
Rubidium-87	$Rb^{87} \rightarrow Sr^{87}$	4.9×10^{10} years

Tables. If three-quarters of the sample is nitrogen-14 and one-quarter carbon-14, then the rock is two half-lives (11.2×10^3 years) old. After three half-lives, the amount of carbon-14 would be cut in half again, so that the sample would be one-eighth carbon-14 and seven-eighths nitrogen-14. See the top boxes in Figure 13-7.

Laboratory studies show that the half-life for each element is not affected by environmental conditions, such as temperature, pressure, or chemical combinations. Thus, when a geologist estimates an age for a particular sample, he or she can be confident that conditions within the earth have not caused an error.

Selecting the Best Radioactive Element for a Sample.

Radioactive dating is a complex process. Decisions must be made to get the best results. First, the sample to be dated must contain a measurable quantity of a radioactive element and its decay product. A sample containing the remains of living organisms is likely to contain radioactive carbon-14.

The next factor to consider is the sample's estimated age. With a half-life of only 5700 years (5.7×10^3 years), carbon-14 can date samples no older than about 50,000 years. On the geologic time scale, this is very recent, covering only the latest epochs of the Cenozoic Era. If the sample is older than 50,000 years, so many half-lives have passed that too little of the original carbon-14 remains to be accurately measured. But uranium-238, with a half-life of 4.5×10^9 years, can measure samples of the oldest rocks on our planet. For very recent samples of rocks, however, too little uranium-238 would have decayed to lead-206 to make the decay product measurable. Thus, a geologist must select the radioactive isotope whose half-life best measures the age of a sample. See Table 13-1.

QUESTIONS

78. Why are radioactive substances useful for measuring geologic time? (1) The disintegration of radioactive substances occurs at a predictable rate. (2) The ratio of decay products to undecayed products remains constant in sedimentary rocks. (3) The half-lives of most radioactive substances are shorter than five minutes. (4) Measurable samples of radioactive substances are easily collected from most rock specimens.

79. When the quantity of a radioactive material decreases, the half-life of that substance will (1) decrease (2) increase (3) remain the same

80. The age of the earth is most accurately estimated from (1) the salinity of the oceans (2) the thickness of sedimentary rock (3) studies of fossils (4) radioactive dating of rock masses

81. Which radioactive substance would probably be used in dating the recent remains of a plant found in sedimentary deposits? (1) carbon-14 (2) potassium-40 (3) rubidium-87 (4) uranium-238

82. The half-life of carbon-14 is 5700 years. After 11,400 years how much carbon-14 would remain? (1) 75% (2) 50% (3) $33\frac{1}{3}$% (4) 25%

83. The carbon-14 method of dating can be used to determine the age of organic remains from which geologic time interval? (1) Precambrian (2) Paleozoic (3) Mesozoic (4) Cenozoic

84. The graph below indicates the radioactive decay rates for three different elements, A, B, and C.

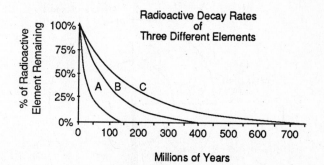

To determine the age of a rock formed during the Cambrian Period, a scientist would use (1) element A, only (2) element B, only (3) element C, only (4) elements A, B, and C

Directions (85–86): Base your answers to questions 85 and 86 on your knowledge of earth science and on the data below, which is a table of statistics gathered from four radioactive models. Each group, containing 100 particles, decayed at a different rate. Each was counted at one-hour intervals and the number of undecayed particles was then listed in the table.

Model	Hr. 0	Hr. 1	Hr. 2	Hr. 3	Hr. 4	Hr. 5	Hr. 6	Hr. 7	Hr. 8
Group A	100	89	80	72	63	53	44	39	34
Group B	100	71	48	36	25	17	13	9	6
Group C	100	51	24	11	6	2	0	0	0
Group D	100	22	6	2	1	0	0	0	0

85. The model of Group *B* would have a half-life of about (1) 1 hour   (2) 2 hours   (3) ½ hour   (4) 5 hours

86. Which graph best represents the data on radioactive decay of the four models?

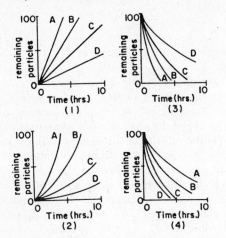

(1)

(3)

(2)

(4)

Directions (87–91): Base your answers to questions 87 through 91 on your knowledge of earth science and the diagram below. The diagram is a model representing a certain amount of carbon-14, having a half-life of 5.7×10^3 years, and the amount of time it takes for various percentages of the carbon-14 to radioactively decay. The shaded portion of the model represents the amount of carbon-14 remaining in a given sample after 34,200 years had passed.

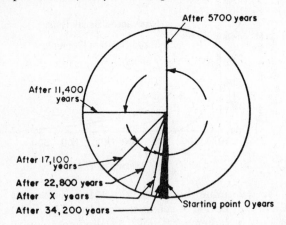

RADIOACTIVE DECAY OF C-14

87. Carbon-14 is useful for dating organic remains from which geologic epoch?   (1) Precambrian   (2) Mississippian   (3) Early Permian   (4) Pleistocene

88. Which graph best represents the decay of carbon-14 as shown in this model?

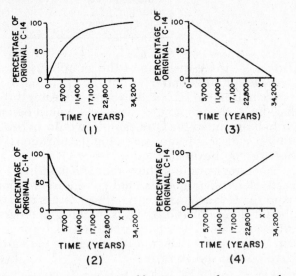

(1)

(3)

(2)

(4)

89. The line represented by *X* years indicates another half-life. How many years does *X* represent in the model?   (1) 25,500 years   (2) 28,500 years   (3) 29,900 years   (4) 39,900 years

90. If the amount of carbon-14 in the original sample had been 48 grams, about how much carbon-14 would have been left after 17,100 years?   (1) 6 grams   (2) 12 grams   (3) 3 grams   (4) 24 grams

91. Which model best represents the radioactive decay that would have occurred if this carbon-14 had been subjected to extreme heat and pressure during the first 5,700 years? [The shaded area represents the amount decayed.]

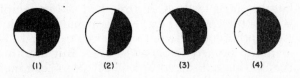

(1)   (2)   (3)   (4)

TOPIC 14 The Development of Landscapes

LANDSCAPE CHARACTERISTICS

A **landscape** is a region on the earth's surface in which physical features, such as hills, valleys, and streams, are related by a common origin. The shape (**topography**) and composition of the landscape are determined by the climate, the local bedrock, geologic structures, and human activities. Landscapes reveal the interaction between the natural and human history of a region.

The heights and shapes of hills, stream patterns, and soil associations are characteristics by which landscapes are described. The shape of a hill is defined by its hillslopes, that is, the sloping surfaces of the hill's sides. A hillslope's steepness (gradient) is measured by the angle the slope forms with a horizontal surface. The steeper the slope, the faster the water will run down it, thus speeding erosion.

As we learned in Topic 8, water falling to the earth runs downhill, forming streams and rivers until the mainstream empties into a lake or ocean at the lowest elevation (base level) in the region. As noted in Topic 9, the stream's gradient (the slope of the streambed) determines how fast water will travel in the stream. The steeper the gradient, the faster the water's velocity, and the more erosion takes place.

A drainage basin is a geographic region in which all of the surface runoff flows into a particular stream. It is an area drained by a stream. Within a drainage basin, the mainstream and its tributaries form a stream **drainage pattern**, which is the arrangement of the streams as seen from above. These stream patterns reflect the geologic features that formed the landscape. (This relationship will be discussed more fully on pages 156 and 157.)

You will recall from Topic 9 that different physical, chemical, and biological processes produce different types of soil. A landscape has a characteristic soil association, that is, soils that are similar and found together. Soils, like landscape regions, depend upon the local bedrock and climate. For this reason, each landscape region has its own characteristic soils.

Landscape Regions.

Most landscape regions can be classified as mountains, plateaus, or plains. See Figure 14-1. Each has its own geologic structures and topographic relief. Topographic relief is the change in elevation between the highest and the lowest places.

Mountain landscapes have the greatest relief between the highest peaks and the deepest valleys. A great variety of rock types, often including igneous and metamorphic rocks (as well as folded and faulted sedimentary rock), are common in mountain landscapes. These structures result from the tectonic forces within the earth that push up mountains. Stream gradients are high, and the fast-moving streams quickly erode deep valleys between the mountain peaks. In landscapes like the Rockies, the Alps, and the Himalayas, much of the land is on steep mountain slopes.

Plateau landscapes are often relatively flat or rolling uplands in which streams have cut deep valleys. Plateaus are commonly underlain by flat layers of sedimentary rock. The Colorado Plateau near the Grand Canyon of northern Arizona is a good example. Although plateaus usually have less topographic relief than mountains, they have more relief than plains.

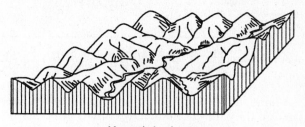

Mountain landscape

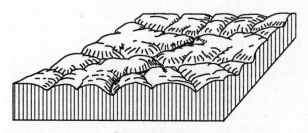

Plateau landscape

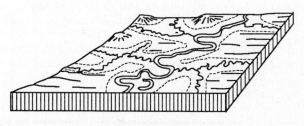

Plain landscape

Figure 14-1. Landscapes are classified on the basis of the shape of the land. Mountain landscapes are dominated by high peaks and steep slopes with great topographic relief. Plateaus usually have a flat or rolling upland which may be cut by stream valleys. Plains are mostly flat and at low elevations.

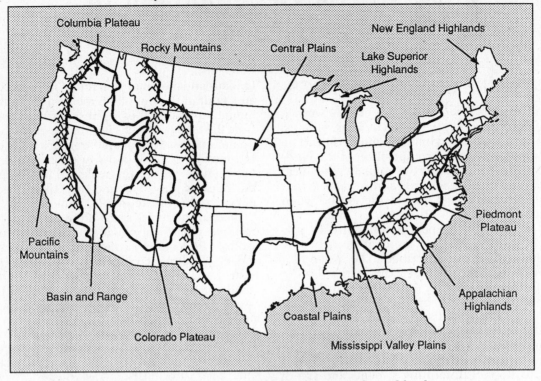

Figure 14-2. The United States can be split into a number of landscape regions. Each region contains landforms of similar appearance and origin.

Plains have the least topographic relief. Although they may contain a few small hills, plains are generally flat and at a low elevation. Plains are commonly underlain by flat layers of sedimentary rock. Most of Florida and the agricultural areas of the midwest exhibit plains topography.

Large areas, such as North America, and even smaller areas, such as New York State, can be divided into various landscape regions. See Figure 14-2. Each landscape region has its own characteristic hillslopes, drainage patterns, and soil associations.

The interfaces (boundaries) between landscape regions are often remarkably distinct. East of Denver, Colorado are the gently rolling Great Plains. The plains landscape ends suddenly just west of Denver, where the Rocky Mountains begin. This abrupt change in landscape is a result of a change from the horizontal sedimentary rocks of the plains to the complex folds and faults of the mountain landscape. In fact, most landscape regions end rather suddenly; thus it is often easy to locate the boundaries between landscapes.

QUESTIONS

1. Hillslopes, stream patterns, and the structure of the bedrock would most likely be helpful in identifying (1) fossils (2) earthquake epicenters (3) landscape regions (4) magnetic north

2. The major landscape regions of the United States are identified chiefly on the basis of (1) similar surface characteristics (2) similar climatic conditions (3) nearness to major mountain regions (4) nearness to continental boundaries

3. Which feature would most likely indicate the boundary between two landscape regions? (1) a highway cutting through a mountain region (2) resistant bedrock composed of more than one type of mineral (3) two adjoining massive bedrock types that have different structures (4) a long, meandering stream flowing across a large, level region

4. The boundaries between landscape regions are usually determined by the location of (1) state boundaries (2) major cities (3) population density (4) well-defined surface features

Landscapes of New York State.

New York State can be divided into several distinct landscape areas. See Figure 14-3. Most of the soils of New York are unsorted sediments that were pushed, dragged, and carried by the most recent continental glacier. However, the great variety of rock types and structures found in the landscapes of New York State were determined mainly by other geologic factors.

The *St. Lawrence/Champlain Lowlands*, New York's northernmost region, is a low-lying plain along the St. Lawrence River and Lake Champlain. This lowland region partially encirlces the Adirondack Mountains. The bedrock is predom-

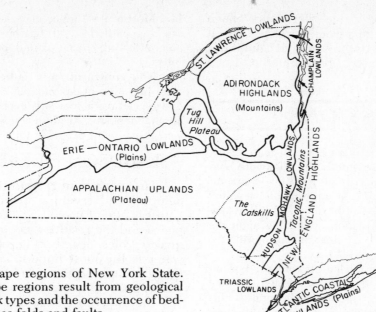

Figure 14-3. Landscape regions of New York State. New York's landscape regions result from geological factors, including rock types and the occurrence of bedrock structures, such as folds and faults.

inantly layers of sedimentary rock that gently slope away from the Adirondacks.

The *Allegheny Plateau* is New York's largest landscape region. The region is underlain by mostly flat layers of sedimentary rocks that were laid down in a shallow, sinking ocean basin (geosyncline) hundreds of millions of years ago. The land was later pushed up thousands of feet to form a plateau and cut into by many streams. The Catskills, near the eastern end of this region, reach nearly a mile in elevation above sea level. The Finger Lakes, near the center of this region, were formed when glaciers moved into existing north-south valleys, widening and deepening them. As the glacier melted back, it deposited till that blocked natural outlets, thus making long north-south lakes.

The *Erie-Ontario Lowlands* lie south of these two great lakes. Although a plains landscape, these lowlands have many hills composed of unsorted glacial till. Layered sediments left by meltwater from the continental glaciers are also common. Good soils deposited and mixed by glaciers, and a climate moderated by the Great Lakes, make this an important agricultural area.

The *Adirondack Mountains* in the northeast are New York's only true mountain landscape. The ancient metamorphic and igneous rocks of this region were pushed up in the middle to form a dome. Most of these rocks are very hard and resistant to erosion. Major valleys commonly run northeast-southwest along joint and fault structures. New York's highest point, Mount Marcy (at 5,344 feet above sea level), is within this region. The lower areas of these highlands are filled with lakes, ponds, and swamps, many of which were formed by glacial deposits.

The *Tug Hill Plateau* is a small region of elevated sedimentary layers near the eastern end of

Lake Ontario. Poor drainage (caused by glacial deposits) and abundant winter snowfall make this one of the least-inhabited and least-used areas of the state.

The *Hudson-Mohawk Lowlands* (plains) follow a zone of easily eroded limestones and shales. The Mohawk River valley, which provided water-level access to the interior of America, was especially important as a trade route in the development of New York in the 1700s and 1800s. Consequently, many towns and cities were established in this region.

The *New England Province (Highlands)*, a region of intensely folded and faulted metamorphic rocks, include the Taconic Mountains along the eastern boundary of the state. The entire area was covered by the last continental glacier, which left rounded hills and a variety of glacial and meltwater deposits. In its southern portion, the highlands split into two prongs. One extends westward toward New Jersey as the Hudson Highlands. The other section extends to the south through Westchester and into the Bronx and Manhattan.

The *Newark Lowlands* are a section of sandstones and shales deposited in a fault basin between the lower portions of the New England Highlands and the Hudson River. The region is geologically younger than the surrounding highlands.

The *Atlantic Coastal Plain*, made up of Staten Island and Long Island, forms a coastal plain largely composed of glacial sediments. Along the north shore and the center of Long Island are two terminal moraines left by the last great glacier that covered the state during the Pleistocene Epoch. The land south of these moraines is composed of sorted material washed out of the glaciers. Landforms of glacial origin, such as *ket-*

tle holes (where buried ice blocks may have melted) and *kames* (where glacial streams slowed down to deposit deltas as they entered calm water at the edge of the glacier), are common on Long Island.

QUESTIONS

5. The formation of the Finger Lakes of central New York State and the formation of Long Island are both examples of (1) climatic changes resulting in a modification of the landscape (2) uplifting and leveling forces being in dynamic equilibrium (3) soil associations differing in composition depending upon the bedrock composition (4) activities of man altering the landscape

6. A hilly region of Long Island is composed of unconsolidated and unsorted sediments. Which erosional agent was probably most influential in forming this landscape? (1) wave action (2) glaciers (3) streams (4) wind

7. The landscape of northeastern New York State was formed mainly by (1) mountain building and glacial erosion (2) faulting and volcanic activity (3) changes in the water level of Lake Ontario (4) erosion of Devonian sedimentary bedrock by rivers

8. The Catskills landscape region is classified as a plateau because the region has (1) deep gorges (2) shallow valleys (3) rock type similar to the Adirondack Highlands (4) landscape characteristics most similar to the Allegheny Plateau.

9. What is the only difference between the Adirondacks and the Catskills that can be distinguished from the *Earth Science Reference Tables*? (1) The Adirondacks have metamorphic bedrock, but the Catskills have sedimentary bedrock. (2) The Adirondacks have mostly rounded hilltops and the Catskills have jagged hilltops. (3) The Catskills have vegetation, but the Adirondacks do not. (4) The Catskills are much higher in elevation than the Adirondacks.

10. According to the *Earth Science Reference Tables*, which New York State landscape region has the lowest elevation, the most nearly level land surface, and is composed primarily of Cretaceous through Pleistocene unconsolidated sediments? (1) the Hudson-Mohawk Lowlands (2) the Atlantic Coastal Plain (3) the Champlain Lowlands (4) the Erie-Ontario Lowlands.

11. According to the *Earth Science Reference Tables*, what type of landscape region is located at 44° 30′ N. and 74° 30′ W.? (1) plateau (2) plain (3) coastal lowland (4) mountainous area

12. According to the *Earth Science Reference Tables*, which New York State landscape region contains mostly Devonian bedrock? (1) Adirondack Mountains (2) Atlantic Coastal Plain (3) Allegheny Plateau (4) Tug Hill Plateau

13. Over the past 2 million years, which erosional agent has been most responsible for producing the present landscape surface features of New York State? (1) ground water (2) wind (3) glaciation (4) human activities

14. Most of the surface materials in New York State can be classified as (1) igneous rocks (2) metamorphic rocks (3) coastal plain deposits (4) transported soils

15. The growth of early settlements in New York State into present-day population centers was chiefly due to (1) favorable weather conditions (2) desirable mineral deposits (3) abundant wildlife resources (4) a combination of desirable topographical features

LANDSCAPE DEVELOPMENT

A landscape results from the opposing forces of uplift and leveling (erosion) in the region. Uplift is often caused by collisions of the earth's plates and the resulting geologic events—earthquakes, volcanoes, faulting, and folding. Running water is the most important leveling force, although wind, glaciers, and gravity acting alone also contribute to erosion.

If the *uplifting forces* have been dominant in a region, elevation and topographic relief are generally high. For example, in mountainous areas, where uplift has been dominant, there are steep slopes and a large range of elevations from high mountain peaks to deep valleys.

If erosion has been dominant, the land surface will be relatively flat and mostly worn down to the level of the streams or other bodies of water.

If uplifting and leveling forces are in balance, the average elevation of the land will remain the same, and the landscape is said to be in *dynamic equilibrium*.

A change in the rate of uplift or leveling will produce changes in hillslopes and drainage patterns. A mountainous area or plateau may be worn down; a landscape that has been worn flat may be pushed up. When a landscape is pushed up, the gradient of its streams increases, thus increasing the velocity of the water in them and the rate of erosion. When a landscape has been worn down, the stream gradient decreases and erosion decreases; and when the landscape becomes very flat, the streams often change their courses to wide, meandering, S-shaped patterns.

Emerging mountain ranges can also change the climate by altering the temperature and wind patterns. The mountains cause the air to rise, cooling it and causing extra precipitation on the windward side. On the leeward (downwind) side, a drier climate with large temperature changes results.

The Influence of Climate. Landscapes in moist climates are generally rounded, while those in arid climates are characterized by sharp angles and steeper slopes. See Figure 14-4. Moisture plays an important part in chemical weathering. Humid climates promote the development of mature soils with a good balance of minerals and humus (organic remains of plants and animals). While you might think that these soils would be quickly eroded by the streams in a

Figure 14-4. Landscapes in humid climates and arid climates. In humid climates, the slopes are not usually as steep as they are in arid climates. This is because a moist climate promotes a lush cover of vegetation.

moist climate, this does not happen. Abundant rainfall throughout the year supports the growth of plant cover. The plant cover protects the soil from rapid runoff and erosion and produces the rounded slopes characteristic of humid climates. The moist climate also maintains many small streams that flow through most of the year.

Arid (dry) climates generally produce thin soils with little humus. Physical weathering, particularly frost action in the colder months, is the dominant form of weathering. This kind of weathering tends to form soils with large and angular grains. There is little fine-grained material to fill the pores and retard rapid and deep infiltration of precipitation. Most plants cannot survive the long periods between rainstorms. While rain is infrequent in desert regions, it often comes down very hard when it does rain. With little plant cover to protect the soil, sediment is readily carried away in time of rainfall. Large areas of exposed bedrock and steep rock faces are the result. Most of the small streams remain dry, except immediately after the widely scattered storms. You may be surprised to know that within the United States, the regions of most rapid stream erosion are the desert areas where rainfall is infrequent.

Thus, the amount and distribution of rainfall influence the landscape features. These include the angle of hillslopes, the number of permanent streams, the vegetative cover, and the nature of the soil.

Glacial Landforms.

If the climate is cold and moist enough that winter snowfall exceeds the amount of snow that can melt in the warmer seasons, the snow will accumulate and change to permanent ice. A mass of ice that does not melt each year is known as a **glacier**. As the ice thickens, it will flow outward or downhill to produce features characteristic of glaciated landscapes. Glaciated landscapes display immature soils with highly variable thicknesses, a wide range of unsorted particle sizes, and a lack of humus. Rocks within the soil may show a mineral composition different from the composition of the underlying bedrock. Glacial landforms include curving ridges of sand and gravel deposited by meltwater in tunnels under the ice (eskers), elongated hills of sediment streamlined by the advancing ice (drumlins), and many small, rounded hills deposited in water at the edge of the ice (kames). Glacial landforms also may include numerous ponds and bogs that mark places where ice blocks melted, leaving a closed depression in the land (kettle holes and kettle lakes) and an irregular pattern of stream drainage. Exposed bedrock may show rounded and polished surfaces, with parallel scratches (striations) caused by abrasion as rocks and sediment were dragged over the bedrock surfaces by the moving ice. Valleys eroded by glaciers are usually U-shaped with steep sides and broad bottoms, unlike the narrow, V-shaped valleys formed by stream erosion. Moraines are piles of unsorted sediment pushed into place along the end or the edge of a glacier. See Figure 14-5.

Coastal Landscapes.

Wave erosion is active in shaping the land along oceans and other large bodies of water. Unlike ice and running water, which flow downhill under the influence of gravity, waves and ocean currents are usually driven by the winds. Wave erosion produces flattened terraces at the water level and steep rock cliffs and bluffs of sediment behind the shore. Waves and currents running parallel to the shore deposit beaches, barrier islands, and sand spits.

Uplifting forces sometimes push these terraces and beaches high above the elevation of sea level where they were originally formed. Conversely, a shoreline where the land is sinking may show drowned stream valleys.

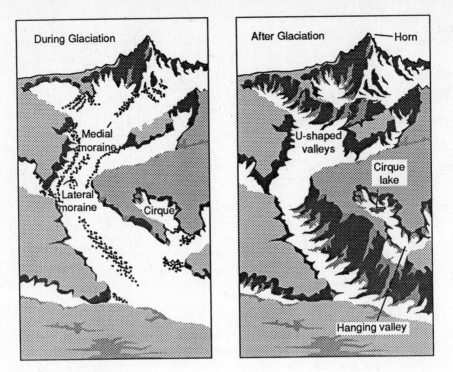

A. Valley Glacier

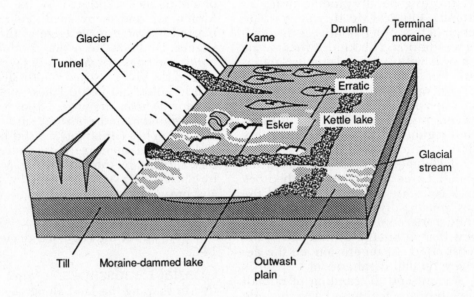

B. Continental Glacier

Figure 14-5. Landscape features of valley glaciers include: (a) Scoured, U-shaped valleys (carved by rocks under the ice); (b) Hanging valleys (left when large valleys are scoured deeper than smaller valleys that join them); (c) Medial and lateral moraines (deposited at the edge of a glacier or between merging glaciers); (d) Cirques (left when rock is scooped away from hollows, forming bowl-shaped basins); (e) Cirque lakes (formed if water fills basins after a glacier has left a valley).

Landscape features of continental glaciers include: (a) Drumlins (formed as a glacier rides up and over piles of sediment being pushed by the glacier); (b) Eskers (deposited as sediments in a stream confined to tunnels under the ice); (c) Terminal moraines (piled up as the ice front stayed in the same location for a time); (d) Kames (deposited where streams under or along the top of the glacier empty into calm waters); (e) Kettles and kettle lakes (left when blocks of ice, caught in the soil, melt).

QUESTIONS

16. Landscapes result from the interaction of what two opposing forces? (1) faulting and folding (2) weathering and abrasion (3) uplifting and erosion (4) potential evapotranspiration and precipitation

17. An area of rugged mountains with steep slopes would most likely be formed if the (1) uplifting forces are greater than the leveling forces (2) leveling forces are greater than the uplifting forces (3) uplifting and leveling forces are equal

18. If the rate of erosion in a particular landscape on the earth's surface increases and the uplifting forces remain constant, the elevation of that landscape will (1) decrease (2) increase (3) remain the same

19. What will happen to the average elevation of an area if a state of dynamic equilibrium exists? (1) The average elevation will decrease. (2) The average elevation will increase. (3) The average elevation will stay the same.

20. As the landscape of a region becomes more level, the rate of erosion due to running water will probably (1) decrease (2) increase (3) remain the same

21. If a change of climate increases the amount of annual precipitation received by an area, what probable effect will there be on the streams draining the area? (1) The volume of the stream flow will increase. (2) The rate of downcutting will decrease. (3) The velocity of the stream flow will decrease. (4) The slope of the streambed will increase.

22. Which change would be occurring in a landscape region where uplifting forces are dominant over leveling forces? (1) topographic features that are becoming smoother with time (2) a state of dynamic equilibrium existing with time (3) streams that are decreasing in velocity with time (4) hill slopes that are increasing in steepness with time

23. The diagrams below represent four different regions that have undergone change as a result of uplifting forces and leveling forces over a period of time starting 20 million years ago (m.y.a.).
Which region has had the *least* amount of uplifting during the last 20 million years?

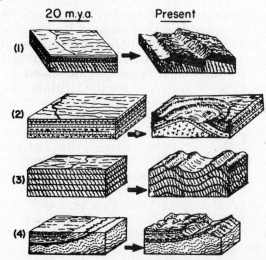

Base your answers to questions 24 and 25 on your knowledge of earth science and on the drawing below of a plateau region.

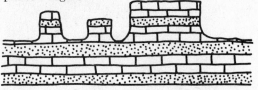

24. Which earth process most recently caused the development of the landscape features? (1) erosion (2) vulcanism (3) deposition (4) folding

25. The climate factor most responsible for the differences in appearance between the landscape features shown in this cross section and those in New York State is the (1) difference in latitude (2) difference in elevation (3) amount of rainfall (4) temperature variations

Directions: Base your answer to question 26 on the diagram below.

26. Which change would probably be noted if the climate in this area became more humid? (1) The elevation of the entire region will increase. (2) The rate of erosion will decrease. (3) The landscape features will become more rounded. (4) The limestone will weather more slowly.

27. Which is the best evidence that more than one glacial advance occurred in a region? (1) ancient forests covered by glacial deposits (2) river valleys buried deeply in glacial deposits (3) scratches in bedrock that is buried by glacial deposits (4) glacial deposits that overlay soils formed from glacial deposits

28. Which occurs as a stream is gradually uplifted? (1) Its ability to erode will probably increase. (2) Its potential energy will probably decrease. (3) Its amount of streambed deposits will probably increase. (4) Its stream discharge will probably decrease.

29. An area contains numerous winding ridges, cone-shaped hills, and small circular lakes. This area was most likely formed by (1) an arid climate (2) folding of rock layers (3) continental glaciation (4) marine flooding

30. Which landscape characteristic best indicates the action of glaciers? (1) few lakes (2) deposits of well-sorted sediments (3) residual soil covering large areas (4) polished and scratched surface bedrock

31. Which observation *least* supports inferences that New York State was covered in the recent past by great sheets of ice? (1) boulders on hilltops (2) increased average annual temperatures (3) stream valleys that have been widened and deepened (4) soils foreign to the bedrock beneath them

32. In the following diagram, the mountains west of point *A* have been rising. If all other factors remain unchanged, what will be the most probable long-range effect on the area around point *A*?

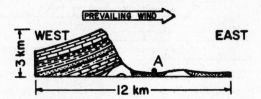

(1) increasing insolation (2) increasing cloud cover (3) decreasing temperature (4) decreasing rainfall

33. Rounded-bottom valleys with almost vertical sides, small hills and ridges composed of unsorted sediments, and exposed bedrock with small, parallel grooves and scratches are observed. Which events probably produced these features? (1) extensive glaciation (2) widespread earthquakes and associated faulting (3) a period of volcanoes and lava flows (4) extensive flooding followed by periods of wind erosion

34. Which diagram best represents a cross section of a valley which was glaciated and then eroded by a stream?

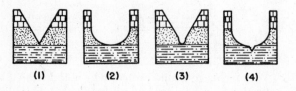

(1)   (2)   (3)   (4)

Directions (35–38): Base your answers to questions 35 through 38 on your knowledge of earth science, the *Earth Science Reference Tables*, and the map below of the landscape regions of New York State.

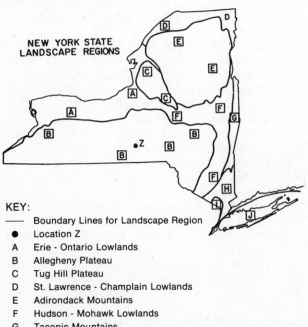

NEW YORK STATE LANDSCAPE REGIONS

KEY:
— Boundary Lines for Landscape Region
● Location Z
A Erie - Ontario Lowlands
B Allegheny Plateau
C Tug Hill Plateau
D St. Lawrence - Champlain Lowlands
E Adirondack Mountains
F Hudson - Mohawk Lowlands
G Taconic Mountains
H New England Province - Hudson Highlands
I Newark Lowlands
J Atlantic Coastal Plain

35. Naturally occurring boundaries have developed between landscape regions in New York State. What is the main reason for these boundaries? (1) differences in underlying bedrock structure and composition (2) similarities in annual climate conditions (3) differences in various forms of vegetation (4) similarities in rate of accumulation of sediments

36. The surface bedrock of the St. Lawrence-Champlain Lowlands is mostly composed of (1) metamorphic rock of Precambrian age (2) sedimentary rock of Cambrian and Ordovician age (3) igneous rock of Triassic age (4) sediments of Pleistocene age

37. Which two landscape regions contain surface bedrock composed of quartzite and marble? (1) *F* and *C* (2) *B* and *D* (3) *H* and *E* (4) *G* and *A*

38. If the climate of the region had been arid during the erosional development of landscape region *B*, which cross-sectional diagram would best represent the appearance of a plateau near point *Z*?

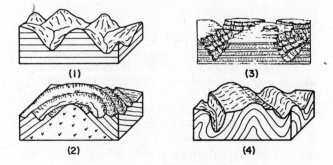

(1)   (3)

(2)   (4)

THE INFLUENCE OF BEDROCK ON A LANDSCAPE

Even in the same climate, locations with different rock types or different structures can develop very different landscape features.

Rocks that are hard and resist weathering and erosion are called **competent rocks**. Competent rocks form the higher portions of a landscape—the plateaus, mountains, and **escarpments** (cliffs). The softer rocks and rocks that have been fractured usually underlie valleys and other low areas.

Softer rock erodes faster than competent rock. If all the exposed bedrock on a hillslope has about the same degree of competence, the slopes will be worn down fairly evenly. If the layers of the hillslope differ in competence, the softer rocks will wear away faster, giving the hillslope an uneven or stepped appearance. The more competent layers will form the steepest slopes and cliffs.

Streams generally follow zones of weakness, such as less competent rock, faults, and joints. Faults and joints particularly influence the stream patterns in mountainous areas of a single rock type.

Figure 14-6 gives some examples of how the bedrock can affect hillslopes, and Figure 14-7 gives examples of different stream patterns that can form on different geological formations.

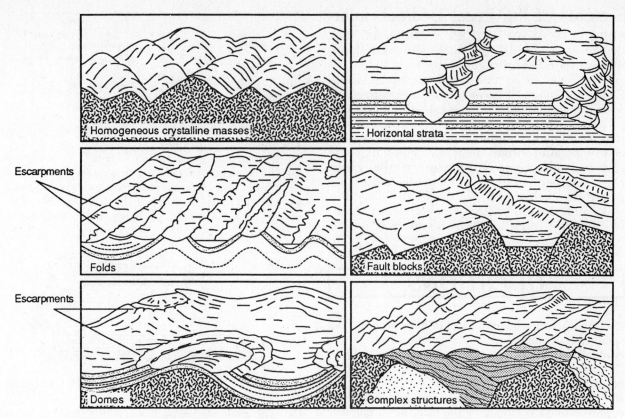

Figure 14-6. The diagrams show how the rock structure can influence landscapes. The highest elevations are usually found where the rock has been pushed up or where the rock is relatively hard. Valleys develop in areas of weak or fractured bedrock.

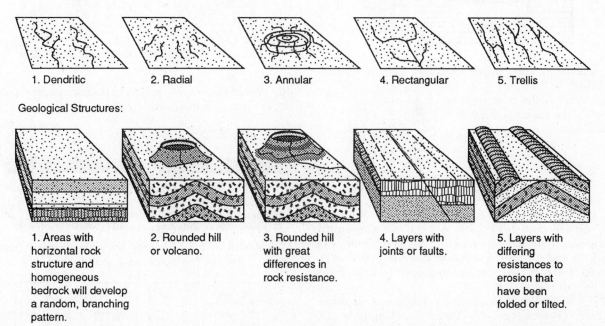

Figure 14-7. Stream drainage patterns and possible associated geological structures. (1) On flat-lying layers of uniform composition, without zones of weakness, a branching, *dendritic pattern* will form. (2) On a volcano or rounded hill (dome) with little difference in rock competence, a *radial pattern* will form. (3) If there are great differences in rock competence, an *annular pattern* of concentric circles will probably form. (4) Joints or faults produce a rectangular or *trellis pattern*. (5) Trellis drainage is often found in areas where rock layers with differing competence have been folded or tilted and eroded to form ridges.

Features of the Local Bedrock Influence the Landscape.

Different rock structures generally produce different landscapes. Rounded hills with summits of similar elevation form in rocks of uniform composition. Flat-lying layers of sedimentary rock often produce plateau landscapes in which the most competent layers form the highest surfaces and steeper slopes. Folded bedrock often makes nearly parallel ridges that may meet in some places. Faults commonly create parallel cliffs. Domes make circular ridges where the more competent rock layers form the ridges and the softer rocks underlie the valleys. A complex mix of surface features often indicates a variety of underlying rock types and structures.

QUESTIONS

39. Which factor has the *least* influence on the development of a landscape over a number of years? (1) average amount of rainfall (2) average rate of uplift (3) composition of bedrock (4) geologic age of bedrock

40. Which earth process most likely formed the depression now occupied by the lake shown below?

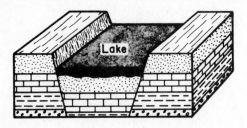

(1) glaciation (2) climate changes (3) erosion (4) faulting

41. What is the best explanation for the shape of the cliff in the diagram?

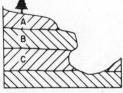

(1) Rocks A and C are made of larger particles than rock B. (2) The particles in rocks A and C are more firmly cemented than those in rock B. (3) The minerals in rocks A and C erode faster than those in rock B. (4) Rocks A and C have not been exposed to weathering as long as rock B.

42. Which would *least* affect landscape development? (1) rock type (2) climate (3) longitude (4) land uplift

Base your answer to question 43 on your knowledge of earth science and on the cross section which represents layers of sedimentary rock that have not been overturned but have been intruded by igneous rock.

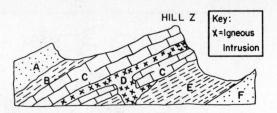

43. Which best explains the presence of hill Z? (1) The intrusion of rock layer D weakened rock layer C. (2) Rock layer D protected rock layer C from erosion. (3) The landscape developed in a moist climate. (4) Rock layer C is more resistant than rock layers above.

44. In the cross section of the hill shown below, which rock units are probably most resistant to weathering?

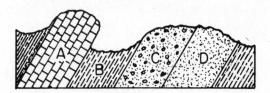

(1) I and II (2) II and III (3) I and III (4) II and IV

45. The diagram below represents a geologic cross section with sedimentary rock layers A, B, C, and D exposed to the atmosphere. Which rock layer in the diagram is most resistant to weathering and erosion?

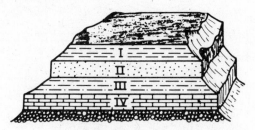

(1) A (2) B (3) C (4) D

46. Which landscape region probably resulted from the erosion of folded rock layers?

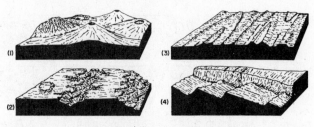

47. Which of the following stream patterns is most characteristic of horizontal rock structure?

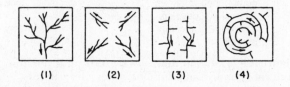

48. Which kind of stream pattern would most likely be found on the type of landscape shown in the following diagram?

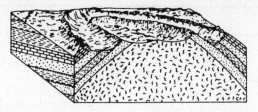

Directions: Base your answer to question 49 on the landscape diagram below.

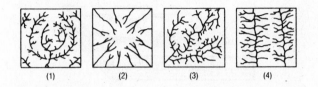

49. Which drainage pattern of streams would most likely develop on this mountain landscape?

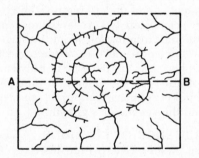

50. The diagram below is a map showing the stream drainage pattern for an area of the earth's crust.

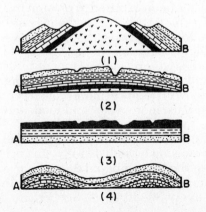

Which geologic cross section shows the most probable underlying rock structure and surface for this area along line *A-B*?

51. Which stream pattern is most commonly found in areas with a nearly level land surface?

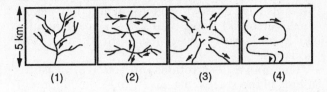

52. Which landscape characteristic indicates a landscape has been formed primarily by streams? (1) residual soil covering a large area (2) coastal sand dunes (3) V-shaped valleys (4) parallel hills of unsorted sediments

53. Which drainage pattern of streams would most likely develop on the illustrated landscape?

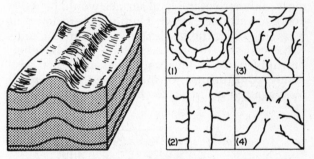

54. Soil formed from local bedrock of the Adirondack Highlands is observed to be different from soil formed from local bedrock in the Appalachian Uplands. Which statement best explains this observation? (1) The elevation of the bedrock in the Adirondacks is different from the elevation of the bedrock of the other region. (2) The type of agriculture found in the Adirondacks is different from the agriculture in the other region. (3) The type of bedrock of the Adirondacks is different from the bedrock of the other region. (4) The stream drainage patterns of the Adirondacks are different from the stream drainage patterns of the other region.

STAGES IN LANDSCAPE DEVELOPMENT

The **maturity** of a landscape depends upon the portion of the land that has been worn down to or near *base level*. Base level is the elevation of the river, lake, or ocean that is at the lowest point in the landscape. Base level for a particular region is not always sea level.

In a *youthful landscape* (Figure 14-8), a large portion of the land is at a high elevation, with steep hillslopes and narrow, fast-running streams that produce deep stream valleys. Waterfalls and rapids occur frequently. Soils are poorly developed in a youthful landscape.

A *mature landscape* is more rounded (particularly in a moist climate) and at a lower elevation, with more gradual hillslopes. Stream valleys are broader, and streams are more likely to have meanders than those in younger landscapes.

The Development of Landscapes

In an *old landscape*, most of the land surface has been eroded down to or near base level. A few hills may rise up above a generally flat area. Streams have a very low gradient and they meander over broad flood plains. Soils are generally thick and well developed with distinct soil horizons.

The above descriptions are relative measurements of the stages in a landscape's development and do not indicate a particular age in years. Should an old landscape be uplifted, its streams would again cut deep, narrow valleys. The landscape would again be young (rejuvenated). This kind of rejuvenation would "restart the clock."

In the early or young stage of a landscape's development, uplifting forces are dominant. But if the leveling force of erosion becomes dominant, more and more of the land surface would be worn down toward base level. The longer erosion is at work, the older the landscape. Sometimes a landscape can stay the same for long periods, when the uplifting and leveling forces are equal (dynamic equilibrium), or the process can start all over again if uplifting forces become dominant.

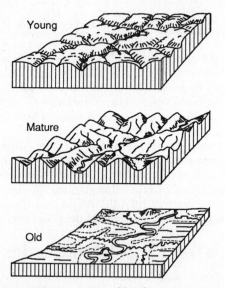

Figure 14-8. Three stages of landscape maturity. As a landscape becomes more mature, more and more of the land surface is worn down to the lowest level in the region (base level). Young landscapes are characterized by a large portion of the land at high elevations. The diagram above shows a youthful plateau underlain by flat-lying layers of sedimentary rock. Youthful landscapes composed of folded, faulted, or contorted rocks will not display the flat uplands shown here, but they will still have little land worn down to base level. As the landscape becomes more mature, erosion wears down the land and makes the stream valleys broader. In old age, streams with little gradient meander over a broad, flat region that may still contain a few hilly remains of the former mountains. Within New York, the most youthful landscapes are within the Adirondack and Catskill mountains. The most mature landscapes are found on the coastal plains of Long Island and along the Great Lakes.

55. Which landscape characteristic is *least* able to be observed and measured? (1) hillslopes (2) stream patterns (3) type of soil (4) age of the surface

56. The three diagrams below represent the same location at different times. What is the best explanation for the differences in appearance of this location?

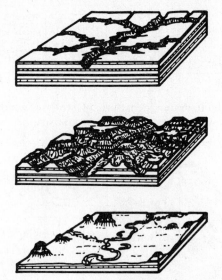

(1) This region was exposed to leveling forces for different lengths of time. (2) This region has different underlying bedrock structures. (3) This region developed in different climate regions. (4) This region has the same type of underlying rock layers.

57. Which characteristics of a landscape region would provide the best information about the stage of development of the landscape? (1) the age and fossil content of the bedrock (2) the type of hillslopes and the stream patterns (3) the amount of precipitation and the potential evapotranspiration (4) the type of vegetation and the vegetation's growth rate

The Influence of Humans.

Technology is the use of scientific principles to create methods and machinery that make our lives more comfortable. Through technology, we have been able to alter the shape of the land in construction projects and mining. In some agricultural areas, the land has been exposed to erosion by wind and water. In the future, these changes are likely to increase for two reasons: (1) As our wealth and technology increase, we are likely to require more and larger excavations for our buildings and other land uses. (2) The increasing population of the earth will require more construction, more raw materials, more water and food, and also will produce more waste to be eliminated.

Until about 200 years ago, the population of the earth grew slowly and steadily. In recent years, however, the human population of our planet has been growing at a rate that would double the population every 30–40 years. See Figure 14-9.

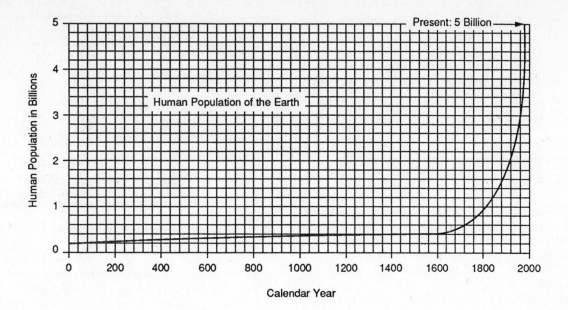

Date	Event	World Population
0	Beginning of the Common Era	0.25 billion
470	Fall of the Roman Empire	0.29
1215	Magna Carta Signed	0.35
1492	Columbus Discovers America	0.40
1776	Declaration of Independence	0.85
1848	California Gold Rush	1.10
1914	World War I	1.70
1939	World War II	2.20
	Present	5.00

Figure 14-9. The population of the earth grew slowly and steadily until the industrial revolution. Since then, the population of our planet has grown explosively due to the control of many diseases and to our increasing ability in providing food and housing.

It is no surprise that environmental changes caused by humans are the greatest where the population density is the greatest. The land in and around our cities has been extensively leveled, dug into, filled, and covered with buildings and pavement. While the cover may protect the land from further changes, it also leaves us vulnerable to new dangers, such as flooding caused by the rapid runoff of precipitation, and the collapse of human structures. Densely populated areas generally produce more air and water pollution. Airborne pollutants, such as acid precipitation, accelerate the weathering of human structures and have a harmful effect on plants and animals.

Humans can make changes in the landscape in a few months that would take nature hundreds of years or more to achieve. It could also take nature hundreds of years to remedy the harmful effects of our technology. Environmental planning and conservation help us to preserve our soil, water, and air from the pollution that often accompanies human changes in the landscape. We can restore polluted portions of our environment through legislation and coordinated efforts.

QUESTIONS

58. Which graph best represents human population growth?

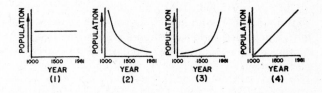

59. The human population of the earth is (1) decreasing (2) increasing (3) remaining the same
60. When human beings' careless activities decrease the amount of plant life, the amount of runoff usually (1) decreases (2) increases (3) remains the same
61. Many landscapes in New York State are presently being altered by (1) glacial activity (2) volcanic action (3) potential evapotranspiration (4) human activities

The Development of Landscapes

62. Which statement is best supported by the graph shown below?

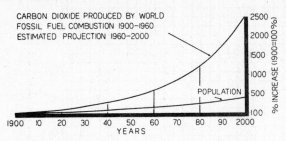

CARBON DIOXIDE PRODUCED BY WORLD
FOSSIL FUEL COMBUSTION 1900–1960
ESTIMATED PROJECTION 1960–2000

(1) From 1960 to 2000 it is anticipated that there will be a decrease in the use of fossil fuels. (2) From 1900 to 1960, the average person continuously used a greater quantity of fossil fuels. (3) By 1980 the world population will be approximately 400 million. (4) From 1970 to 2000 the world population will remain relatively constant.

63. Legislation by federal, state, and local governments dealing with the problem of pollution has come about mainly as a result of (1) people's ability to solve this problem with technology (2) nature's ability to clean itself, given enough time (3) people's belief that natural resources are inexhaustible (4) people's action because of their needs, awareness, and attitudes

64. Which graph best shows the relationship between atmospheric transparency and the concentration of pollution particles in the air?

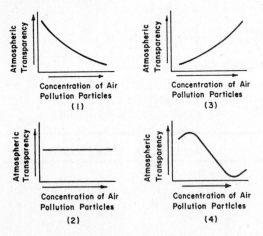

Directions (65–69): Base your answers to questions 65 through 69 on your knowledge of earth science and the air pollution field map shown below. The isolines represent the concentration of pollutants measured in particles/cm³.

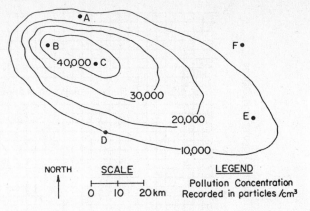

NORTH SCALE LEGEND
0 10 20 km
Pollution Concentration
Recorded in particles /cm³

65. The major source of air pollution is most likely at point (1) *A* (2) *B* (3) *E* (4) *D*

66. The winds responsible for this air pollution pattern are most likely blowing from the (1) northeast (2) northwest (3) southeast (4) southwest

67. The most rapid increase in air pollution would be encountered when traveling between points (1) *A* and *B* (2) *A* and *F* (3) *C* and *D* (4) *D* and *E*

68. The air pollution field illustrated by the map is located in a heavily populated area. Which is the *least* probable source of the pollution? (1) human activities (2) industrial plants (3) automobile traffic (4) natural processes

69. Which graph best represents the relationship between the pollution concentration and distance from point *B* toward point *E*?

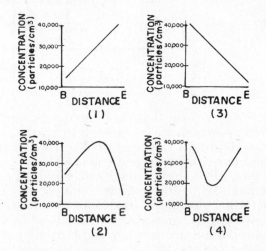

Reference Tables and Charts

Surface Ocean Currents

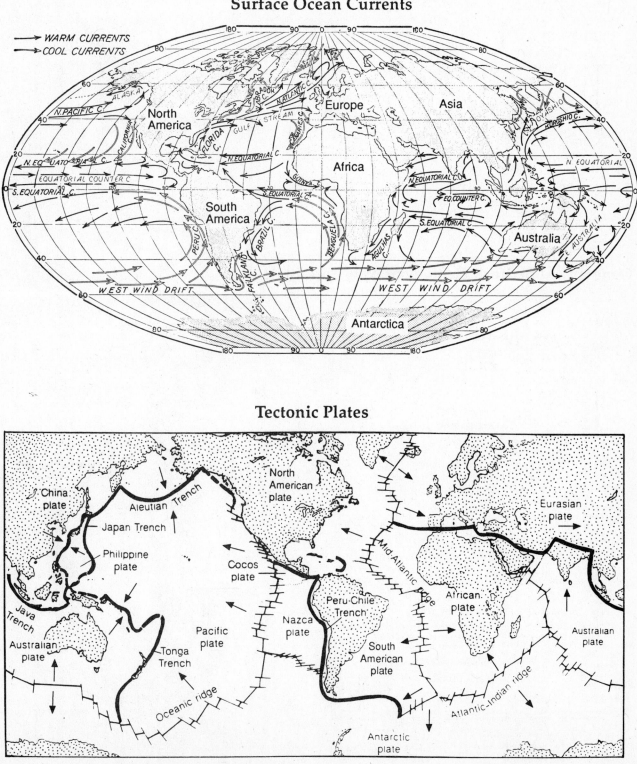

Tectonic Plates

Generalized Landscape Regions of New York State

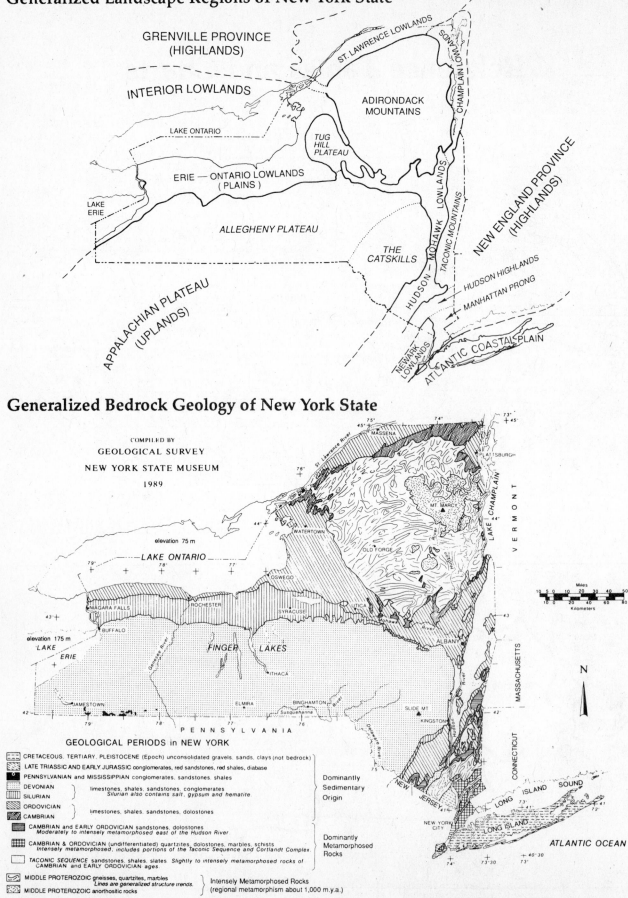

Generalized Bedrock Geology of New York State

COMPILED BY

GEOLOGICAL SURVEY

NEW YORK STATE MUSEUM

1989

GEOLOGICAL PERIODS in NEW YORK

CRETACEOUS, TERTIARY, PLEISTOCENE (Epoch) unconsolidated gravels, sands, clays (not bedrock)

LATE TRIASSIC AND EARLY JURASSIC conglomerates, red sandstones, red shales, diabase

PENNSYLVANIAN and MISSISSIPPIAN conglomerates, sandstones, shales

DEVONIAN — limestones, shales, sandstones, conglomerates

SILURIAN — *Silurian also contains salt, gypsum and hematite.*

ORDOVICIAN

CAMBRIAN — limestones, shales, sandstones, dolostones

} Dominantly Sedimentary Origin

CAMBRIAN and EARLY ORDOVICIAN sandstones, dolostones. *Moderately to intensely metamorphosed east of the Hudson River.*

CAMBRIAN & ORDOVICIAN (undifferentiated) quartzites, dolostones, marbles, schists *Intensely metamorphosed, includes portions of the Taconic Sequence and Cortlandt Complex.*

TACONIC SEQUENCE sandstones, shales, slates *Slightly to intensely metamorphosed rocks of CAMBRIAN and EARLY ORDOVICIAN ages.*

} Dominantly Metamorphosed Rocks

MIDDLE PROTEROZOIC gneisses, quartzites, marbles *Lines are generalized structure trends.*

MIDDLE PROTEROZOIC anorthositic rocks

} Intensely Metamorphosed Rocks (regional metamorphism about 1,000 m.y.a.)

Rock Cycle in Earth's Crust

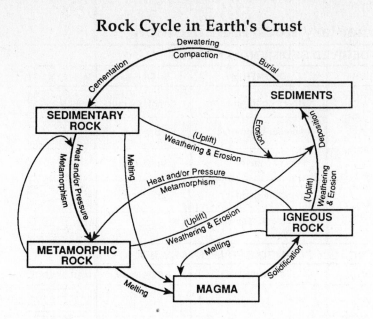

Relationship of Transported Particle Size to Water Velocity*

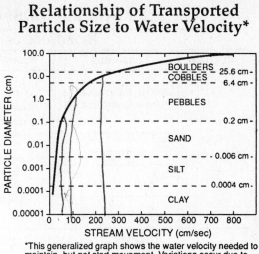

*This generalized graph shows the water velocity needed to maintain, but not start movement. Variations occur due to differences in particle density and shape.

Scheme for Igneous Rock Identification

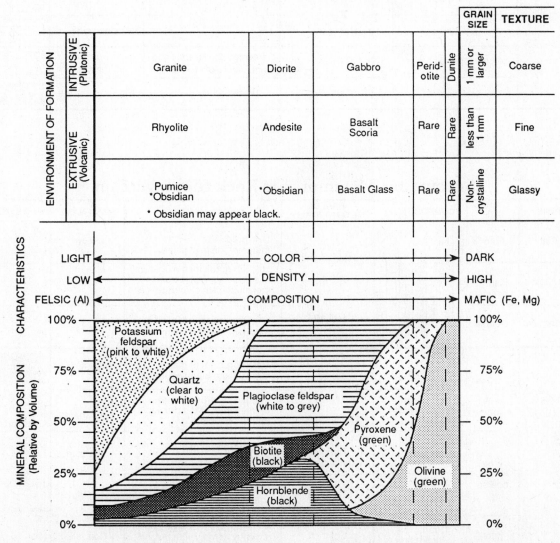

Note: The intrusive rocks can also occur as exceptionally coarse-grained rock, Pegmatite.

Scheme for Sedimentary Rock Identification

INORGANIC LAND-DERIVED SEDIMENTARY ROCKS

TEXTURE	GRAIN SIZE	COMPOSITION	COMMENTS	ROCK NAME	MAP SYMBOL
Clastic (fragmental)	Mixed, silt to boulders (larger than 0.001 cm)	Mostly quartz, feldspar, and clay minerals; May contain fragments of other rocks and minerals	Rounded fragments	Conglomerate	
			Angular fragments	Breccia	
	Sand (0.006 to 0.2 cm)		Fine to coarse	Sandstone	
	Silt (0.0004 to 0.006 cm)		Very fine grain	Siltstone	
	Clay (less than 0.0006 cm)		Compact; may split easily	Shale	

CHEMICALLY AND/OR ORGANICALLY FORMED SEDIMENTARY ROCKS

TEXTURE	GRAIN SIZE	COMPOSITION	COMMENTS	ROCK NAME	MAP SYMBOL
Nonclastic	Coarse to fine	Calcite	Crystals from chemical precipitates and evaporites	Chemical Limestone	
	Varied	Halite		Rock Salt	
	Varied	Gypsum		Rock Gypsum	
	Varied	Dolomite		Dolostone	
	Microscopic to coarse	Calcite	Cemented shells, shell fragments, and skeletal remains	Fossil Limestone	
	Varied	Carbon	Black and nonporous	Bituminous Coal	

Scheme for Metamorphic Rock Identification

TEXTURE	GRAIN SIZE	COMPOSITION	TYPE OF METAMORPHISM	COMMENTS	ROCK NAME	MAP SYMBOL
FOLIATED — Slaty	Fine	CHLORITE / MICA / QUARTZ / FELDSPAR / AMPHIBOLE / GARNET / PYROXENE	Regional	Low-grade metamorphism of shale	Slate	
FOLIATED — Schistose	Medium to coarse			Medium-grade metamorphism; Mica crystals visible from metamorphism of feldspars and clay minerals	Schist	
FOLIATED — Gneissic	Coarse		(Heat and pressure increase with depth, folding, and faulting)	High-grade metamorphism; Mica has changed to feldspar	Gneiss	
NONFOLIATED	Fine	Carbonaceous		Metamorphism of plant remains and bituminous coal	Anthracite Coal	
NONFOLIATED	Coarse	Depends on conglomerate composition		Pebbles may be distorted or stretched; Often breaks through pebbles	Meta-conglomerate	
NONFOLIATED	Fine to coarse	Quartz	Thermal (including contact) or Regional	Metamorphism of sandstone	Quartzite	
NONFOLIATED		Calcite, Dolomite		Metamorphism of limestone or dolostone	Marble	
NONFOLIATED	Fine	Quartz, Plagioclase	Contact	Metamorphism of various rocks by contact with magma or lava	Hornfels	

Dewpoint Temperatures

Dry-Bulb Temperature (°C)	Difference Between Wet-Bulb and Dry-Bulb Temperatures (C°)														
	1	2	3	4	5	6	7	8	9	10	11	12	13	14	15
−20	−33														
−18	−28														
−16	−24														
−14	−21	−36													
−12	−18	−28													
−10	−14	−22													
−8	−12	−18	−29												
−6	−10	−14	−22												
−4	−7	−12	−17	−29											
−2	−5	−8	−13	−20											
0	−3	−6	−9	−15	−24										
2	−1	−3	−6	−11	−17										
4	1	−1	−4	−7	−11	−19									
6	4	1	−1	−4	−7	−13	−21								
8	6	3	1	−2	−5	−9	−14								
10	8	6	4	1	−2	−5	−9	−14	−28						
12	10	8	6	4	1	−2	−5	−9	−16						
14	12	11	9	6	4	1	−2	−5	−10	−17					
16	14	13	11	9	7	4	1	−1	−6	−10	−17				
18	16	15	13	11	9	7	4	2	−2	−5	−10	−19			
20	19	17	15	14	12	10	7	4	2	−2	−5	−10	−19		
22	21	19	17	16	14	12	10	8	5	3	−1	−5	−10	−19	
24	23	21	20	18	16	14	12	10	8	6	2	−1	−5	−10	−18
26	25	23	22	20	18	17	15	13	11	9	6	3	0	−4	−9
28	27	25	24	22	21	19	17	16	14	11	9	7	4	1	−3
30	29	27	26	24	23	21	19	18	16	14	12	10	8	5	1

Relative Humidity (%)

Dry-Bulb Temperature (°C)	Difference Between Wet-Bulb and Dry-Bulb Temperatures (C°)														
	1	2	3	4	5	6	7	8	9	10	11	12	13	14	15
−20	28														
−18	40														
−16	48	0													
−14	55	11													
−12	61	23													
−10	66	33	0												
−8	71	41	13												
−6	73	48	20	0											
−4	77	54	32	11											
−2	79	58	37	20	1										
0	81	63	45	28	11										
2	83	67	51	36	20	6									
4	85	70	56	42	27	14									
6	86	72	59	46	35	22	10	0							
8	87	74	62	51	39	28	17	6							
10	88	76	65	54	43	33	24	13	4						
12	88	78	67	57	48	38	28	19	10	2					
14	89	79	69	60	50	41	33	25	16	8	1				
16	90	80	71	62	54	45	37	29	21	14	7	1			
18	91	81	72	64	56	48	40	33	26	19	12	6	0		
20	91	82	74	66	58	51	44	36	30	23	17	11	5	0	
22	92	83	75	68	60	53	46	40	33	27	21	15	10	4	0
24	92	84	76	69	62	55	49	42	36	30	25	20	14	9	4
26	92	85	77	70	64	57	51	45	39	34	28	23	18	13	9
28	93	86	78	71	65	59	53	47	42	36	31	26	21	17	12
30	93	86	79	72	66	61	55	49	44	39	34	29	25	20	16

GEOLOGIC HISTORY OF NEW

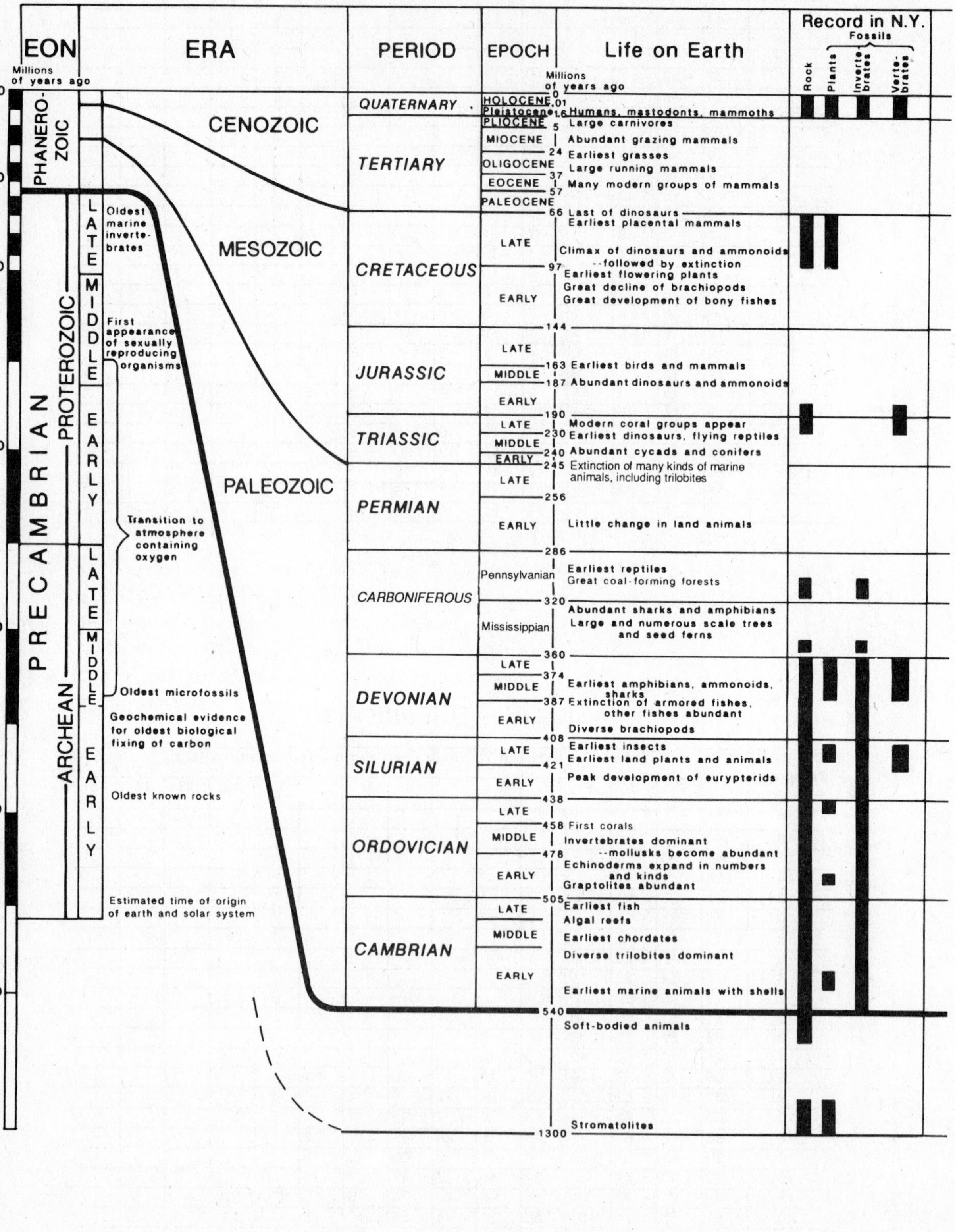

EON
ERA
PERIOD
EPOCH
Life on Earth
Record in N.Y.
Fossils
Rock
Plants
Inverte-brates
Verte-brates
Millions of years ago
0
500
1000
2000
3000
4000
5000
PHANERO-ZOIC
PRECAMBRIAN
PROTEROZOIC
ARCHEAN
LATE
MIDDLE
EARLY
CENOZOIC
MESOZOIC
PALEOZOIC
Oldest marine inverte-brates
First appearance of sexually reproducing organisms
Transition to atmosphere containing oxygen
Oldest microfossils
Geochemical evidence for oldest biological fixing of carbon
Oldest known rocks
Estimated time of origin of earth and solar system
QUATERNARY
TERTIARY
CRETACEOUS
JURASSIC
TRIASSIC
PERMIAN
CARBONIFEROUS
DEVONIAN
SILURIAN
ORDOVICIAN
CAMBRIAN
HOLOCENE
Pleistocene
PLIOCENE
MIOCENE
OLIGOCENE
EOCENE
PALEOCENE
Pennsylvanian
Mississippian
0
.01
1.6 Humans, mastodonts, mammoths
5 Large carnivores
Abundant grazing mammals
24 Earliest grasses
Large running mammals
37
Many modern groups of mammals
57
66 Last of dinosaurs
Earliest placental mammals
Climax of dinosaurs and ammonoids
--followed by extinction
97 Earliest flowering plants
Great decline of brachiopods
Great development of bony fishes
144
163 Earliest birds and mammals
187 Abundant dinosaurs and ammonoids
190
Modern coral groups appear
230 Earliest dinosaurs, flying reptiles
240 Abundant cycads and conifers
245 Extinction of many kinds of marine animals, including trilobites
256
Little change in land animals
286
Earliest reptiles
Great coal-forming forests
320
Abundant sharks and amphibians
Large and numerous scale trees and seed ferns
360
374
Earliest amphibians, ammonoids, sharks
387 Extinction of armored fishes, other fishes abundant
Diverse brachiopods
408
Earliest insects
421 Earliest land plants and animals
Peak development of eurypterids
438
458 First corals
Invertebrates dominant
478 --mollusks become abundant
Echinoderms expand in numbers and kinds
Graptolites abundant
505 Earliest fish
Algal reefs
Earliest chordates
Diverse trilobites dominant
Earliest marine animals with shells
540
Soft-bodied animals
1300 Stromatolites

YORK STATE AT A GLANCE

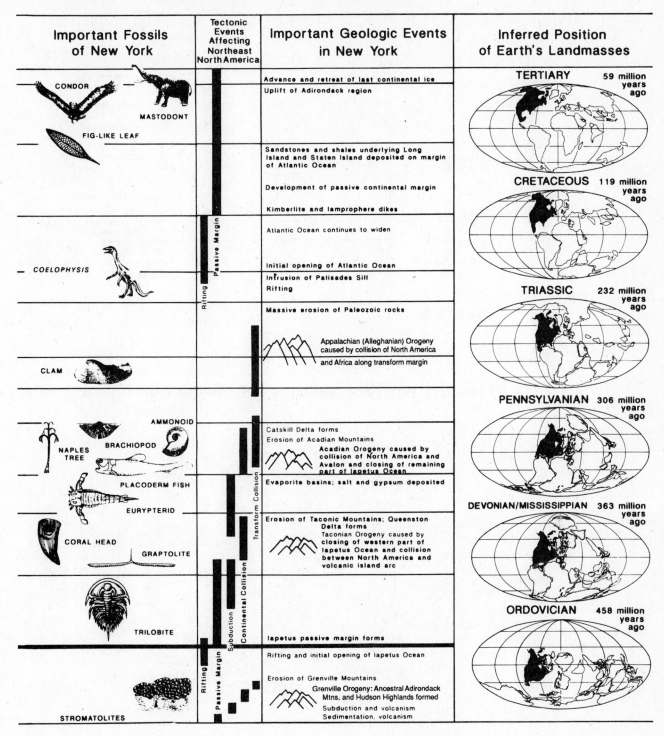

| Important Fossils of New York | Tectonic Events Affecting Northeast North America | Important Geologic Events in New York | Inferred Position of Earth's Landmasses |

Important Fossils of New York

CONDOR
MASTODONT
FIG-LIKE LEAF
COELOPHYSIS
CLAM
AMMONOID
BRACHIOPOD
NAPLES TREE
PLACODERM FISH
EURYPTERID
CORAL HEAD
GRAPTOLITE
TRILOBITE
STROMATOLITES

Tectonic Events Affecting Northeast North America

Rifting
Passive Margin
Transform Collision
Continental Collision
Subduction
Rifting
Passive Margin

Important Geologic Events in New York

Advance and retreat of last continental ice
Uplift of Adirondack region

Sandstones and shales underlying Long Island and Staten Island deposited on margin of Atlantic Ocean

Development of passive continental margin

Kimberlite and lamprophere dikes

Atlantic Ocean continues to widen

Initial opening of Atlantic Ocean

Intrusion of Palisades Sill
Rifting

Massive erosion of Paleozoic rocks

Appalachian (Alleghanian) Orogeny caused by collision of North America and Africa along transform margin

Catskill Delta forms
Erosion of Acadian Mountains
Acadian Orogeny caused by collision of North America and Avalon and closing of remaining part of Iapetus Ocean

Evaporite basins; salt and gypsum deposited

Erosion of Taconic Mountains; Queenston Delta forms
Taconian Orogeny caused by closing of western part of Iapetus Ocean and collision between North America and volcanic island arc

Iapetus passive margin forms

Rifting and initial opening of Iapetus Ocean

Erosion of Grenville Mountains
Grenville Orogeny: Ancestral Adirondack Mtns. and Hudson Highlands formed
Subduction and volcanism
Sedimentation, volcanism

Inferred Position of Earth's Landmasses

TERTIARY — 59 million years ago

CRETACEOUS — 119 million years ago

TRIASSIC — 232 million years ago

PENNSYLVANIAN — 306 million years ago

DEVONIAN/MISSISSIPPIAN — 363 million years ago

ORDOVICIAN — 458 million years ago

Selected Properties of Earth's Atmosphere

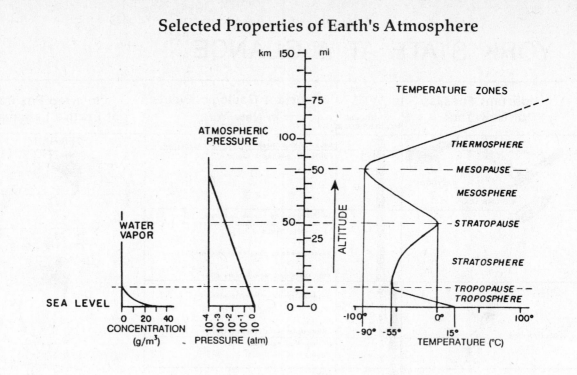

Planetary Wind and Moisture Belts in the Troposphere

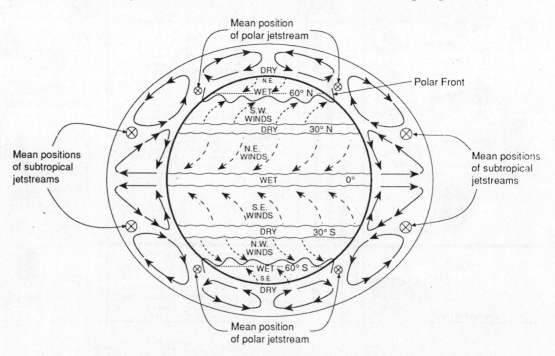

The drawing shows the locations of the belts near the time of an equinox. The locations shift somewhat with the changing latitude of the Sun's vertical ray. In the Northern Hemisphere the belts shift northward in summer and southward in winter.

Reviewing Earth Science

Equations and Proportions

Equations

Percent deviation from accepted value	deviation (%) =	$\dfrac{\text{difference from accepted value}}{\text{accepted value}} \times 100$
Eccentricity of an ellipse	eccentricity =	$\dfrac{\text{distance between foci}}{\text{length of major axis}}$
Gradient	gradient =	$\dfrac{\text{change in field value}}{\text{change in distance}}$
Rate of change	rate of change =	$\dfrac{\text{change in field value}}{\text{change in time}}$
Circumference of a circle	$C = 2\pi r$	
Eratosthenes' method to determine Earth's circumference	$\dfrac{\angle a}{360°} = \dfrac{s}{C}$	
Volume of a rectangular solid	$V = \ell wh$	
Density of a substance	$D = \dfrac{m}{V}$	
Latent heat	$\begin{cases} \text{solid} \longleftrightarrow \text{liquid} & Q = mH_f \\ \text{liquid} \longleftrightarrow \text{gas} & Q = mH_v \end{cases}$	
Heat energy lost or gained	$Q = m\,\Delta T C_p$	

C_p = specific heat
C = circumference
d = distance
D = density
F = force
h = height
H_f = heat of fusion
H_v = heat of vaporization
$\angle a$ = shadow angle
ℓ = length
s = distance on surface
m = mass
Q = amount of heat
r = radius
ΔT = change in temperature
V = volume
w = width
Note: $\pi \approx 3.14$

Proportions

Kepler's harmonic law of planetary motion	(period of revolution)$^2 \propto$ (mean radius of orbit)^3
Universal law of gravitation	force $\propto \dfrac{\text{mass}_1 \times \text{mass}_2}{(\text{distance between their centers})^2}$ $\left(F \propto \dfrac{m_1 \, m_2}{d^2}\right)$

EURYPTERID
New York State Fossil

Physical Constants

Properties of Water

Latent heat of fusion (H_f)	80 cal/g
Latent heat of vaporization (H_v)	540 cal/g
Density (D) at 3.98°C	1.00 g/mL

Specific Heats of Common Materials

MATERIAL		SPECIFIC HEAT (C_p) (cal/g·C°)
Water	solid	0.5
	liquid	1.0
	gas	0.5
Dry air		0.24
Basalt		0.20
Granite		0.19
Iron		0.11
Copper		0.09
Lead		0.03

Radioactive Decay Data

RADIOACTIVE ISOTOPE	DISINTEGRATION	HALF-LIFE (years)
Carbon-14	$C^{14} \longrightarrow N^{14}$	5.7×10^3
Potassium-40	$K^{40} \begin{smallmatrix} \longrightarrow Ar^{40} \\ \searrow Ca^{40} \end{smallmatrix}$	1.3×10^9
Uranium-238	$U^{238} \longrightarrow Pb^{206}$	4.5×10^9
Rubidium-87	$Rb^{87} \longrightarrow Sr^{87}$	4.9×10^{10}

Astronomy Measurements

MEASUREMENT	EARTH	SUN	MOON
Mass (m)	5.98×10^{24} kg	1.99×10^{30} kg	7.35×10^{22} kg
Radius (r)	6.37×10^3 km	6.96×10^5 km	1.74×10^3 km
Average density (D)	5.52 g/cm^3	1.42 g/cm^3	3.34 g/cm^3

Lapse Rate

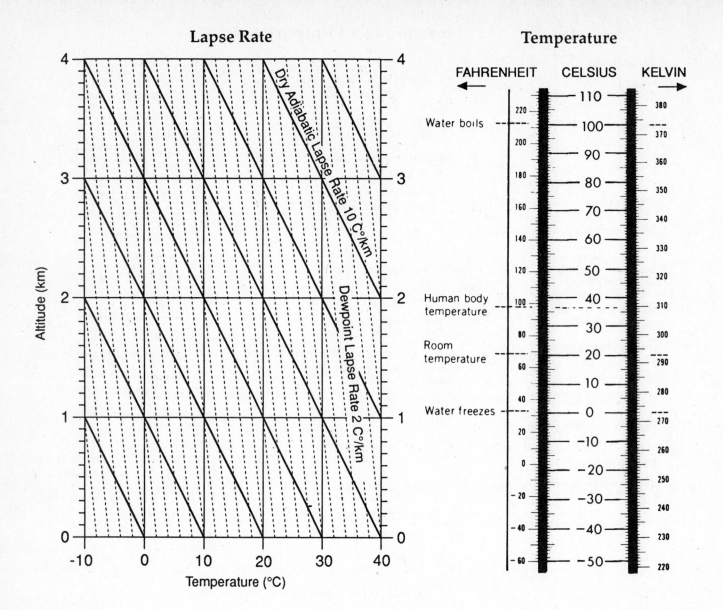

Altitude (km) vs Temperature (°C)

Dry Adiabatic Lapse Rate 10 C°/km

Dewpoint Lapse Rate 2 C°/km

Temperature

FAHRENHEIT — CELSIUS — KELVIN

Water boils — 100 — 370
Human body temperature — 40 — 310
Room temperature — 20 — 290
Water freezes — 0 — 270

Weather Map Information

STATION MODEL

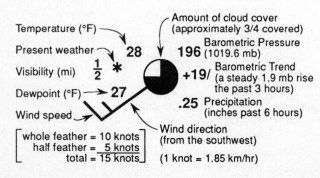

Temperature (°F) → 28
Present weather → *
Visibility (mi) → ½
Dewpoint (°F) → 27
Wind speed →

Amount of cloud cover (approximately 3/4 covered)
196 Barometric Pressure (1019.6 mb)
+19/ Barometric Trend (a steady 1.9 mb rise the past 3 hours)
.25 Precipitation (inches past 6 hours)
Wind direction (from the southwest)

[whole feather = 10 knots
half feather = 5 knots
total = 15 knots]

(1 knot = 1.85 km/hr)

PRESENT WEATHER SYMBOLS

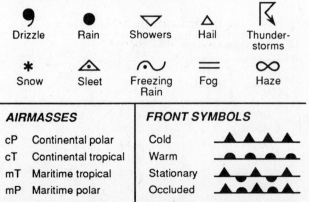

Drizzle   Rain   Showers   Hail   Thunder-storms
Snow   Sleet   Freezing Rain   Fog   Haze

AIRMASSES

cP Continental polar
cT Continental tropical
mT Maritime tropical
mP Maritime polar

FRONT SYMBOLS

Cold
Warm
Stationary
Occluded

Pressure

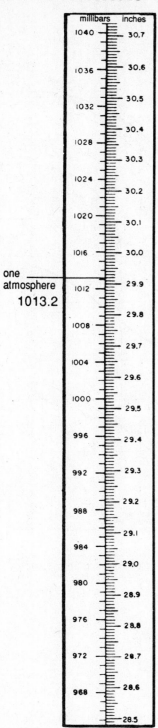

one atmosphere
1013.2

Electromagnetic Spectrum

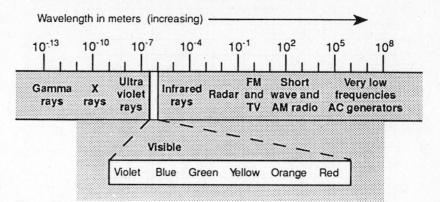

Wavelength in meters (increasing) →

10^{-13} 10^{-10} 10^{-7} 10^{-4} 10^{-1} 10^{2} 10^{5} 10^{8}

| Gamma rays | X rays | Ultra violet rays | Infrared rays | Radar | FM and TV | Short wave and AM radio | Very low frequencies AC generators |

Visible

| Violet | Blue | Green | Yellow | Orange | Red |

Solar System Data

Planet	Mean Distance from Sun (millions of km)	Period of Revolution	Period of Rotation	Eccentricity of Orbit	Equatorial Diameter (km)	Density (g/cm^3)
MERCURY	57.9	88 days	59 days	0.206	4,880	5.4
VENUS	108.2	224.7 days	243 days	0.007	12,104	5.2
EARTH	149.6	365.26 days	23 hours 56 min 4 sec	0.017	12,756	5.5
MARS	227.9	687 days	24 hours 37 min 23 sec	0.093	6,787	3.9
JUPITER	778.3	11.86 years	9 hours 50 min 30 sec	0.048	142,800	1.3
SATURN	1,427	29.46 years	10 hours 14 min	0.056	120,000	0.7
URANUS	2,869	84.0 years	11 hours	0.047	51,800	1.2
NEPTUNE	4,496	164.8 years	16 hours	0.009	49,500	1.7
PLUTO	5,900	247.7 years	6 days 9 hours	0.250	2,300	2.0

Average Chemical Composition of Earth's Crust, Hydrosphere, and Troposphere

ELEMENT (symbol)	CRUST		HYDROSPHERE	TROPOSPHERE
	Percent by Mass	Percent by Volume	Percent by Volume	Percent by Volume
Oxygen (O)	46.40	94.04	33	21
Silicon (Si)	28.15	0.88		
Aluminum (Al)	8.23	0.48		
Iron (Fe)	5.63	0.49		
Calcium (Ca)	4.15	1.18		
Sodium (Na)	2.36	1.11		
Magnesium (Mg)	2.33	0.33		
Potassium (K)	2.09	1.42		
Nitrogen (N)				78
Hydrogen (H)			66	

Earthquake P-wave and S-wave Travel Time

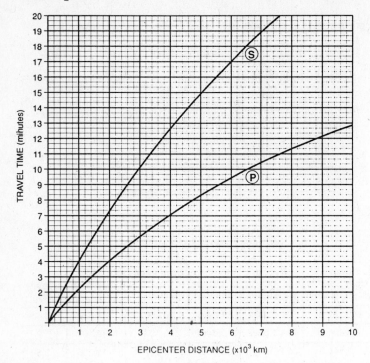

Inferred Properties of Earth's Interior

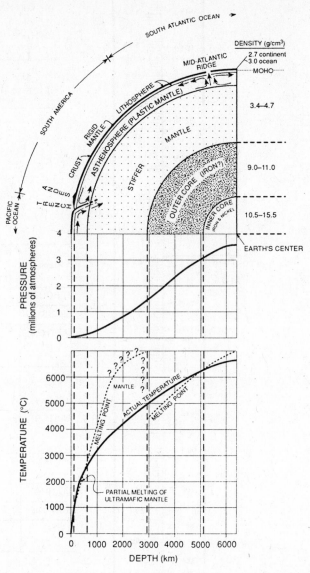

Science, Technology, and Society

The SETI Project: Anyone Out There?

In 1982, a group of the world's foremost astronomers issued the following statement.

"Intelligent organisms are as much a part of the universe as stars and galaxies. It is hard to imagine a more exciting astronomical discovery or one that would have greater impact on human perceptions than the detection of extraterrestrial intelligence."

Ten years later, at 3:00 P.M. on October 12, 1992, the most ambitious hunt for such organisms was launched when astronomer Jill Tarter flipped a switch at Arecibo, Puerto Rico, the site of the world's largest radiotelescope. Tarter is the Project Scientist, or director, of NASA's SETI program. And SETI stands for the pulse-quickening phrase: Search for Extra-Terrestrial Intelligence.

When Tarter threw the switch, the 300-meter-wide aluminum dish at Arecibo began to collect radio waves zipping to Earth from outer space. Scientists expected that most of the radio waves would be irregular and random. Such waves are generated naturally by stars. But what if the telescope, or others that are part of the 10-year SETI project, picked up a signal that was not irregular or random?

Scientists would then set in motion a series of actions to check, recheck, and check again the nature and source of the signals. After careful analysis and confirmation by researchers around the world, a spokesperson for NASA would announce to the world, "We are not alone."

But what would be the significance of such a discovery? According to Arthur C. Clarke, who wrote the best selling novel *2001: A Space Odyssey*, a message from extraterrestrials (or ETs) might "contain answers to almost all the questions our philosophers and scientists have been asking for centuries, and solutions to many of the practical problems that beset mankind."

If this event comes to pass, a great deal of credit will have to go to Cornell University scientists Frank Drake, Giuseppe Cocconi, and Philip Morrison who, in the late 1950s and early 1960s, suggested that a survey of space might turn up signals produced by ETs. Although many other scientists considered this idea far-fetched, the Cornell researchers continued to press for the establishment of a hunt for ETs. As Cocconi and Morrison put it in an article published in 1959, "The probability of success is difficult to estimate, but if we never search, the chance of success is zero."

In the beginning, the search, undertaken by Drake in 1960, was limited to only two stars that were very similar to the sun. Their names were Tau Ceti and Epsilon Eridani and they lay 11 light-years from Earth.

Drake had chosen the stars because he reasoned that sunlike stars would be most likely to possess a planetary system with Earthlike planets. And, as far as he or anyone else knew, life similar to that on Earth could only evolve on a planet like Earth. The logic was sound. But after a short 150-hour search, the results were negative.

Although Drake's search had ended in failure, he and other scientists knew that in the Milky Way galaxy—our home family of stars—there were millions of stars like the sun. Did intelligent beings inhabit one or more of these? To find the answer would require advanced technology, time, money, and very persuasive arguments.

By the late 1970s, such arguments had persuaded officials at NASA to seek funds to launch a search. Many members of Congress were reluctant to allocate money for what they considered foolish endeavors. But the scientists persisted and, finally, $100 million dollars was made available to launch a 10-year full-scale search for ETs.

The money was there. So was the time. What's more, technology not available to Drake three decades earlier was now available. For

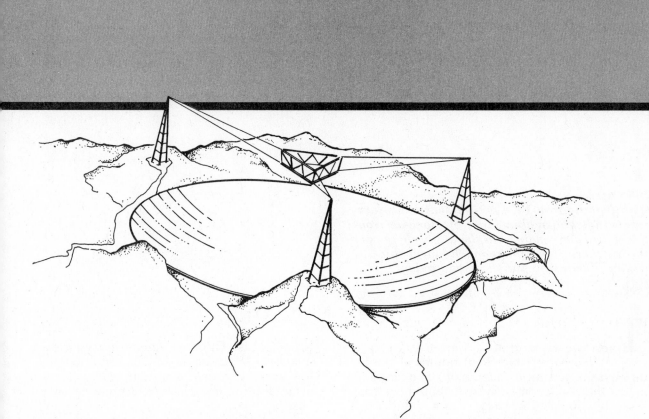

example, Drake had had to painstakingly analyze radio wave data to determine whether it might represent messages from ETs. Today, modern computers can do the job in seconds.

SETI is really a two-part project. One part, the "targeted search," will be carried out by huge radiotelescopes, like the one at Arecibo. Since these telescopes provide a narrow view, they will focus on individual, sunlike stars. These stars—1000 of them—will all be within about 80 light-years of Earth. (Because radio waves travel at the speed of light, and since a light-year is the distance light travels in a year, a message from an ET 80 light-years away would take 80 years to reach us.) The other part, the "sky survey," will be carried out by many smaller radiotelescopes that can scan larger areas of space. These radiotelescopes will systematically survey the rest of the sky.

Should we spend $100 million on the remote chance that we will be able to carry on century-long conversations with ETs or receive descriptions of their civilization? Is $100 million possibly "the biggest bargain in history," as Drake claims. What do you think?

Questions

1. An early pioneer in the search for ETs was
   a. Jill Tarter.   c. Frank Drake.
   b. Arthur C. Clarke.   d. SETI.

2. The "target search" will focus on about
   a. 2 stars.   c. 100 stars.
   b. 10 stars.   d. 1000 stars.

3. If we receive a message from ETs that live 40 light-years from the Earth, that message was sent
   a. 20 years ago.   c. 80 years ago.
   b. 40 years ago.   d. 160 years ago.

4. Distinguish between each part of the SETI project.

5. Explain why you agree, or disagree, with Frank Drake's characterization of SETI as possibly "the biggest bargain in history."

The Ozone Hole: What Made It?

News item:
Washington, April 14, 1993—Satellite measurements indicate an abundance of ozone-destroying chemicals remained in the atmosphere over the Northern Hemisphere much longer this winter than last, researchers said today.

These words, written by Warren E. Leary for *The New York Times*, sent ripples of alarm through the scientific community. The news meant that a phenomenon first sighted over the sparsely populated Antarctic was now lurking over the highly populated regions of North America and Europe, where hundreds of millions of people live. What was the phenomenon? What had caused it? And what could be its consequences?

The answer to the first question is easy. Concentrated in Earth's stratosphere (a layer of atmosphere that extends from 10–50 km above Earth's surface) is a layer of ozone. And something is punching a hole through that ozone layer. But why should anyone care? And what is ozone anyway?

Ozone is a form of oxygen. But unlike oxygen you breathe, which consists of two atoms of oxygen bonded together, a molecule of ozone consists of three atoms of oxygen. This oxygen triplet possesses a unique and important property. It absorbs ultraviolet (UV) radiation streaming in from the sun. So what? you might ask. So this: UV radiation can kill living things. It can also cause skin cancer in human beings.

For a number of years, scientists had known that substances called chlorofluorocarbons (CFCs) were at least partly responsible for destroying ozone high in the sky. And this meant that human beings were also responsible.

That's because CFCs are chemicals we use as coolants in refrigerators and air conditioners. They were also used in various kinds of aerosol cans and in the manufacture of products such as insulating foams.

When CFCs escape into the air—and they do—they rise into the stratosphere where they can survive for 50 to 100 years. During that time, the CFCs break up, releasing free chlorine. The highly reactive chlorine atoms can do two things. They can react with ozone—thinning out the ozone layer—to form a new compound called chlorine monoxide (ClO) or they can react with nitrogen—leaving the ozone layer in one piece—to form chlorine nitrate ($ClONO_2$).

Obviously, as far as people are concerned, a reaction with nitrogen is preferable to one with ozone. But this doesn't happen to a great enough extent, even though there is plenty of nitrogen in the stratosphere. As a matter of fact, about 80 percent of the stratosphere consists of nitrogen. So why doesn't the nitrogen hook on to the chlorine? That's the question many scientists tried to answer.

Initially, researchers investigated strange clouds found in the stratosphere that were tens of kilometers long and a few kilometers thick. They looked like huge red eyes with green pupils. But a study of these clouds revealed that they were made of pure water. They had no ef-

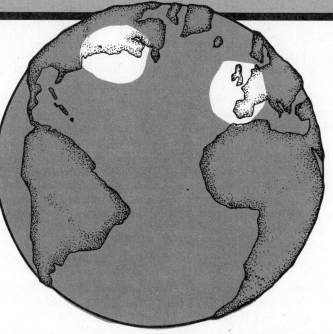

fect on the nitrogen in the stratosphere. There were, however, other clouds in the stratosphere, so thin and so spread out that they were invisible to the unaided eye. What were they made of?

The answer was as startling as it was revealing. These unseeable clouds contained a mixture of water and . . . nitric acid (HNO_3)! The nitrogen that might otherwise have neutralized the chlorine set loose from CFCs was already tied up, which left the chlorine free to break up ozone molecules.

There is general agreement, however, that if we did not pump CFCs into the atmosphere to begin with, no harm would come to the ozone layer. So the ultimate responsibility rests with us, not the clouds above our heads.

What then, can we do to save the ozone layer? What is being done about it? What do you think?

Questions

1. The stratosphere extends above Earth's surface from
   a. 0–10 km.   c. 10–50 km.
   b. 10–20 km.   d. 10–100 km.

2. The ozone layer absorbs
   a. ultraviolet radiation.   c. CFCs.
   b. nitrogen.   d. water.

3. CFCs are used in all the following devices except
   a. refrigerators.   c. aerosol cans.
   b. televisions.   d. air conditioners.

4. Describe how nitrogen might protect the ozone layer and why its effect is limited.

5. On a separate sheet of paper, express your views on what people—or society—might do to protect the ozone layer. Include measures already undertaken by various governments, and a discussion of the impacts of your proposals.

The Gaia Controversy

Early in the 1960s, NASA scientists were eagerly working on one of the most dramatic explorations of space. They were planning the two Viking missions to Mars, which they hoped would answer the question of whether life did exist—or had ever existed—on the rosy-colored planet.

Many experts were consulted to help design the instruments that would hunt for signs of life after the Vikings had settled on the Martian surface. Among these was a British scientist and inventor by the name of James E. Lovelock.

Before Lovelock tackled the problems of instrumentation, he studied data about Martian chemistry that had been gathered by NASA's infrared telescopes. The chemistry of Mars turned out to be very stable. This, concluded Lovelock, was a clear sign that living things did not inhabit Mars. Living things, Lovelock pointed out, constantly change the environment in which they live, as happens on Earth.

The Viking spacecraft, which landed on Mars in 1976, supported Lovelock's conclusion. Instruments aboard the vehicles detected no signs of life. But why were there no living things on Mars? There were a number of answers to that question, the most obvious of which was that it was simply too cold to support life as we know it. Could there be life on Venus, our other planetary neighbor? No, concluded Lovelock. That planet was too hot.

This led Lovelock to ask himself an intriguing question and, in answer, to propose a startling hypothesis. Why, he asked, was Mars too cold, Venus too hot, but Earth just the right temperature to support life?

Lovelock proposed that living things actually controlled the environment of Earth so that it remained supportive of life. Since this kind of control is a property of life—like the way your body automatically controls its temperature—Lovelock further suggested that Earth as a whole behaved as if it were a living organism. Lovelock called this idea the Gaia (GUY-ah) hypothesis, after the Greek goddess of Earth.

Scientists did not dispute the fact that organisms affected Earth's environment. After all, through photosynthesis green plants released oxygen into the air and soaked up carbon dioxide. As a matter of fact, green plants had been responsible for producing the oxygen-rich atmosphere that had made the evolution of oxygen-breathing animals possible.

Just so, Lovelock and his supporters argued. However, they went a step further, one that critics could not accept. The supporters of the Gaia hypothesis proposed that living things on Earth work together to promote an environment that is good for them. Lovelock assigned a kind of *purpose*—almost a consciousness—to the activities of Earth's living community. That is, they act *symbiotically,* or cooperatively, to alter their environment so as to improve their chances of survival. And this the critics could not accept. Among other things, they argued that survival was promoted by competition rather than cooperation.

To get a better idea of what the Gaia hypothesis is all about, consider the following statements, which present currently accepted assumptions about Earth:

- About 3.8 billion years ago, when life began to evolve, the average temperature of Earth was about 23 degrees Celsius.
- The average temperature of Earth today is about 15 degrees Celsius and, within a relatively small range, has remained so for the past 3.8 billion years.
- The sun has burned hotter as time has passed.
- Earth now receives 25–30 percent more heat and light from the sun than it did 3.8 billion years ago.

Question: How could the temperature of Earth remain relatively constant while heat from the sun increased?

Question: Did the evolution of life somehow keep Earth cooler than it otherwise would have been?

According to the Gaia hypothesis, the questions can be answered as follows. We have evi-

dence that about 4 billion years ago—prior to the evolution of life on Earth—the atmosphere held great amounts of carbon dioxide, perhaps up to 98%. Today, Earth's atmosphere is only 0.03% carbon dioxide. Since this gas is known to allow sunlight to pass through to Earth's surface, but to limit heat from escaping from the surface, an abundance of carbon dioxide in Earth's early atmosphere should have caused Earth's temperature to rise.

According to the best evidence we have, the first living things to evolve on Earth were bacteria. And, like living things to follow, bacteria required carbon atoms to build chemicals vital to their survival, like proteins and enzymes. Where did the bacteria get the carbon they needed? From the carbon dioxide in the atmosphere. What's more, the green algae that were soon to evolve also pulled carbon out of the air. By doing this, these organisms lowered the percentage of carbon dioxide in the atmosphere and, therefore, reduced the average temperature of Earth, making it a better place for more complex living things to evolve.

Thus, the chemical activities of early forms of life made possible the evolution and survival of later forms of life. But if the bacteria and algae used up all the carbon dioxide, they could not survive. How, then, was carbon dioxide kept in the air? Animals, whose existence had been made possible by the bacteria and algae, cooperated by exhaling carbon dioxide into the atmosphere.

Can living things regulate Earth's environment for their own benefit? Have they done so in the past? And if they've done so, need we worry about such things as pollution? Or can we count on living things to automatically set our environment right? What do you think?

Questions

1. About 3.8 billion years ago, the average temperature of the Earth was
   a. 2°C.   c. 23°C.
   b. 15°C.   d. 72°C.

2. The percentage of carbon dioxide in the Earth's atmosphere today is about
   a. 0.   c. 0.3.
   b. 0.03.   d. 98.

3. The first living things to evolve on Earth were
   a. bacteria.   c. animals.
   b. green algae.   d. human beings.

4. What led James Lovelock to assume no life existed on Mars?

5. On a separate sheet of paper, give your views of the Gaia hypothesis. Do library research to find data and arguments to support your position. Include references to these data and arguments.

Doomsday Rocks: Cause for Concern?

Its name is Swift-Tuttle. It's 10 km wide. It's a comet that sweeps by Earth about every 130 years. And, like a few other comets and some asteroids, it crosses Earth's orbit from time to time. The next time Swift-Tuttle is scheduled to do this is sometime in July of the year 2126. If the date turns out to be July 26, look out! Why? That's the date when Earth will be near the same point in its orbit where the comet would cross. Result? Collision!

However, according to comet and asteroid expert Brian G. Marsden of the Smithsonian Astrophysical Observatory in Cambridge, Massachusetts, Swift-Tuttle should cross Earth's orbit on July 20, 2126 not on July 26. If Marsden's prediction is accurate, your great-great-grandchildren will have nothing to worry about. Earth will be about 24 million kilometers away when Swift-Tuttle visits.

But the paths of comets are not always easy to predict. Swift-Tuttle itself gave Marsden a hard time. In 1973, he had predicted its return to the vicinity of Earth in 1981 or 1992, depending on the effects of different variables.

The year 1981 came and went and Swift-Tuttle failed to show up. Time passed as Marsden and other astronomers kept an eye on the sky in search of the tardy Swift-Tuttle. Then, on September 27, 1992, the comet was spotted against the background of the Big Dipper's stars. Marsden recalculated the date the comet would reach a point closest to the sun, or *perihelion*, which is a kind of landmark for comets. According to Marsden's best estimate, the date would be November 25, 1992.

But as Swift-Tuttle whizzed through space, something unseen happened. Perhaps it may have been one or more bursts of gas from the comet, triggered by heat from the sun. Like the effects of rockets on a space vehicle, these bursts of gas altered the path of Swift-Tuttle. Result? The comet reached perihelion on December 12 instead of November 25.

Marsden was unconcerned. As he put it, "A 17-day error out of 130 years is good enough for me." But if a similar error occurs in the year 2126, will it be good enough for Earth's inhabitants of that time?

This brings up a key question. Why should we worry about a comet or asteroid hitting Earth? Scientists explain that a collision with even a small comet or asteroid, say one-half kilometer across, would cause an explosion with a force equal to more than one million tons of TNT! That's equivalent to 50 times the force of the atom bomb that completely wiped out the Japanese city of Hiroshima at the end of World War II.

Has such a natural explosion ever rocked Earth? Yes, say many scientists, about 65 million years ago. If the scientists are correct, and there is mounting evidence to support their view, such a collision and explosion may have caused the extinction of thousands of species including the dinosaurs.

But we don't have to go back millions of years to find evidence of such explosions. On June 30, 1908, vast areas of forest along the Tunguska River in Siberia were leveled and charred, along with the animals who lived there. Evidence points to a "rock from space" as the culprit.

In fact, impacts like this happen every 100 years or so. What's more, near misses occur even more frequently. In January, 1991, an asteroid zipped past Earth only about 160,000 km away. What's disturbing is that the asteroid was discovered only a few hours before its brush with our planet.

For all of these reasons, many astronomers are urging that a comet and asteroid watch system be set up. This would consist of five special telescopes positioned around the world. These telescopes would be designed to spot comets and asteroids. The orbits of these objects would be quickly determined to find out whether they were headed our way. Such a system of observatories might give us a few year's warning of a comet or asteroid whose path led directly to Earth. Armed with this information we might be able to head off the collision. How?

A number of ideas have been proposed. Among these would be sending a space vehicle to the comet or asteroid. The vehicle could deposit a rocket on the "rock" which, when fired, would alter its orbit so it would miss Earth. Another idea is to explode a nuclear bomb on one side of the space rock, again pushing it out of its path toward Earth.

Setting up a tracking system to spot doomsday rocks would take millions of dollars—your family's tax dollars. Should we spend the money to possibly avoid an event that might not occur in your lifetime, or in the lifetime of your children, or grandchildren? What do you think?

Questions

1. Swift-Tuttle crosses Earth's orbit about once every
   a. 13 years.
   b. 130 years.
   c. 1300 years.
   d. 2126 years.

2. Perihelion is the point in space when a moving object like a comet is
   a. closest to Earth.
   b. farthest from Earth.
   c. closest to the sun.
   d. farthest from the sun.

3. Scientists estimate that a collision between a "rock from space" and Earth, like the one that occurred in Siberia in 1908, occurs on average every
   a. 10 years.
   b. 100 years.
   c. 1000 years.
   d. 10,000 years.

4. What do many scientists believe happened 65 million years ago?

5. On a separate sheet of paper, express your views on whether an expensive comet and asteroid watching system should be installed around the world. Back up your views with appropriate data.

Electricity From Space: A Bright Idea?

Electricity provides energy to light homes and cities and to run factories and businesses. In a real sense it is the energy of progress—the energy that improves our standard of living. Yet we pay a price for that energy. And the price involves more than dollars and cents.

According to many scientists, the price we pay is the pollution of our environment. That's because much of our electricity is generated in a process that starts with the burning of coal or oil. The by-products of this burning include carbon dioxide, which may cause Earth to heat up, and gases containing sulfur, which irritate people's eyes and skin, and cause acid rain.

Although there are sources of "clean" electricity, such as flowing water used to run hydroelectric power plants, windmills that run electric generators, and arrays of solar panels that convert sunlight into electricity, none of these sources has been able to satisfy the energy needs of the world's people. And as the population of our planet grows, the problem of providing people with the energy they need will grow also.

As engineer Peter Glaser puts it, "In 2030 there will be 8 billion people in the world" who will be seeking a standard of living like the one we now enjoy and "the only thing stopping them will be energy," or the lack of it.

But if this energy will not be available on Earth, will the world's people have to settle for lower standards of living? No, says Glaser. There's plenty of energy in space. All we have to do is find a way to collect it and transport it to Earth.

The energy is contained in sunlight. If you had a bucket whose bottom had a surface area of one square meter, you could gather 1400 joules per second of solar energy in space. And if you could transmit that power continuously to your home, you could run your stereo and every other appliance in your house—not to mention its lights—indefinitely.

That's one of the reasons why Peter Glaser advocates putting solar power satellites (SPSs) in space. If an SPS were positioned 36,000 km above Earth in a stationary orbit, it would be in almost constant sunshine. Photovoltaic solar cells could convert that sunlight into electricity. In turn, the electricity would be converted into microwaves, like those produced in a microwave oven. Like all electromagnetic waves, microwaves could be beamed down to an antenna on Earth. Once down there, the microwaves can be reconverted into electricity and fed into power grids serving large areas of Earth.

Although the principle is simple, the engineering feats required to make it work in practice are considerable. For example, engineers estimate that for an SPS to be a practical source of electricity for Earth dwellers it would have to have a surface area of about 55 square kilometers, or about the area of Manhattan Island. Moreover, by the time the spreading beam of microwaves reached Earth, it would cover an area the size of a medium-sized city. A receiving antenna would have to be the same size. And land would have to be set aside for the device, which would look like a huge oval dish.

Regardless of the problems, Glaser believes that SPSs will end up being a major source of electricity in the 21st Century. He proposes that the development of the technology should advance in steps. A first step might be to design an SPS that would provide electricity for the planned space station, *Freedom*. And if people go back to the moon, a second step might be to build an SPS to provide the moon colony with electricity. Along the way, engineers would have opportunities to solve SPS problems as they arise.

This idea of clean energy from the sky may sound good—and it may be good—but it is not without its detractors. At least three concerns have been expressed by critics: (1) When the microwaves knife through Earth's upper atmosphere they will heat it up. What effects would this have? (2) How will beams of microwaves affect television and radio signals on Earth? (3) How would the incoming microwaves affect living things, including people, near the receiving antennas?

Should we spend millions of dollars on building SPSs in space? Do the problems and concerns associated with such a project outweigh its potential benefits? Or do the potential benefits to the world's people and their environment make going ahead with such a program worthwhile, even essential? What do you think?

Questions

1. In the year 2030, the number of people on Earth will be about
   a. 8 million.
   b. 8 billion.
   c. 80 million.
   d. 80 billion.

2. Each square meter just above Earth's atmosphere receives about
   a. 140 joules per second of solar energy.
   b. 1400 joules per second of solar energy.
   c. 14,000 joules per second of solar energy.
   d. 140,000 joules per second of solar energy.

3. As it approaches Earth from space, a beam of microwaves
   a. spreads out.
   b. narrows down.
   c. is unchanged.
   d. first spreads out and then narrows down.

4. What are three concerns expressed by critics of SPSs that beam microwaves to Earth?

5. On a separate sheet of paper, give your views on whether we should invest tax dollars in the development of SPSs. Give reasons for your position.

Turning Darkness to Dawn: Should We?

"It was nothing I'd ever seen before. First, there was a pulsating object that flashed very bright every one and a half seconds, which I'm sure was the *Banner* spacecraft tumbling through space." The words were those of astronomer Terence Dickinson of St. Lawrence College in Kingston, Ontario, as reported in *The New York Times* on February 5, 1993.

The spacecraft, called *Znamya* by its Russian builders—*Banner* in English—was basically nothing more than an aluminum disc 20 meters in diameter, equipped with a motor. Originally folded up like a Japanese fan, it had been part of the space cargo ship *Progress*, which had been sent on a resupply mission to Russia's *Mir* space station.

After the two cosmonauts aboard the *Mir* unloaded the supplies they needed, the *Progress* separated from the space station and deployed *Banner*. *Banner's* motor unfolded the "fan" and, through commands from Earth, rockets aboard *Progress* positioned *Banner* so it would reflect sunlight to Earth's surface. And that's what Terence Dickinson reported seeing in the early morning sky.

If that were all *Banner* was about, you might shrug your shoulders and think, "So what?" What good is a mirror in space anyway? After all, you could hardly use it to make sure your hair was combed.

That's true. However, *Banner* was not put in space for cosmetic purposes. It was put there to test a concept that could literally change the face of Earth, or, at least, part of its face. As project engineer Nikolai N. Sevastyanov put it: "The reflector was a big success because it proved the concept was right." But to what concept was the Russian engineer referring?

The concept was as dramatic as it was simple. Its aim was to turn night into day or, at least, a kind of twilight. But for what purpose? To illuminate ballparks? To shed light on high crime areas in big cities? To make night driving safer on interstate highways? Although these ideas may have merit, the Russian designers of *Banner* had something else in mind.

They envisioned a reflector many kilometers in diameter; one which would be controlled by a guidance system that would allow it to throw a huge beam of sunlight onto a given spot on the nightside of Earth. For the chosen spot, this would bring daylight saving time on a grand scale.

The advantages? Energy use in the area would plummet because people would not have to use as much electricity to light homes, businesses, and factories. Crops would get higher doses of sunlight. They would grow faster and yield more food. Growing seasons would also be stretched out, and perhaps more than one crop could be harvested a season. Food would be more plentiful and more of the world's people would be better fed.

So what's the downside? First of all, what parts of the world will be chosen for the night-to-day treatment? Who would do the choosing? And what would be the criteria for the choices? How would the local environment be affected by fiddling with nature's day-night cycle? And what would be the effect on the behavior of people robbed of regular periods of darkness? Would the change affect their behavior in some unwanted way?

The Russian experiment seems to indicate that the technology to turn night into day is likely to be available soon. Their next step is to put a 200-meter-diameter mirror into space, provided they can raise the millions of rubles needed to do so.

But will the ultimate goal do more good for society than harm? What factors should be considered before investing more money in the

program, part of which the Russians are seeking from western companies, including some in the United States? What do you think?

Questions

1. The *Banner* space vehicle was used to
   a. bring supplies to a space station.
   b. carry two cosmonauts.
   c. reflect sunlight to Earth.
   d. send TV signals to Earth.

2. When deployed, the *Banner* space vehicle's diameter was
   a. 2 m.
   b. 20 m.
   c. 200 m.
   d. 2000 m.

3. The goal of the program pioneered by *Banner* is to
   a. increase crop production and energy use.
   b. decrease crop production and energy use.
   c. increase crop production and decrease energy use.
   d. decrease crop production and increase energy use.

4. What problems would have to be investigated before the *Banner* concept was put into effect?

5. On a separate sheet of paper, describe actions you would propose be taken before making a commitment to build and launch a huge version of the *Banner* space vehicle.

Can a Little Child Help Predict the Weather?

Meteorologists call him El Niño, or "little boy" in Spanish, and her La Niña, or "little girl." Both grow up in the Pacific Ocean. And, if scientists are correct, detecting the growth of one or the other can lead to weather predictions months, or even a few years, in advance.

As you might guess, El Niño and La Niña are not human. To find out what they are and how they affect the weather, you've got to take a long journey to the western part of the Pacific Ocean. Let's say you did this in the spring of 1991. You would have found a huge patch of warm water above Australia that stretched eastward for a few thousand kilometers.

As weeks passed, you would have noticed that the winds that normally blow from east to west over the Pacific were becoming weaker. Result? You would have observed the patch of warm water slowly drifting eastward. By June, waters to the east that only a few months earlier had been relatively cool would have become 1°C to 1.5°C warmer.

You might well have predicted that the ominous patch of warm water would arrive off the coast of South America by December, 1991. If you had done this, your prediction would have agreed with that of a number of scientists who call such an event, which occurs every four to seven years, an El Niño.

Was El Niño really on the way in the spring of 1991? To scientists, this was a very important question, since in the past the coming of an El Niño heralded dramatic changes in weather patterns in different parts of the world, including the United States. Two years earlier, computers at Columbia University's Lamont-Doherty Geological Observatory in Palisades, New York had predicted that an El Niño would indeed arrive in late 1991. Computers at other institutions had, however, come up with other predictions.

Then in November of 1991 great thunderstorms began to rumble over the eastern Pacific Ocean. El Niños are thought to trigger such atmospheric disturbances. The storms prompted Chester Ropelewski of the National Meteorological Center in Camp Springs, Maryland to venture, "From the observations, it looks as though we're in the middle of a warm event," or an El Niño.

You might think that a "warm event" is something to look forward to. Certainly, beaches bathed in warm water are attractive to surfers and other lovers of sand and sea. But an El Niño brings more than warm water to a nearby coastline. And what it brings may not be welcome at all.

First of all, El Niño's thunderstorms change the atmosphere in predictable, but troubling ways. The storms transport heat from the ocean's surface into Earth's atmosphere. As the heat rises it runs into great streams of air that constantly move around Earth from west to east. These rivers of air are called jet streams. And the heat changes the course of their flow.

This might be of little consequence except for the fact that jet streams control the movements of large masses of air across the world. Some of these masses are wet and warm. Others are dry and cold. As you know from personal experience, the arrival of a wet and warm air mass over your head brings different kinds of weather than the arrival of a dry and cold air mass. So El Niño affects local weather. What's more, since jet streams circle the globe, the effects of El Niño are felt all over the world.

Although by Thanksgiving of 1991 El Niño had not yet arrived off the coast of South America, weather forecasters of the National Weather Service became convinced it was on its way. Based on this conviction, the agency issued a long-range weather forecast for the coming few months. The prediction included heavy rains along the Gulf Coast and southeast sections of the United States. The northern part of the continent, the forecasters said, would be abnormally warm. What happened?

During the winter, heavy rains drenched parts of the southern United States. For example, between December and February, 25 inches of it poured down on south-central Texas. As a matter of fact, the amount of rain that fell on Texas was double what it would normally be. And "sunny California" seemed also to be a victim of El Niño. Within 10 days in February, three storms dumped 8 inches of rain on Los Angeles. Reports of still heavier rains came from the mountains to the east of the city.

Up north—from Alaska east through Canada—people were enjoying an unusually warm December. Many inhabitants of these usually cold regions tapped thermometers to make sure the instruments were recording correct temperatures, which were 3°C to 7°C above average.

People in other parts of the world were also feeling the effects of El Niño. Australia and India were abnormally dry. So was southeastern Africa. But wet weather drenched the usually dry northwest coast of South America. El Niño had turned the weather in these places upside down. The predictions of scientists had turned out to be correct.

But of what benefit are such long-range weather forecasts? Ropelewski suggests that farmers who normally plant crops that thrive in relatively dry weather could switch to water-loving crops when an El Niño is scheduled to deliver torrents of rain. And people who live in areas slated for unusually dry weather could take measures to lessen the effects of droughts.

By now you're probably wondering about the other "child" in this story, La Niña. What is "she?" La Niñas pop up when winds from the east blow more and more strongly, pulling up cold, deep water off the coast of South America and driving it toward the west. By late June, 1992 this was exactly what was happening. What kind of weather does La Niña bring to Australia, India, southeast Africa, and the northern and southern parts of the United States? What do you think?

Questions

1. When El Niño arrives in parts of the Pacific Ocean, the temperature of the water
   a. stays the same.
   b. increases by 1°C–1.5°C.
   c. decreases by 1°C–1.5°C.
   d. increases by 3°C–7°C.

2. El Niños occur every
   a. 1–3 years.
   b. 2–4 years.
   c. 3–5 years.
   d. 4–7 years.

3. You would expect a La Niña to bring weather that is
   a. the same as that brought by an El Niño.
   b. opposite to that brought by an El Niño.
   c. similar but less severe than that brought by an El Niño.
   d. similar but more severe than that brought by an El Niño.

4. How do El Niños affect weather over land?

5. On a separate sheet of paper, explain how knowledge of El Niños and La Niñas may be used to benefit society.

The Greenhouse Effect: Is It Black and White?

The greenhouse effect, that global warming due to an increase of carbon dioxide and certain other gases in the atmosphere, is coming! Or is it?

Arguments rage on both sides of this issue. And since the effects of global warming could be devastating to life on our planet, the issue has to be carefully examined so that the world's citizens can make informed decisions—decisions that could have far-reaching environmental, social, and economic impact.

To evaluate the dangers of a greenhouse effect, you must take into consideration three basic factors: (1) the causes of the greenhouse effect; (2) data that supports or refutes the idea that the greenhouse effect is actually happening; and (3) the evaluation of feedback processes, or events that tend to increase or decrease global warming.

First of all, we can agree—along with all scientists—on two facts: primarily due to the burning of fossil fuels, greenhouse gases (mostly carbon dioxide) are building up in the atmosphere, and these gases trap heat near the planet's surface, which *tends* to increase Earth's temperature. But has the temperature actually increased and, if so, has the increase been because of the greenhouse effect?

There's no question that the amount of carbon dioxide in the atmosphere has increased since the beginning of the Industrial Revolution in the 19th century. As a matter of fact, the amount of carbon dioxide in the air has jumped 25 percent by mass in the last 100 years. And the concentration of other greenhouse gases has also gone up.

According to some scientists, this should have produced an increase in average global temperatures of between 0.75°C and 1.5°C. The actual figure is 0.5°C. Nevertheless, some researchers say, any increase in global temperatures is a concern because such increases could trigger positive feedback processes that would speed the warming trend. But what's a feedback process and how does it work?

You don't have to look farther than your own body for examples. For instance, one feedback process in your body stimulates perspiration as your body's temperature increases above normal, say, when you are exercising on a hot day. This is a *negative* feedback because it tends to reverse, or work against, the warming trend.

In this example, a negative feedback is healthy. If the feedback was *positive*, however, your temperature would soar and you would be in danger of passing out from heat stroke. This is the kind of feedback that worries scientists who believe a dangerous greenhouse effect is coming.

Let's examine some positive feedback processes that might aggravate the greenhouse effect. As carbon dioxide builds up in the atmosphere, temperatures would begin to increase near Earth's surface. Water from the world's oceans begins to evaporate at an increasing rate. This water vapor traps more heat, and global temperatures would get a boost upward.

Vast sheets of glistening white ice begin to melt in the Arctic and Antarctic, reducing the amount of heat and light they reflect away from Earth's surface. The uncovered land and water absorb more heat and grow still warmer.

As the frozen arctic tundra warms, the water trapped in its soil melts. Under these conditions, organic matter in the soil begins to oxidize. In the process, huge amounts of methane gas are produced and released into the air. Methane is a powerful greenhouse gas. The temperature climbs still higher.

The heat begins to dry out other parts of the world, including areas where great numbers of green plants thrive. These plants don't grow as well, and insect pests gobble up many that are weakened by drought. Fires devastate vast parched forests and grasslands. Since plants remove carbon dioxide from the air during photo-

synthesis, this reduction in plant life allows even more of the gas to build up in the atmosphere.

What could be the result of all these positive feedbacks? An uncontrollable, runaway greenhouse effect that, according to a report of Japan's Advisory Panel on Environment and Culture, could "... cause the destruction of the entire planet and every living thing on it." But will nature and people conspire to hold back or reverse the greenhouse effect?

Certainly, people can help by doing such things as regulating the use of fossil fuels, by preventing the cutting down of forests for lumber, by controlling population growth, and by limiting the growing of rice and the raising of cattle (two activities that add methane to the atmosphere). But critic S. Fred Singer of the Science and Environmental Policy Project in Washington, D.C., says that such activities could condemn "billions [of people] to continued poverty, starvation and misery." This would be especially tragic if the greenhouse effect were never to happen. More studies and much patience are needed before such measures should be undertaken, urge the critics.

Of course, scientists and environmentalists who see the greenhouse effect as becoming uncontrollable if something is not done to check it soon say we can't wait. What do you think?

Questions

1. Since the beginning of the Industrial Revolution, the amount of carbon dioxide in the atmosphere has
   a. increased by 25%.
   b. decreased by 25%.
   c. remained unchanged.
   d. become zero.

2. During the past 100 years, the average global temperature has
   a. been unchanged.
   b. increased 0.5°C.
   c. increased 0.75°C.
   d. increased 1.5°C.

3. Perspiring on a hot day is an example of
   a. positive feedback.
   b. negative feedback.
   c. neither positive nor negative feedback.
   d. the greenhouse effect.

4. Explain how the shrinking of polar ice caps produces positive feedback.

5. On a separate sheet of paper, describe those governmental policies you would support concerning the greenhouse effect. Explain why you would support those policies.

Beaches: Should We Leave Them Alone?

In the winter of 1992–93, a series of powerful storms battered the east coast of the United States. Thundering waves unleashed tremendous torrents of energy on beaches along the coasts of New Jersey and New York. Beaches vanished. Homes were swept away. Pounding seas driven by ferocious winds cut new inlets where none had existed before.

Homeowners, merchants, and local politicians called for relief. Many asked that protective barriers be erected to hold back the sea when future storms strike. To many people, placing such barriers on beaches made sense. To others, including some geologists who specialize in beach erosion, putting up barriers was an invitation to disaster. How come?

Beaches, like other landforms, are changed by *erosion,* or wearing away by wind and moving water. Some of the changes are triggered by natural events like storms, the ebb and flow of tides, and the steady lapping of waves. These forces often strip away sand in one place only to deposit it somewhere else.

In most cases, such erosion and deposition tends to preserve beaches over time. But when people interfere with these natural processes, an unbalanced erosion can occur that destroys beaches, perhaps forever.

What kinds of human activities speed up erosion of beaches? Anything that interferes with the movement of sand along or onto a coastline.

This happens, for instance, when people build rock jetties that jut into the sea. Although the jetties produce relatively calm water for harbors and vacationers, they block the migration of sand along a coastline, say, from north to south. Beaches to the north still lose their sand, but beaches to the south that would ordinarily gain this sand are blocked from getting it by the jetties.

Similarly, any kind of construction, such as a home or parking lot, that is built too close to the water of a beach may keep the sands from migrating naturally.

Sometimes sand robbers are located far from beaches. For example, some beaches get their sand from rivers and creeks that constantly sweep *silt,* fine grains of eroded rock, toward the sea. When such rivers are dammed to produce hydroelectricity, or the bottoms and sides of creeks are paved with concrete to inhibit flooding, the flow of silt is interrupted. The sand of the beaches that is carried away by natural forces is not replenished and the beaches shrink.

Clearly, we need electricity, we can't put up with flooding rivers and creeks, and we should have the right to build homes near the shoreline. But what about a beach's right to *its* sand? Should that be protected too? Put another way, don't the beaches belong to all of us and, if so, shouldn't something be done to protect our right to have beaches?

A beach's right to its sand and our right to enjoy unspoiled beaches is a concern of Los Angeles lawyer Katherine E. Stone. Ms. Stone suggests that "certain kinds of resources are held in common for everyone under a trust. Those resources include the air, the sea, fish swimming in the sea, and the shore of the sea as well."

In recent years, local, state, and federal governments have recognized such rights by passing laws or instituting regulations that require builders not to interfere with the natural flow of sand or, if they do, to replace the sand at their own expense. This, of course, increases the cost of construction, electricity, and flood control, which people have to pay for when they buy products or pay taxes.

What's more, some people say such laws and regulations are unconstitutional. What happens, they say, if a person buys a piece of oceanfront land and then is not permitted to build on it. The value of the land plummets and the person loses a lot of money. Isn't this the same as the government taking land and not compensating the owner for it, which is a violation of the Fifth Amendment to the U.S. Constitution?

No, say supporters of beach erosion control. The government isn't taking the land. It is only regulating how the land can be used.

Clearly, this is a complex issue with reasonable arguments on both sides. Which arguments make more sense? What do you think?

Questions

1. A rock jetty causes erosion by
   a. wearing away a beach.
   b. protecting a harbor.
   c. controlling floods.
   d. preventing the movement of sand.

2. One source of sand is silt from
   a. rivers.   c. jetties.
   b. dams.   d. storms.

3. Katherine E. Stone believes
   a. people should build homes where they want.
   b. a beach has a right to its sand.
   c. builders should not have to replace sand.
   d. the Fifth Amendment is unconstitutional.

4. With regard to beaches, what are some causes of natural and unnatural erosion?

5. Look up the Fifth Amendment to the U.S. Constitution. On a separate sheet of paper identify the part that applies to the protection of beaches. Then look up the Supreme Court decision of 1992 in the case of *Lucas* v. *South Carolina Coastal Commission*. Explain why you do or do not agree with the Supreme Court's decision.

Ice Ages: What Gets Them Started?

They've come before. They're scheduled to come again—and soon. But this time something will be different. This time great civilizations, billions of people, and some of the world's finest cities will be in the way.

"They" are 3000-meter-thick tongues of ice that, although they creep along the ground at a snail's pace, can level everything in their paths. Last time, that meant grass, shrubs, and trees. Next time it could mean the twin spires of the World Trade Center in New York City, the soaring Sears Tower in Chicago, and all the other buildings in between.

These tongues of ice are the shock troops of an ice age. By about 20,000 years ago they had advanced almost halfway from Earth's polar regions toward the equator. They never got that far. But in the Northern Hemisphere they did not stop their march until they had reached points a third of the way down the East Coast and as far down in the Midwest as the Ohio River. What gave them the order to march? Can we countermand that order?

About 70 years ago, a Serbian astronomer by the name of Milutin Milankovitch proposed a hypothesis which suggested that ice ages are caused by motions of Earth in space. The motions, said Milankovich, affect how intensely sunlight falls on the northern and southern hemispheres of Earth and, hence, the temperatures of these hemispheres. When the temperatures drop, ice ages follow. Conversely, when the temperatures rise, ice ages end.

Milankovitch identified three motions of Earth that could cause such fluctuations in temperature. The first is a change in the angle of Earth's tilt on its axis. It's now about 23.5 degrees. But it varies from 21.5 degrees to 24.5 degrees, making one complete cycle every 41,000 years. The greater the tilt, the greater the difference in winter and summer temperatures.

The second motion involves a change in the shape of Earth's orbit from more elliptical to almost circular. When the orbit becomes more elliptical—which happens every 100,000 years—the distance between Earth and the sun in one season, say winter in the northern hemisphere, is greater than when the orbit is more circular. This would make for colder winters.

Finally, the third motion is a kind of wobble that affects Earth as it spins. A complete wobble takes 23,000 years. Taken together, the wobble and the shape of Earth's orbit either maximize or minimize the amount of sunlight that strikes the northern and southern hemispheres.

As geologists Wallace S. Broecker and George H. Denton put it in an article in the January, 1990 issue of *Scientific American:* "When these . . . controllers of seasonality reinforce each other in one hemisphere, they oppose each other in the opposite hemisphere." That is, there would be times when winter and summer temperatures in North America would vary more greatly than they would in South America. At such time, winter snows could pile up to great depths in North America and would not melt over the summer. As time passed, the weight of the snow would compress it into ice that would spread southward in a new ice age.

These three factors, suggested Milankovitch, produced the ice ages. What's more, Milankovitch proposed that the timing of these factors should produce ice ages at regular intervals of 23,000, 41,000, and 100,000 years. Based on the analysis of sediments brought up from the ocean bottom—which provide clues concerning when Earth was covered with the most and least ice—Broecker and Denton report: "Over the past 800,000 years, the global ice volume has peaked every 100,000 years . . . In addition, 'wrinkles' superimposed on each [100,000-year] cycle . . . have come at intervals of roughly 23,000 and 41,000 years. . . ."

The Milankovitch hypothesis, as it had come to be known, seemed to be supported by the ocean-bottom data. Then in October of 1992 came evidence that questioned the validity of this hypothesis.

The evidence had been gathered by a team of scientists at an open, water-filled fault zone called Devils Hole in south-central Nevada. The team, lead by Isaac J. Winograd of the

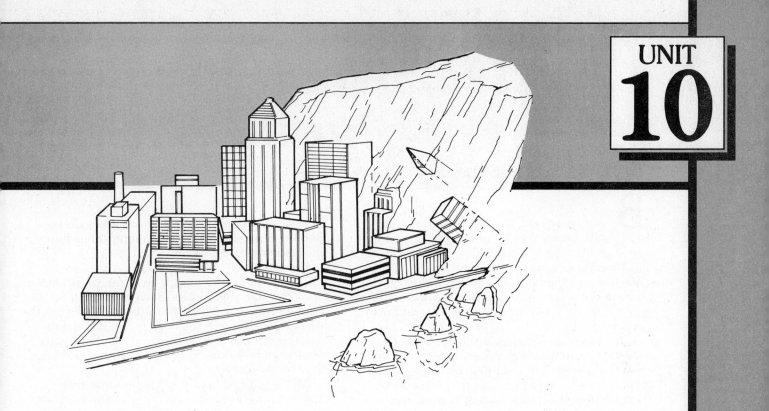

United States Geological Survey, had obtained a core of a mineral called calcite from underwater rock, deep in Devils Hole. Scuba divers had brought the 36-centimeter-long core, a cylinder about the size and shape of the cardboard tube in a roll of paper toweling, from about 30 meters under the water.

The core held deposits of calcite that had been laid down between 60,000 and 560,000 years ago. By analyzing 285 samples of the core taken every 1.26 mm along its length, the researchers were able to date increases and decreases in ice that had occurred on Earth's surface over the 500,000-year period. (Each slice of the core represented a period of about 1,800 years.)

Result? Oddly, some northern hemisphere ice ages appeared to end at times when sunlight was *weakest* in that region. According to the Milankovitch hypothesis, that should have been a time when the ice ages were beginning. Moreover, the length of the ice ages did not follow the cycles of Earth's motions in space.

Whose data was correct? And what did they mean? The scientific jury is still out on both questions. However, Winograd suggests that the data gathered by his team points to a complex interaction of Earth's atmosphere, oceans, and other factors as the cause of ice ages. If this is true, then human activities, such as those that pump greenhouse gases into the atmosphere, may bring on or prevent the next ice age.

Could we interfere with nature by deliberately creating a greenhouse effect? Should we? What do you think?

Questions

1. The tilt of Earth's axis varies between
   a. 0 and 21.5 degrees.
   b. 21.5 and 23.5 degrees.
   c. 21.5 and 24.5 degrees.
   d. 45.0 and 90.0 degrees.

2. A complete cycle in Earth's "wobble" takes
   a. 100,000 years.
   b. 41,000 years.
   c. 23,000 years.
   d. 500,000 years.

3. Data gathered at Devils Hole
   a. supported the Milankovitch hypothesis.
   b. refuted the Milankovitch hypothesis.
   c. had nothing to do with ice ages.
   d. was gathered from the ocean bottom.

4. What is the Milankovitch hypothesis?

5. On a separate sheet of paper, suggest what could be done to avert the next ice age. Discuss other implications of your suggestion.

Nuclear Waste: Where Should It Go?

By the year 2000, 48,000 tons of nuclear waste will have piled up in temporary storage areas around the United States. These wastes are by-products of both the military weapons industry and the civilian nuclear industry. Among other things, the wastes contain radioactive plutonium, one of the deadliest chemical poisons on Earth.

For decades, the United States government has been searching for a "permanent" resting place for these "hot" substances. And permanent means a lot of years. Why a lot of years? The isotope of plutonium that is used in nuclear bombs and in nuclear power plants—Pu-239—has an extremely long half-life of 24,100 years. That means that half of the Pu-239 placed in storage today will still be producing lethal radioactivity 24,100 years from now.

By the early 1990s, the search had narrowed down to a barren hump of land in southwestern Nevada called Yucca Mountain. The site was picked for a number of reasons.

For one thing, the mountain—really a long ridge—is fairly far from a populated area. The nearest city, bustling Las Vegas, is 90 miles to the southeast, and hardly anyone lives in between.

For another thing, the area is extremely dry. On average, only 6 inches of rain fall on the dusty slopes of Yucca Mountain each year. And almost all of that evaporates in the blazing Nevada sun. Only about one fiftieth of an inch of the precipitation soaks into the soil. Since moisture would tend to corrode the barrels in which the wastes were stored, its absence increases the likelihood of the containers staying in one piece.

Finally, Yucca Mountain rock is rich in a family of minerals called zeolites. And zeolites possess a property that make them ideal as a safe-deposit "box" for radioactive materials. The zeolites bind, or hang on to, such materials.

Okay, so let's start shipping all those tons of radioactive waste to Yucca Mountain. Not so fast, say critics of the plan, as well as four out of five citizens of Nevada. What gives these people cause for concern? Among other things, the geology of the region.

If you visited the area around Yucca Mountain, a number of geologic features would catch your eye. One would be Busted Butte, a strange hill rising out of the desert to the southeast. Why strange? It's only half a hill. Long ago the other half was destroyed by an earthquake. In addition, to the west you would spot four old volcanoes.

All this might lead you to conclude that Yucca Mountain lies in an active geological region, and you would be correct. But would this pose a danger to the storage facility and, in turn, to the people of Nevada?

Yes, declares engineering geologist Jerry Szymanski, Yucca Mountain's most vocal critic. Szymanski points to veins of a mineral called calcite that snake up and down through the rock of Yucca Mountain. These veins, insists Szymanski, were deposited by groundwater rising from below the mountain through cracks caused by earthquakes and other geologic activity.

Says Szymanski, "Groundwater will rise again in the next 10,000 years. It is as certain as death." And when the groundwater floods the storage areas in the mountain, the plutonium-containing barrels would corrode, eventually leaking their deadly contents into the environment.

Not likely, say other scientists who point to evidence that the calcite veins were deposited top to bottom, probably by rainwater. According to a report issued in April, 1992 by a 17-member panel of scientists, ". . .There is no evidence to support the assertion [by Szymanski] that the water table has risen periodically hundreds of meters from deep within the crust. In fact, the evidence strongly supports a surface process origin from rainwater. . ."

One piece of evidence supporting a "surface process" is that calcite deposits caused by the upwelling of groundwater usually form mounds on the surface. There are no such mounds on

Yucca Mountain. In addition, water moving upward produces relatively pure deposits. But water moving downward produces deposits that are full of sand, clay, and volcanic cinders—which is what is found in Yucca Mountain. Finally, at least some of the calcite veins don't go all the way down through the mountain. If they rose from beneath the mountain they would be almost bottomless.

Nevertheless, some people are not convinced that Yucca Mountain is a safe depository for nuclear wastes. Seismologist Charles Archambeau of the University of Colorado believes it's Szymanski's aggressive personality, not his science, that turns people off to his ideas. Says Archambeau: "People get irritated by Szymanski's style, but what matters is the science . . . My own conclusion is that [Yucca Mountain] . . . is a dangerous place."

Nevada officials, including Governor Bob Miller and U.S. Senator Richard Bryan see the villain as the nuclear industry, which is overloaded with nuclear wastes and which mounted a television and radio advertising campaign to convince Nevadans that Yucca Mountain was a safe haven for the wastes. Governor Miller views the industry's media blitz as an attempt "to brainwash Nevadans." Senator Bryan calls it nothing less than "a declaration of war against the people of Nevada."

Should Yucca Mountain be chosen as the storage site for the country's nuclear wastes? Should the objections of Nevadans outweigh the needs of the nuclear industry? Should other factors be considered? What do you think?

Questions

1. By the year 2000, the number of tons of nuclear waste in the United States will be about
   a. 4800.
   b. 48,000.
   c. 480,000.
   d. 4,800,000.

2. The half-life of Pu-239 is
   a. 2410 years.
   b. 239 years.
   c. 10,000 years.
   d. 24,100 years.

3. Zeolites are
   a. radioactive chemicals.
   b. minerals.
   c. buttes.
   d. critics of Szymanski.

4. What evidence exists to support the idea that Yucca Mountain is in a geologically active area?

5. On a separate sheet of paper, discuss the pros and cons of placing a nuclear waste facility in Yucca Mountain. Express your own view and support it with data provided in this article and/or with library research.

Earthquake Prediction: On Shaky Ground?

The Parkfield Cafe looks like many others of its kind until you notice the words painted on a large water tank next to the building. First of all, who would want to be there "when it happens"? Most people would go out of their way to avoid an earthquake.

But seismologists trying to find ways to predict earthquakes are not "most people." Like mountain climbers who head for the craggiest peaks "because they're there," seismologists trek to earthquake country because that's where the earthquakes are. And the California town of Parkfield is a virtual treasure chest of earthquakes.

Perched atop a segment of the infamous San Andreas Fault, Parkfield has attracted scores of seismologists bent on finding ways to predict earthquakes so that people can be warned of the coming of a temblor in time to seek safety. These scientists come with a wide variety of instruments designed to detect signs that precede an earthquake.

For example, instruments can detect effects of stress that build up as two sides of a fault press more and more forcefully against each other. Some of these devices measure bulges or tilts in the land. Others are used to detect slight movements as one side of a rocky fault creeps past the other side.

But, besides the fact that the Parkfield area is a particularly active earthquake region, there was something else that lured instrument-packing seismologists to this spot. That something was a prediction made in 1985 by the United States Geological Survey (USGS) that a major earthquake would strike the area before the end of 1992. Moreover, this was the first long-range earthquake prediction ever officially made by American seismologists. And the scientists wanted to be there not only when it happened but during the period before, too. Why?

They hoped to discover changes that precede earthquakes. In other words, they wanted to uncover the signs of coming quakes, signs that would allow for accurate quake predictions.

Why had Parkfield been chosen for what turned out to be a $19 million, seven-year experiment? Put another way, what had led seismologists to believe a big earthquake would strike at or near Parkfield before 1992? The answer: history!

Records revealed that since 1857 the region had been rocked six times by earthquakes whose magnitudes were between 5.5 and 6.0 on the Richter scale. More significantly, the earthquakes had occurred at remarkably regular intervals, once about every 22 years, with the last one in 1966. This was one factor that led the seismologists to make their prediction.

What happened? In early October of 1992, a series of small earthquakes shook the town of Middle Mountain, 10 km north of Parkfield. But none scored higher than 3.1 on the Richter scale. Then, on October 19, a 4.7-level quake rumbled through the ground halfway between Middle Mountain and Parkfield. This prompted the state of California to announce what is called an A-level earthquake alert.

There are five levels of alert, ranging from A to E. An E essentially means little or no chance of a major earthquake. An A means the chances are very good that one is about to strike. The A-level alert translated into a prediction by the California Office of Emergency Services that there was a 33 percent probability that a 6.0-magnitude earthquake would shake the area within three days.

But the predicted earthquake never struck. Nor had it struck by mid-1993. Both the long-range and short-range predictions had missed the mark. Did this mean that earthquake prediction was impossible? No, said John O. Langbien of the USGS, pointing out that: "Scientifically . . . if the earthquake doesn't come now, but in three years, we'd be pretty happy with the results."

Langbien and other seismologists emphasize that many factors, some of them yet to be identified, affect the occurrence of earthquakes. For

example, seismologists Robert Simpson of the USGS and Terry Tullis of Brown University suggest that the 6.5 quake that struck Coalinga, 30 km northeast of Parkfield, in 1983 might have relieved some of the stress that had built up in the San Andreas Fault under Parkfield. This, they hypothesize, could cause a delay of a few years in the arrival of the originally predicted Parkfield quake.

The main problem with predicting earthquakes based on history, says Harvard University's Yehuda Ben-Zion, is that, "If you think in terms of a simple [historical] clock, you have no hope of predicting earthquakes," because the crust is too complex and too many factors interact to cause temblors.

Does that mean that the Parkfield experiment was a waste of money and scientific time? No, declares Ben-Zion, adding "you have to work on details" to understand how an earthquake is triggered, and "Parkfield is essential to that." Do you agree with Ben-Zion? Should we spend more money to discover whether earthquakes can be predicted? What do you think?

Questions

1. The San Andreas Fault is located in
   a. Nevada.
   c. Arizona.
   b. California.
   d. New Mexico.

2. The USGS predicted that a major earthquake would strike the area around Parkfield, CA before the end of
   a. 1966.
   c. 1992.
   b. 1985.
   d. 1995.

3. Historically, the period between earthquakes at Parkfield has been about
   a. 2 years.
   c. 22 years.
   b. 12 years.
   d. 40 years.

4. What kinds of "signs" do seismologists look for before an earthquake?

5. On a separate sheet of paper, explain why you would or would not favor spending money on continued earthquake prediction research.

Diamond Dust and Dinosaurs

If our modern society had flourished some 65 million years ago and you had been alive at the time, you might have tuned into the weather segment of a local newscast to hear: "Today's forecast: cloudy as usual with steady diamond-dust showers, heavy at times."

Since human beings would not evolve for at least another 63 million years, no such broadcast ever occurred. But the event apparently did. In 1991, diamond dust was found in 65-million-year-old rocks. What's more, this particular discovery provided still another clue to the solution of one of science's most intriguing mysteries: what caused the extinction of the dinosaurs?

The mystery began with the discovery that a great many species, including virtually all of the dinosaurs, did not survive beyond what geologists call the Cretaceous-Tertiary, or K-T, boundary. This is a boundary in time which marks the end of the Cretaceous Period and the beginning of the Tertiary Period. The date of the boundary is roughly 65 million years ago. What prevented so many living things from crossing this boundary? Put another way, what happened 65 million years ago to kill off the dinosaurs and a horde of other animals and plants?

No single event, said many scientists who contended that the living things that died out did so gradually over millions of years. But at least two scientists did not agree. They were a father and son team, geologist Walter Alvarez and his Nobel-Prize-winning physicist father, Luis.

Walter Alvarez had made a curious discovery in the late 1970s. He had found a layer of rock holding extraordinarily high concentrations of the element iridium. That in itself might not have caused Alvarez's pulse to quicken, save for the fact that iridium in high concentrations is not generally found in earthly rocks. It is, however, among the elemental passengers of space rocks: meteorites and asteroids. But even more astounding was the uncovering of a startling coincidence. The layer of rock was just about 65 million years old. It marked the K-T boundary.

Like most scientists, Walter and Luis Alvarez did not believe in coincidences in nature. They were sure that the iridium layer and the extinction of the dinosaurs were connected, and proposed what turned out to be a very unpopular hypothesis. Their premise? A large object from space crashed into Earth 65 million years ago. The impact from the collision threw vast amounts of dust into the air. This dust shrouded the sun for many years, changing Earth's climate. The change disrupted the life cycles of plants and animals, setting loose a chain of events that led to the abrupt extinction of the dinosaurs and other living things.

The controversy raged through the 1980s. Critics pointed out that the fossils of certain dinosaurs and other animals seemed to vanish in layers of rocks that were older than 65 million years. This was evidence, the critics said, that these creatures died out gradually, starting before 65 million years ago.

The Alvarezes and a growing band of supporters felt they should look harder for dinosaur fossils near the K-T boundary. Soon paleontologists were scouring the rocks in such places as the Hell Creek Formation along the border of Montana and North Dakota, one of the richest treasure chests of dinosaur fossils.

A team of fossil hunters led by Peter M. Sheehan of the Milwaukee Public Museum spent three summers systematically hunting for dinosaur fossils in the rocks of the Hell Creek Formation. Their painstaking work was rewarded with the discovery of dinosaur fossils in all layers of rock near the K-T boundary but not in layers above it. This suggested that the extinctions had not been gradual but sudden. The asteroid-impact hypothesis had gained supporting evidence.

But skeptics were hard to convince. If the ex-

tinctions were caused by an asteroid impact, where, they asked, was the telltale crater? Tiny bits of glass found around the Caribbean Sea provided a clue to the answer to this question. The bits of glass, called *tektites,* are produced when large objects from space crash into Earth. Tektites start out as molten bits of rock that are sprayed into the sky when a large object from space hits the ground. As the drops of molten rock fall, they solidify into glass.

The discovery of tektites around the Caribbean led some scientists to believe that, if they looked hard enough, they might find a crater in or near the Caribbean Sea. Sure enough, in February of 1991, *The New York Times* reported: "Scientists . . . have identified a buried crater near Merida, Yucatan, that is more than 100 miles wide, extending out under the Gulf of Mexico." The crater was the largest ever found on Earth. And how old was the crater? About 65 million years!

Some scientists are still not convinced that an asteroid smashing into Earth was responsible for the extinction of the dinosaurs. They suggest that slower changes in climate may have been responsible. What do you think? (By the way, before you tackle this question, you might be wondering just what diamonds might have to do with dinosaur extinctions. Diamonds are a form of carbon that has been transformed by extreme heat and pressure. Could an asteroid im-

pact have produced the 65-million-year-old diamond dust found in 1991?)

Questions

1. The K-T boundary is how many years old?
   a. 6.5 million
   b. 65 million
   c. 650 million
   d. 6.5 billion

2. The significance of the iridium find is that
   a. dinosaur bones are rich in the element.
   b. Earth rocks are rich in the element.
   c. objects from space are rich in the element.
   d. diamonds are rich in the element.

3. Tektites are
   a. fossils.
   b. bits of glass.
   c. objects from outer space.
   d. diamonds.

4. Describe the reasoning that led Walter and Luis Alvarez to develop their hypothesis.

5. On a separate sheet of paper, discuss and evaluate the evidence presented to support the argument that an impact by an object from space caused the extinction of the dinosaurs.

Runoff: A Runaway Problem?

Huge thunderheads glide ominously across the land. Within minutes, the sky turns from bright blue to a deep charcoal-gray. Lightning bolts streak to the ground. Thunder rumbles, and torrents of rain pour down.

The storm sweeps over a forest and then over vast farmlands. It rushes over a small city. In past years, much of the water dumped on the region would have seeped slowly into the soil. The flow of the water into streams, rivers, and lakes would have been controlled by carpets of grass and shrubs and great stands of trees—the living inhabitants of a *watershed,* a large area of land that receives water from rain or snow and feeds it into local bodies of water.

But great areas of the forest have been cut down for lumber. Farmers have cleared the land to plant crops. And cement and asphalt have replaced vegetation in cities and suburbs. Result? The water runs off the land like spilled milk off a glass tabletop. As it rages along, this run-off water picks up dirt, fertilizers, pesticides, and various metals, only to deposit them later in streams, rivers, and lakes.

The fresh water that came from the sky is now polluted water. And the pollution can clog bodies of water with choking silt and contaminate them with poisonous chemicals. The toll in dead fish will be large. Moreover, people will be robbed of sources of clean, fresh water for drinking and for recreation.

Runoff due to the destruction of watersheds is not just a local problem. In June of 1989, the Environmental Protection Agency (EPA) reported that no fewer than 17,000 bodies of water in the United States had been degraded, most of them by uncontrolled runoff. Yet, according to some scientists and engineers, few governmental agencies—local or federal—were doing much to correct the problem.

As environmental engineer Diane M. Cameron put it in an article published in the magazine *Environment* in March of 1990: ". . . runoff is at the bottom of our priority list." But what's it doing down there? you might ask.

For one thing, we need the products whose production adds to the run-off problem. For example, we need the corn and wheat from such states as Iowa and Nebraska. There's no question that land has to be cleared to make room for such food crops. What's more, to grow healthy and bountiful crops farmers apply fertilizer and pesticides to the soil and plants.

Unfortunately, when rain splashes onto farmland, it picks up some of the fertilizers and pesticides and sweeps them into nearby streams, rivers, and lakes. In her article, Cameron states that, "In Iowa . . . agricultural runoff is blamed for more than 95 percent of the water-quality problems in the state. . ."

Farms are not the only contributors to the problem. Developers of suburban homes and city dwellers also contribute. For example, an area in Maryland near Washington, D.C., called the Anacostia watershed is now one-third paved over or covered with buildings. In the summer, rain falling on the sizzling pavement has been known to warm to an astounding 92°F. When this hot water pours into the Anacostia River, the lives of fish and other inhabitants of the river are seriously threatened.

Logging, especially a practice called *clearcutting*—the cutting down of all the trees in a particular part of a forest—also promotes uncontrolled runoff and the accumulation of silt in rivers. In some parts of the country, sheep and cattle that munch away grass set the stage for rampant runoff. In other areas, mining practices may allow acids and heavy metals to escape into rainwater.

So what's to be done? Many states rely on education and voluntary programs to control runoff and its problems. The federal government also has programs to do this. However, "... federal programs lack statutory muscle, regulatory clout, and adequate funding...," says Diane Cameron. How come? Cameron explains that, "... the particular groups who cause runoff ... are not politically palatable targets for regulation ... [Nevertheless] the consequences of this neglect are staggering."

How can we curb runaway runoff and restore watersheds without infringing on the rights of farmers, city folk, loggers, and miners, or giving up the products we need? What do you think?

Questions

1. In 1989, the EPA reported that the number of degraded bodies of water in the U.S. was
   a. 7000.
   c. 70,000.
   b. 17,000.
   d. 170,000.

2. Agricultural runoff is thought to account for what percent of the water-quality problems of Iowa?
   a. none
   c. 95%
   b. 10%
   d. 100%

3. Mining practices may contaminate rainwater with
   a. fertilizers.
   c. hot water.
   b. pesticides.
   d. acids and heavy metals.

4. How does farming contribute to water pollution?

5. Pick one cause of uncontrolled runoff and, on a separate sheet of paper, recommend how it might be controlled. Consider and describe the economic and social effects of your proposal.

Glossary of Earth Science Terms

Abrasion: A form of physical weathering caused by friction between rock particles.

Absolute age: The age of a rock unit, a fossil, or an event expressed in units of time, such as years.

Absolute humidity: The moisture content of the air more commonly expressed as a vapor pressure in millibars.

Absolute zero: The coldest possible temperature, $-273°C$. At absolute zero, molecules have no energy of vibration (heat).

Absorption (energy): The taking in of energy.

Actual evapotranspiration: The amount of water that is lost by the soil in evaporation and transpiration within a given period of time.

Adiabatic temperature change: The change in the temperature of a gas caused by expansion (cooling) or compression (warming).

Aerobic bacteria: Microscopic organisms that must live in water with dissolved oxygen.

Aerosol: Tiny particles or droplets suspended in a gas.

Agent of erosion: A medium, such as water, wind, or glacial ice, that transports weathered sediments.

Air mass: A large body of air that has relatively uniform conditions of temperature and pressure. The character of an air mass depends upon its origin.

Altitude: The height, measured in degrees, of an object above the horizon of an observer.

Anaerobic bacteria: Bacteria that can live in water without dissolved oxygen. See **aerobic bacteria**.

Angle of insolation: The angle of the sun above the horizon.

Angular diameter: The angle formed between two sides of an object and an observer's eye.

Annular drainage pattern: A stream pattern of concentric circles formed on a mountain whose rocks have differing competence.

Anticyclone: A high-pressure system that usually brings cool, clear weather as its winds rotate clockwise and away from the center; a zone of divergence.

Aphelion: The farthest approach of a satellite to its primary; where a satellite moves the slowest in its orbit.

Apparent: What seems true, whether or not it really is.

Apparent diameter: How large an object looks, which depends upon its size and distance from an observer.

Apparent solar day: The time required for the sun to go from its highest point in the sky on one day to its highest point the next day.

Apparent solar time: Time based upon the position of the sun in the sky. It is usually a few minutes ahead of, or behind, clock time (mean solar time).

Arc: A uniformly curved line that is a part of a circle; the path of the sun or a star through the sky.

Arctic air mass: An extremely cold air mass.

Arid: Dry; a climate in which there is little precipitation or a climate in which the potential evapotranspiration exceeds the precipitation.

Asthenosphere: The part of the earth's interior below the lithosphere that is plastic in response to stress.

Atmosphere: The shell of gases that surrounds the earth.

Atmospheric pressure: A measure of the force exerted by the atmosphere.

Atmospheric variables: The observable or measurable characteristics of the air, such as temperature, pressure, humidity, wind speed, and wind direction.

Axis: The imaginary line around which an object rotates.

Banding: A type of layering (foliation) found in some metamorphic rocks that is caused by the movement or growth of minerals into homogeneous layers.

Basaltic: Igneous rock composed mostly of dark-colored, dense minerals containing compounds of iron and magnesium.

Base level: The lowest level to which streams can erode.

Basic unit: A unit of measure, like mass, length, or time, that cannot be expressed in terms of a combination of other units.

Bedrock: The solid layer of rock that extends into the earth. Bedrock can always be found beneath the soil.

Bench mark: A metal disk, or other marker, placed in rock or concrete that shows a location or surveyed position and known elevation above sea level.

Boiling temperature: The temperature at which a substance changes from a liquid to a gaseous phase.

Bonding: Attachments; the way that atoms are connected to adjacent atoms.

Calorie: The amount of heat energy needed to raise the temperature of one gram of pure water one Celsius degree; a common measuring unit of heat energy.

Calorimeter: A closed energy system used to determine the specific heat of a substance.

Capillarity: The ability of a soil to draw water upward into tiny pores.

Capillary water: Water held within the aerated zone of the soil above the water table.

Carbon-14: A radioactive form of the element carbon that has been used to find the absolute age of recent fossils and geologic events.

Celestial object: An object in the sky outside the earth's atmosphere; the sun, moon, stars, and planets.

Celestial sphere: An imaginary sphere encircling the earth on which all objects in the night sky appear projected.

Cement (natural): A mineral or another fine matrix that fills the pores between the grains of sediments, forming sedimentary rock.

Chemical weathering: A change in the chemical composition of a rock caused by adjustment to conditions at the surface of the earth.

Circumference: The distance around a circle, or the straight-line distance around a sphere.

Classification: The organization of objects, ideas, or information into groupings.

Cleavage: The way that a mineral splits between layers of atoms that are joined by weak bonds.

Climate: The average weather conditions over many years of observation.

Cloud: A large mass of water droplets or ice crystals suspended in the air.

Coalesce: Combine. Cloud droplets must coalesce to fall as precipitation.

Colloid: Tiny particles or droplets suspended in a gas or a liquid indefinitely.

Competent rock: Hard rock that resists weathering and erosion.

Compression: A reduction in the volume of a substance through the application of a force.

Compressional waves: See **P-waves**.

Condensation: The process by which a gas changes into a liquid; a way in which clouds form.

Condensation nuclei: See **condensation surface**.

Condensation surface: A surface on which water vapor may change into a liquid.

Conduction: The way in which heat energy is transferred through matter by the direct contact of molecules.

Conglomerate: A sedimentary rock composed of cemented gravel, pebbles, or cobbles.

Contact metamorphism: Chemical and physical changes in a rock, caused mostly by heat, next to an intrusion or extrusion of molten liquid rock.

Continental air mass: A body of arid air that is low in humidity because it formed over a land area.

Continental climate: A climate in which there are large seasonal changes in temperature due to the absence of nearby bodies of water to moderate the climate.

Continental crust: Rocks within the continents, usually a thin layer of sedimentary rocks over granitic rocks, that are lighter than oceanic crust.

Continental drift: The idea that the continents move over the surface of the earth like rafts on water.

Contour interval: The difference in height between two adjacent contour lines.

Contour line: A line on a map that connects places with the same elevation and shows the shape of the land.

Contour map: A map that shows the shape of the land with contour lines; a map showing an elevation field.

Convection: The circulation of a heated fluid (a liquid or a gas) caused by density currents; a form of heat flow in which the heated material moves.

Convection cell: The circular path of convection flow.

Convergence: The coming together of winds as they blow into a cyclone (low-pressure system); the coming together of tectonic plates.

Coordinate system: A grid in which each location has a unique designation defined by the intersecting of two lines. Latitude and longitude are the most common coordinates used on the earth.

Core: The innermost layer of the earth, thought to be composed mostly of iron and nickel.

Coriolis effect (force): The apparent curvature of the winds, ocean currents, or objects moving long distances along the earth's surface; caused by the rotation of the earth on its axis.

Correlation: A matchup of rock layers in different locations by age or by rock types.

Crust: The thin, outermost layer of the solid earth.

Crystal: The solid form of a mineral with a regular shape caused by the internal arrangement of atoms.

Crystallization: The formation of intergrown crystals as a liquid cools to form a solid.

Cyclic change: A change that repeats itself, like the annual cycle of the seasons or the apparent daily motion of the sun through the sky.

Cyclone: A low-pressure system in which the winds rotate counterclockwise in the Northern Hemisphere and converge to the center.

Decay product: The element produced by the decay of a radioactive isotope.

Decay product ratio: The ratio between the mass of a radioactive element and its decay product.

Deficit: Within the water budget, a shortage of water because there is not enough water available from precipitation and storage to satisfy the potential evapotranspiration.

Dendritic: A pattern resembling tree branches.

Density: The mass per unit volume of a substance.

Deposition: The settling out or release of sediments by an agent of erosion.

Derived units: Units of measure that consist of combinations of basic units.

Dew point: The temperature at which the air would be saturated with moisture.

Direct rays: Sunlight that strikes the earth from straight overhead; vertical rays.

Discharge: The quantity of water flowing past a certain point in a stream per unit of time.

Distorted structures: Bedding, fossils, or other features of a rock that have been warped or otherwise changed by metamorphism.

Divergence: The outward movement of winds from a high-pressure zone (anticyclone).

Drainage pattern: The arrangement of adjoining streams as seen from above.

Drumlin: An oval-shaped mound of unsorted glacial till.

Duration of insolation: The length of time that the sun is in the sky from sunrise to sunset.

Dynamic equilibrium: A state of balance in which something is changing, but the amount remains constant.

Earthquake: Natural vibrations, sometimes destructive, that radiate from a sudden movement along a fault zone within the earth or from sudden movements of magma (molten rock) under a volcano.

Eccentricity: The degree of elongation of an ellipse.

Eclipse: A shadowing of a celestial object. A lunar eclipse occurs when the earth lies between the moon and the sun. A solar eclipse occurs when the moon passes between the earth and the sun.

Electromagnetic energy: A form of energy, such as heat waves, visible light, and X rays, that can radiate through empty space.

Electromagnetic spectrum: The complete range of electromagnetic energy from long-wave radiowaves to short-wave gamma rays.

Ellipse: A closed curve around two fixed points known as the foci. All orbits are ellipses.

Energy: The ability to do work.

Energy sink: See sink.

Energy source: See source.

Epicenter: A location along the earth's surface that is directly above the focus of an earthquake. An earthquake is felt most strongly at its epicenter.

Equator: An imaginary line that circles the earth halfway between the North and South Poles.

Equilibrium: A state of balance between opposing forces in a system.

Equinox: The time at which the sun is directly above the equator, and all places on the earth have 12 hours of daylight and 12 hours of darkness. The equinoxes are near the end of March and September, and they mark the beginning of spring and autumn.

Era: A large division of geologic time.

Erosion: The transportation of weathered material (sediments) by water, wind, or ice away from their place of origin and the deposition of them elsewhere.

Erosional-depositional system: A river system within which energy transformations from potential energy to kinetic energy are constantly occurring.

Escarpment: A steep slope or cliff where resistant layers of sedimentary rock overlie weaker layers.

Esker: A winding ridge of sand and gravel deposited by a stream confined to a tunnel under a glacier.

Evaporation: A change in state from a liquid to a gas (vapor); also known as vaporization.

Evaporite: A sedimentary rock that is deposited as minerals in a saturated solution settle out of an evaporating body of water.

Evapotranspiration: A combination of evaporation from the ground and evaporation from plants (transpiration). Within the water budget, water enters the air by evapotranspiration.

Event: A change or series of changes in the earth's environment.

Evolution (organic): The principle that living things have changed in form through the history of the earth from a few simple organisms to a great diversity of organisms, including simple and complex forms.

Extrusion: Molten, liquid rock (lava) flowing out onto the surface of the earth; a fine-grained igneous rock formed by the rapid crystallization of lava at or near the surface of the earth.

Fault: A break in the rock of the earth's crust along which there has been displacement (movement).

Felsic: Rocks composed mostly of feldspar and quartz.

Field: A region of space in which the same quantity can be measured at every point or location.

Flotation: The transportation of sediments along the surface of a stream.

Fluid: A substance that can flow; liquids and gases.

Focus: One of two fixed points that determine the shape and position of an ellipse; an earthquake's point of origin within the earth.

Folded strata: Layers of rock that have been bent by forces within the earth.

Foliation: The alignment or segregation of minerals in a metamorphic rock, giving it a layered appearance.

Formation: A mappable unit of rock of uniform age or composition.

Fossil: Any preserved remains or traces of life.

Foucault pendulum: A swinging weight that is free to rotate as it swings back and forth. The slow change in direction of a swinging Foucault pendulum is proof of the rotation of the earth.

Fracture: The uneven splitting of a mineral sample.

Freezing temperature: The temperature at which a liquid will start to change to a solid.

Front: A boundary, or interface, between different air masses.

Frost action: A form of physical weathering in climates with seasonal temperature changes alternately above and below 0°C.

Gas: A state of matter in which molecules or atoms flow freely and are not bound closely together.

Geocentric model: An early model of the solar system and universe in which the earth is a stationary object located at the center of the universe around which all celestial objects revolved.

Geologic time scale: Divisions of the history of the earth originally based upon observations of fossil evidence. Through the use of radioactive isotope measurements, it has changed from a relative scale to an absolute scale.

Geosyncline: A shallow-water basin along the edge of a continent that is sinking as it accumulates thick layers of sediment.

Glacial erratic: A large rock that has been transported by a glacier.

Glacier: A large mass of moving ice.

Graded bedding: Layers of sediment that change from coarse particles at the bottom of each layer to progressively finer particles toward the top.

Gradient: The rate of change in field values between two points in a field; the average slope.

Grains: The particles of which rocks are made.

Granitic: Rocks composed mostly of light-colored, low density minerals like quartz and feldspar.

Gravity (gravitational force): An attractive force between objects that is directly proportional to the product of their masses and inversely proportional to the square of the distance between the centers of their masses; gravity holds objects on the earth.

Greenhouse effect: A process in which infrared heat waves are trapped in the earth's atmosphere by gases like carbon dioxide.

Greenwich Mean Time: Time based upon observations of the sun along the prime meridian.

Groundwater: Water found below the water table in the ground.

Half-life: The time required for half of a radioactive element's atoms in a sample to change to the decay product.

Heat energy: The total potential and kinetic energy that can be released as heat from an object.

Heat of fusion: Latent potential energy absorbed when a solid melts and released when a liquid freezes.

Heat of vaporization: Latent potential energy absorbed when a liquid vaporizes and released when a gas condenses.

Heliocentric model: The modern model of the solar system and universe in which the planets revolve around the sun and the earth undergoes daily rotation.

High-pressure system: An anticyclone; a dense mass of air in which the atmospheric pressure is the highest at the center; a zone of divergence.

Horizontal sorting: A gradual change in the size, density, and shape of particles deposited when a stream slows down as it reaches calm water. The largest, most dense, and roundest particles settle first while the smaller, least dense, and flatter particles are carried farther out into the calm water.

Humid: Moist; describes a climate in which there is abundant precipitation or in which the precipitation exceeds the potential evapotranspiration.

Humidity: A measure of the moisture, or water vapor content, of the air.

Humus: Organic remains that are in the soil.

Hydrosphere: The liquid water part of the earth including the oceans, lakes, streams, and groundwater.

Igneous rock: Rock formed by the cooling and crystallization of molten rock (magma or lava).

Index fossil: A fossil that can be found over a large geographic area but existed for a brief period of geologic time. An index fossil is useful in determining the geologic age of the rock in which it is found.

Inference: A scientific conclusion based upon observations and experiences; something that is thought out, but not directly observed; an interpretation.

Infiltration: Water seeping into the ground.

Infrared waves: Long-wave heat radiation.

Inner core: The central portion of the earth's core that is thought to be composed mostly of iron and nickel in the solid state.

Insolation: A contraction of the words, "*in*coming *sol*ar radi*ation*." Electromagnetic energy that the earth receives from the sun.

Insolation-temperature lag: The time delay between maximum or minimum insolation and maximum or minimum air temperature.

Instrument: A device that makes observations or measurements easier to perform or more precise.

Intensity: Strength.

Interface: A boundary between different materials or systems.

Intrusion: Molten, liquid rock (magma) being pushed into cracks within the earth; a body of coarse-grained igneous rock formed by slow cooling in the earth.

Isobar: A line on a weather map connecting places with the same atmospheric pressure.

Isoline: A line connecting points of the same value within a field.

Isostasy: The theory that the earth's crust floats on the denser rock beneath it in a state of equilibrium.

Isosurface: A surface in which all points have the same field value.

Isotherm: A line connecting places of the same temperature within a temperature field or on a weather map.

Isotope: A form of an element with more or fewer neutrons than other forms of the same element.

Joint: A crack in a rock produced by shrinkage or uneven pressure. Unlike a fault, no displacement along a joint surface occurs.

Kame: A delta deposited by a stream at the end of a glacier.

Kettle: A lake left when a block of glacial ice melts.

Kinetic energy: Energy of motion.

Landscape: The general shape of a region on the earth's surface.

Latent heat: Energy absorbed or released in a change in state. Latent heat is so named because it does not show up as a temperature change.

Latitude: The angular distance in degrees north or south of the equator. It varies from 0° at the equator to 90° at the poles.

Lava: Molten rock at the surface of the earth.

Leaching: A process in which groundwater carries dissolved minerals deeper into the soil as the water infiltrates farther into the ground.

Leeward: The downwind side of a mountain range. Usually the side with less precipitation.

Length: The distance between two points, measured in meters or other units of length.

Liquid: A state of matter in which the molecules or atoms are close together but are free to move about.

Lithosphere: The solid portion of the earth below the atmosphere and hydrosphere; a solid layer that includes the crust and the upper portion of the earth's mantle.

Longitude: The angular distance in degrees east or west of the prime meridian. Longitude varies from 0° at the prime meridian to 180° near the middle of the Pacific Ocean.

Low-pressure system: A weather system in which the atmospheric pressure is lower than surrounding areas; a cyclone.

Luster: The way that the surface of a mineral reflects light.

Mafic: Composed of dark minerals rich in iron and magnesium.

Magma: Molten rock within the earth.

Magnitude: The total energy released by an earthquake, measured by the Richter scale.

Mantle: The portion of the earth below the crust and above the core.

Marine (maritime) air mass: A body of air that is relatively moist because it formed over an ocean.

Marine climate: A climate in which seasonal temperature changes are moderated by large bodies of water.

Mass: The quantity of matter in an object, measured in grams or other units of mass.

Maturity: A relative measure of the development of a landscape as either young, mature, or old.

Meander: A natural looping bend, or S-shaped curve, in a stream.

Mean solar day: The average length of the day as measured from noon to noon (24 hours).

Measurement: An observation, made with an instrument, of a quantity.

Melting temperature: The temperature at which a substance starts to change from a solid to a liquid phase.

Meridian: An imaginary semicircle, drawn around the earth from the North Pole to the South Pole, that represents a constant longitude.

Metamorphic rock: A sedimentary or igneous rock that has been changed in texture or composition by heat or pressure, or both, without melting.

Meteorite: A natural object that has fallen to the earth from space.

Mid-ocean ridges: A system of submerged mountain ranges that encircles the earth and often connects with mountain ranges on the continents.

Millibar: A metric unit of atmospheric pressure.

Minerals: The natural, crystalline inorganic substances of which rocks are made.

Model: A representation of an object or natural event. Maps, graphs, and mathematical formulas are models.

Moho: The interface between the earth's crust and mantle.

Mohs scale: A series of ten minerals used as a scale of hardness.

Moisture: The presence of water or water vapor, particularly in the atmosphere.

Monomineralic: Describes a rock composed of a single mineral.

Moraines: Irregular, hilly, unsorted deposits made at the end of an advancing glacier when the melting ice front stays at the same position for a period of time; ridges deposited along the sides of a glacier.

Mountain: A landscape region characterized by non-horizontal rock structure and great topographic relief; a landscape feature usually characterized by high elevation and steep slopes.

Navigation: The science of locating your position on the earth.

Nonsedimentary rocks: Igneous or metamorphic rocks that were not formed directly by sedimentary processes.

North Star: Polaris; the star located almost directly above the North Pole. It is often used for navigation or to find the local latitude.

Oblate spheroid: The nearly spherical shape of the earth, slightly flattened at the poles and slightly bulging at the equator.

Observation: Information obtained directly from the senses.

Occluded front: A type of weather front that is produced when a cold air mass overtakes a warm air mass, isolating the warm air above the ground.

Ocean-floor spreading. The theory that the oceanic crust has been constructed by material from deep within the earth that rises and spreads apart at the mid-ocean ridges.

Oceanic crust: The relatively thin, dense layer of basaltic rock that underlies the ocean sediments and lies on top of the mantle layer.

Orbit: The path (usually an ellipse) of any satellite around its primary.

Orbital speed: The measure of a satellite's orbital motion.

Organic evolution: See **evolution**.

Organic sedimentary rock: Rock formed by the accumulation of plant or animal remains.

Origin time: The time when an earthquake occurs at its epicenter.

Orogeny: The process of mountain building.

Outcrop: Bedrock that is exposed at the surface because it is not covered by soil.

Outer core: The outside portion of the earth's core that is thought to consist mostly of iron and nickel in the liquid state because S-waves can not go through it.

Outwash: Layered deposits left by water from a glacier.

Pangaea: The ancient supercontinent that broke apart millions of years ago to form the present continents.

Parallel: An imaginary line, drawn around the earth and parallel to the equator, that represents a constant latitude.

Percent error: A mathematical method of comparing a measurement with the commonly accepted value for that measurement; percent deviation from accepted value.

Perihelion: The closest approach of a satellite to its primary; where a satellite moves the fastest in its orbit.

Period: The amount of time required for a complete cycle; in geologic time, a subdivision of an era.

Permeability: The ability of a soil to transmit water.

Phase: The physical state of matter; solid, liquid, or gas; the shape of the lighted portion of a celestial object, like the phases of the moon.

Physical weathering: The mechanical breakdown of rocks without any change in chemical composition.

Plains: A landscape region characterized by horizontal rock structure and low topographic relief.

Planetary wind belts: Latitude zones of prevailing wind conditions caused by uneven heating of the earth and the earth's rotation; the mid-latitude westerlies, the polar easterlies, the trade winds, and the doldrums.

Plate tectonics: A unified theory of crustal motions that incorporates continental drift and ocean-floor spreading; the theory that the earth's surface is composed of about a dozen large, rigid plates that carry the continents with them as they diverge and converge.

Plateau: A landscape region characterized by horizontal rock structure and high topographic relief. A plateau is usually a relatively flat or rolling uplands area deeply cut by stream valleys.

Polar air mass: A cool air mass.

Polaris: See **North Star**.

Pollution: Any substance or form of energy in sufficient concentration to harm living things or the natural environment.

Polymineralic: Describes a rock composed of more than one mineral.

Porosity: The portion or percentage of empty space within a soil; the number of pores in a material compared with its volume.

Potential energy: Energy in storage, energy of position, or energy involved in a change in state.

Potential evapotranspiration: The demand of the atmosphere for moisture; the amount of water that could be lost by the soil in evaporation and transpiration within a given period of time, if plenty of water were available.

Precipitation: Water, in the form of rain, snow, or sleet, falling from the sky; a sedimentary process that involves substances settling out of a water solution that is saturated.

Prediction: An inference made about future events.

Pressure gradient: The rate of change in air pressure between two points on a map.

Primary: An object (lying along the major axis of an ellipse) around which a satellite moves. The sun is the primary of the orbiting earth, and the earth is the primary of the moon.

Primary waves: See **P-waves**.

Prime Meridian: An imaginary line (semicircle) that runs through Greenwich, England from the North Pole to the South Pole.

Probability: The likelihood of an event.

Profile: A side view of the elevations along a baseline crossing contour lines on a topographic map.

P-waves: Compressional (longitudinal) waves that are the fastest form of seismic waves to radiate from an earthquake; also known as primary waves.

Radial drainage: A pattern of streams that runs away from a central mountain, like a volcano.

Radiation: The emission and transfer of heat energy by means of electromagnetic waves, and the only way that energy can travel through empty space; rays or particles given off by an unstable radioactive substance.

Radiative balance: An equilibrium between absorbed radiant energy and radiant energy given off.

Radioactivity: The emission of energy rays or nuclear particles from the breakdown of an unstable isotope.

Recharge: In the water budget, infiltrating water that enters storage in the root zone of the soil.

Reflection: The process by which energy waves bounce off a surface or interface.

Refraction: The way that energy waves change direction as they move from one medium to another.

Regional metamorphism: The process by which large masses of rock are changed by deep burial within the earth.

Relative age: A comparative age; age expressed as before or after other events without specifying the age in units of measure.

Relative humidity: The ratio between the actual amount of water vapor in the air and the maximum amount of water vapor the air can hold at a given temperature.

Relief (topographic): Changes in elevation from one place to another.

Residual soil: Soil that remains on top of the bedrock from which it forms.

Retrograde motion: The apparent backward motion of planets, such as Mars, through the stars. Retrograde motion is in a direction opposite to the more common direction of motion.

Reversed magnetic polarity: Refers to an igneous rock that was formed at a time in the geologic past when the north and south magnetic poles of the earth had the opposite polarity that they have at the present.

Revolution: The orbital motion of a satellite around its primary. The earth revolves around the sun in an annual cycle.

Rift: A linear feature of the earth where new crust is being created.

Ring of Fire: The zone of volcanoes, earthquakes, and mountain building that surrounds the Pacific Ocean.

Rock: A natural piece of the solid earth, usually composed of one or more minerals.

Rock cycle: A model of natural changes in rocks and sediment.

Rotation: The spinning of a body around an internal axis. The earth's rotation causes day and night.

Runoff: Precipitation that is unable to infiltrate the soil, so it moves overland into streams. In the water budget, runoff is surplus water.

Satellite: An object that moves elliptically around another object. The earth is a satellite of the sun. The moon is a satellite of the earth.

Saturation: A weather condition in which the air holds as much water vapor as it can at a given temperature; a saturated solution is one that can hold no more of a particular substance dissolved in it.

Saturation vapor pressure: The portion of air pressure that could be caused by the weight of water vapor alone, if the air were saturated with water vapor.

Scalar: A measured quantity that has magnitude (size), but no direction. Temperature is a scalar quantity because it has no direction.

Scattering: Random reflections from irregular surfaces.

Scientific notation: A mathematical shorthand in which numbers are written in the form $M \times 10^n$, where M is a number between 1 and 10, and 10^n is a power of 10.

Seasons: The annual cycle of weather conditions as the earth orbits the sun.

Secondary waves: See **S-waves**.

Sediment: Accumulations of particles of weathered rock, organic remains, or both.

Sedimentary rock: Rock formed by the compression and cementation of particles of sediment.

Seismic waves: Vibrational energy that radiates through the earth from an earthquake.

Seismograph: An instrument designed to measure and record the magnitude of an earthquake.

Senses: Any of the five means by which we directly observe our environment; sight, hearing, smell, taste, and touch.

Shear waves: See **S-waves**.

Silica tetrahedron: A four-sided pyramid formed by four oxygen atoms bonded to one silicon atom in the center; the structural unit of silicate minerals.

Silicates: The large family of minerals that has the silicon-oxygen tetrahedron as its basic structure.

Sink (energy): An object or region that absorbs energy because it is cooler than its surroundings.

Slope: See **gradient**.

Soil: Weathered rock mixed with organic remains at the top of the lithosphere.

Soil association: Soils that are similar and found together.

Soil horizon: A layer within the soil showing a particular stage of soil development.

Solar noon: The time when the sun is at its highest point in the sky.

Solar system: The earth and eight other planets that revolve around the sun.

Solid: A state of matter in which the molecules or atoms are rigidly held together in a three-dimensional network known as a crystal lattice.

Solstice: The longest or shortest day (hours of daylight) of the year when the sun is directly above the Tropic of Cancer or the Tropic of Capricorn. The solstices occur about December 21 and about June 21, and they mark the beginning of winter and summer.

Sorted: Separated by particle size or other characteristics.

Source (energy): An object or region that gives off energy because it is hotter than its surroundings.

Source region: The place where an air mass originates.

Species: A group of living organisms with similar characteristics, a common name, and the capability to interbreed.

Specific gravity: The ratio of a substance's density to that of water.

Specific heat: The amount of heat energy required to raise the temperature of one gram of a substance by one Celsius degree. Water, with a specific heat of 1, is the common standard.

Spectrum: See **electromagnetic spectrum**.

Sphere: A round object on whose surface all points are equidistant from its center.

State of matter: See **phase**.

Static equilibrium: A state of balance in a system in which no movement or change occurs in any of the system's components.

Stationary front: An interface between two air masses that is not moving.

Storage: Within the water budget, water held in the root zone that can be used for evapotranspiration.

Strata: Layers or beds of rock, usually sedimentary.

Streak: The color of the powder of a mineral revealed by rubbing the mineral along a white, unglazed porcelain plate.

Streambed: The bottom of a stream.

Stream discharge: See **discharge**.

Striations (glacial): Parallel scratches on a rock surface caused by the movements of a glacier.

Subduction zone: The region in which the earth's crust is destroyed as it is pulled down into the mantle.

Sublimation: A direct change in state from a solid to a gas or from a gas to a solid without the liquid phase occurring.

Subsidence: The gradual sinking of a portion of the earth's crust.

Superposition (law of): The principle that the lowest layers in a sequence of rock strata must have been deposited before the layers above, unless the rock strata have been turned upside down. The oldest rocks are generally found at the bottom of an outcrop.

Surplus: In the water budget, water that becomes runoff or sinks below the water table when precipitation is greater than potential evapotranspiration and storage is full.

Suspension: A fluid containing large particles that can be filtered out but are too small to settle out on their own. A cloud is a suspension of tiny water droplets in the sky.

S-waves: Transverse earthquake waves that arrive after the P-waves and that cannot travel through a liquid such as the outer core of the earth; also known as secondary or shear waves.

Synoptic weather map: A map showing a variety of field quantities, like temperature, pressure, and sky conditions, at a particular time and over a large geographic area.

Talus: Rock fragments that accumulate at the base of a cliff.

Tectonics: The study of large-scale deformations of the earth.

Temperature: A measure of the average vibrational kinetic energy in a substance.

Terrace (marine): A series of flat areas, cut by wave or stream action, that go up from a shoreline like steps.

Tetrahedron: See **silica tetrahedron**.

Texture: The shape or feel of a surface; particularly the shape, arrangement, and size of mineral crystals on a rock surface.

Thermal energy: See **heat energy**.

Till: Unsorted sediments deposited directly by glacial ice.

Tilted strata: Beds of rock (usually sedimentary), thought to have been deposited flat and level, that have been pushed into a different inclination (angle), usually by motions of the earth's crust.

Time: A measurable period in which an event or process occurs.

Topographic map: See **contour map**.

Topography: The shape of the land surface.

Track: The route followed by a weather system.

Traction: The transportation of large particles along a streambed by rolling and bouncing.

Transition zone: Rock adjacent to an igneous intrusion that has been altered by the heat of the intrusion; a region of contact metamorphism that gradually intensifies toward the contact.

Transparency: The quality of a mineral that determines how it transmits light.

Transpiration: The process by which living plants release water vapor to the atmosphere.

Transported soil: Soil eroded and deposited away from its parent bedrock.

Transverse wave: An energy wave that vibrates perpendicular to the direction of travel, like S-waves and electromagnetic energy.

Trellis drainage: A drainage pattern in which most of the streams occupy parallel valleys; usually develops on folded strata of rocks with differing competence.

Trench (ocean): An ocean floor depression that marks the zone where crust is being subducted.

Tropic of Cancer: The farthest north that the vertical ray of sunlight ever gets (at the June solstice), $23\frac{1}{2}°$ north of the equator.

Tropic of Capricorn: The farthest south that the vertical ray of sunlight ever gets (at the December solstice), $23\frac{1}{2}°$ south of the equator.

Tropical air mass: A warm air mass.

Troposphere: The lowest layer of air, from the surface of the earth up to about 12 km, that contains most of the mass of the atmosphere.

Turbidity current: A down-slope underwater flow of a dense mixture of sediment and sea water that can deposit a layer of graded bedding.

Unconformity: A gap in the geologic record caused by the erosion of sediments or rock before they are protected by layers above.

Uniformitarianism: The principal that most of the geologic events of the past are similar to processes that we can observe in the present.

Uplift: The rising of the earth's crust from forces within the earth, generally related to motions of the tectonic plates.

Usage: Within the water budget, water from storage that is used for evapotranspiration because there is not enough precipitation to satisfy the potential evapotranspiration.

Vaporization: See evaporation.

Vapor pressure: The portion of the total air pressure caused by the weight of water vapor alone.

Vector: A quantity that has both magnitude (size) and direction. Wind is a vector quantity because the wind is specified by both a speed (magnitude) and a direction.

Vein: A small inclusion of crystalline rock within a pre-existing rock; formed by intrusion, partial melting, or deposition in cracks by mineral-laden groundwater.

Vertical ray: Sunlight that strikes the earth from directly overhead (the zenith). At any given time, the vertical ray of sunlight strikes the earth at a single location.

Vertical sorting: The sorting of particles from bottom to top in a layer, with the roundest, largest, and densest particles settling at the bottom and the flattest, smallest, and least dense particles at the top.

Visibility: A measure of the transparency of the atmosphere. Fog, haze, precipitation, and pollution reduce the visibility of the air.

Volcanic ash: Cinders that are blown into the air by a volcano, and that are useful in correlating rock outcrops in different locations.

Volume: The amount of space that matter occupies.

Walking the outcrop: A method of following rock layers to correlate layers within the same outcropping.

Water budget: An accounting procedure that models the annual movement of water through the soil for any given location.

Water cycle: A model of the circulation of water at or near the surface of the earth.

Water table: A boundary at the top of the saturated zone within the soil.

Water vapor: Water in the form of a gas.

Wavelength: The distance between corresponding points on two successive crests or two successive troughs of a wave. For visible light, the wavelength determines the color. Heat radiation (infrared) and red light have longer wavelengths than violet, ultra-violet, or X rays.

Weather: The local condition of the atmosphere and the short-term changes in the condition.

Weathering: A change in the physical form or chemical composition of rock material at or near the surface of the earth.

Weight: A measurement of the pull of gravity on an object.

Wind: The natural movement of air along, or parallel to, the earth's surface; convection within the atmosphere.

Windward: The side of a mountain range where warm, moist air is forced to rise, leading to cloud formation and precipitation.

Year: The time required for a planet (the earth) to complete one orbit around its primary (the sun).

Zenith: The point on a celestial sphere that is directly overhead with respect to an observer (90°).

Zone of aeration: The part of the soil above the water table in which most of the interconnected pores are filled with air.

Zone of crustal activity: An area around an ocean ridge or continental mountain range where volcanoes and earthquake epicenters are concentrated.

Zone of saturation: The portion of the soil below the water table, in which the pores are filled with groundwater.

Index

Abrasion, 93, 97
Absolute humidity, 64
Absolute zero, 40, 42
Absorption, 45–46
Acid precipitation, 93
Acid rain, 83
Acid test, for minerals, 109
Actual evapotranspiration, 86
Actual vapor pressure, 64
Adiabatic cooling, 69, 89
Adiabatic lapse rates, 69–70
Adiabatic temperature changes, 69–70
Adiabatic warming, 69
Aerobic bacteria, 84
Aerosols, 51
Air, convection currents in, 42
Air masses, 70–73
Air pressure gradient, 59
Air temperature, 57, 60
Alaska current, 89
Altitude, 15–16
   climate and, 89
   finding, of star with astrolabe, 16
   of stars, 27
Aluminum, 6, 19
Aluminum silicate minerals, 112
Anaerobic bacteria, 84
Annular patterns, in stream drainage, 157
Antarctic Circle, 30
Antarctic zone, 49
Anticyclones, 71
Aphelion, 37
Apparent motion, 29
Apparent solar day, 29, 38
Apparent solar zone, 29
Arctic Circle, 30
   duration of insolation and, 50
Arctic zone, 49
Argon, 19
Arid climates, 86, 153
Asbestos, 108
Asthenosphere, 130, 131
Astrolabe, 16
Astronomy, 15–16
Atlantic Ocean, 90, 130
   birth of, 128
Atmosphere, 10, 19
   elevation changes in, 65
   energy in, 66–67
Atmospheric pressure, 22
   measuring, 57–58
   wind and, 59
Atoms, 42, 47
   decay of, 146
   in minerals, 107
Autumnal equinox, 29, 33, 49

Axis, of earth, 28, 30
Azimuth, of star, 28

Bacteria, 94
   aerobic, 84
   anaerobic, 84
Bar graphs, 13
Barometer, 3, 58
Basalt, 112, 132
Base level, 159
Bedrock, 79, 94
   in landscapes, 156–158
Bench marks, 118
Boiling temperature, 47, 66

Calcite, 106, 108, 110, 135
Calcite reefs, 139
Calcium, 19, 94
Calorie, 40
Calorimeter, 44
Cambrian Period, 139
Capillarity, 81
Capillary water, 79
Carbon dioxide, 11, 19, 66, 93
   greenhouse effect and, 53
   pollution and, 83
Carbon-14, 146, 147
Celestial North Pole, 27
Celestial objects
   angular diameters of, 33
   geocentric model of, 28
   motions of, 27
Celestial sphere, 27
   locating stars on 27–28
Celsius, 40, 41, 47
Cenozoic Era, 147
Change, energy and, 10–11
Chemical sedimentary rocks, 110–111
Chemical weathering, 93, 94
Circumference of earth, 15
   determining, 18–19
Cirque lakes, 154
Cirques, 154
Classification systems, 1
Cleavage, 108
Climate, 86–87
   factors affecting, 88–90
   influence of, on landscape, 152–153
   storm tracks and, 90
Climatologists, 11
Closed energy system, measuring heat flow in, 43–44
Cloud(s), 19
   adiabatic cooling in, 69
   definition of, 96

formation of, 69, 89, 90
   reflection of insolation, 51
Coal, 115, 127
   formation of, 110
Coastal climates, 89
Cold fronts, 71, 73
Colloids, 96
Competent rocks, 156
Compressional waves, 121
Condensation, 47, 69, 70
Condensation nuclei, 69
Conduction, 42
Conglomerate, 110, 116
Contact metamorphism, 114
Contact metamorphism zone, 134
Continental air mass, 70
Continental climates, 89
Continental crust, 122
Continental drift
   ocean-floor spreading and, 128–129
   origin of, 127–129
   reversed magnetic polarity and, 128
Continental glacier, 54, 98
Contour interval, 23
Contour lines, 22–23
   definition of, 22
Contour maps, 22–23
   making profiles from, 24
Convection, 42
Convection cells, in mantle, 130, 131
Convection model, of plate motion, 132
Coordinate system, 12, 20, 21
Copernicus, 28
Coquina, 110
Coral, 136
Coral reefs, 127
Core, of earth, 123
Coriolis effect, 28, 29, 59, 60, 71
Correlation, 138
Correlation by continuity, 138
Crustal motions
   local evidence of, 118
   regional evidence of, 118–119
Crust, of earth
   chemicals within, 13
   creation of, 129
   isostasy theory of, 126
   movement of sediments and, 126
Crystal lattice, 46
Crystalline cement, 110
Crystallization, 111
Crystals, 108, 110
Cycle, in electromagnetic waves, 45

213

Cyclic change, 10
Cyclones, 71

Darwin, Charles, 139
Dating, in geology, 134–136
    correlating of rock strata in, 138
    evolution of life and, 139
    geologic events of past, 143
    geologic time scale in, 139
    radioactive, 146–147
    volcanic ash falls and, 138
Day, changing length of, 38
Daylight hours, 30
Decay product, 146
Decay-product ratio, 146–147
Deforestation, 53
Dendritic patterns, in stream
    drainage, 157
Density, 5–8
    flotation and, 8
    measuring, 6–7
    of solids, 7
Deposition, 100–105
    erosional-depositional systems,
        103–104
    by glaciers, 103
    rates of, 100
    sorting of sediments in, 100–101
Derived units, 2–3
Desert regions, 153
Devonian fossils, 139
Dew-point temperature, 60–61
Dew-point temperature chart, 61
Diameter measurements, 15
Dinosaurs, 136
Doldrums, 60
Dolomite, 110
Domes, 157, 158
Drainage basin, 149
Drumlins, 153, 154
Dry-bulb thermometer, 61
Dry ice, 48
Dynamic equilibrium, 10–11, 104,
    152, 160

Earth
    axis of, 30
    circumference of, determining,
        18–19
    dimensions of, 15, 18
    as energy sink, 42
    insolation absorbed by, 50–51
    layers of, 122–123
    locating positions on surface of,
        20–22
    models of, 15–19
    observations of, from astronomy,
        1
    parallelism of, 30
    parts of, 19
    photographs of, from space, 15
    radiative equilibrium of, 83
    rotation of, 28–29
    shape of, 15–19
    structure of, 19–20
    sun and, distance between, 33

temperature and, 54
Earth fields, *see* Fields
Earthquakes, 118, 120–122
    earthquake shadow zones, 123
    epicenter, 120, 131
    finding epicenter, 121
    measuring, 120–121
    origin time of, 122
    seismic waves, 120
Eccentricity, of ellipse, 36
Eclipses, 35
Electrical power, 84
Electromagnetic energy, 45
Electromagnetic spectrum, 45
Electromagnetic waves, 45
Electrons, 47
Elevation changes, in atmospheric
    variables, 65
Ellipses, 36
Energy, 40–44
    in atmosphere, 66–67
    change and, 10–11
    conduction, 42
    convection, 42
    definition of, 40
    heat flow, 42
    kinetic heat energy, 40
    law of conservation of, 44
    pollution, 84
    potential, 40
    specific heat, 41
    transfer of, between two objects,
        42
    vapor pressure, 64–65
Energy sink, 40, 42
Energy source, 40, 42
Energy waves, 45
Environment, 11
Environmental pollution, *see*
    Pollution
Epicenter, of earthquake, 120, 131
    finding, 121
Epicycles, 28
Epochs, 139
    Pleistocene, 151
Equator, 20
    duration of insolation, 50
    winds at, 59–60
Equilibrium, 10
Equinoxes, 30, 33
    angles of insolation at different
        latitudes, 49
Eras, 139
    Cenozoic Era, 147
Eratosthenes, 18
Erosion, 94, 96–98
    agents of, 96, 97, 98
    human technology and, 98
    in landscape development, 152
    plant cover in, 98
    rivers in, 126
    by water, 96–97
    by wind and ice, 97–98
Erosional-depositional systems,
    103–104
Erratics, 103
Escarpments, 156
Eskers, 153, 154

Evaporation, 66–67
    rates of, 67
Evaporites, 110
Evapotranspiration, 66, 85
Events, definition of, 10
Evolution of life, 139
Extinction, 139
Extrusion, 34, 111–112, 134

Fahrenheit, 40
Faults, 118, 134, 157
Feldspars, 93, 112
Field map, 22
Fields, 22–26
    definition of, 22
    mapping, 22–26
    scalars, 22
    vectors, 22
Flattened terraces, 153
Flotation, 8
    in erosion, 96
Folds, in rock strata, 134
Fossil coral reefs, 127
Fossil fuels, 83
Fossils, 111, 126, 127, 136
    evolution and, 139
    geologic time scale and, 139
    index, 138
    marine, 118
    Precambrian, 139
Foucault, Jean, 28
Foucault pendulum, 28, 29
Fracture, 108
Fragmental sedimentary rocks, 110
Freezing temperature, 48
Fronts, 71
Frost action, 93
Frosts, 153
Fuels
    coal, 115, 127
    fossil, 83
Full moon, 35

Gabbro, 112
Galileo, 28
Gaseous state, 46
Gases
    air temperature of, 57
    as conductors, 42
    convection in, 42
    sublimation, 48
Geocentric model, 28
Geologic events, of past, 143–144
Geologic time scale, 139
Geometry of orbits, 36
Geosyncline, 126
Glacial deposits, 151
Glacial drifts, 103
Glacial erratics, 103
Glacial landforms, 153
Glacial rocks, 97
Glacial till, 103, 127, 151
Glacial valleys, 98
Glaciers, 79, 89, 98, 153
    continental advances of, 54
    deposition by, 103, 151

Theory of organic evolution, 139
Thermal energy, 40
Thermal equilibrium, 44
Thermometers, 40, 60–61
Thermosphere, air temperature in, 65
Time, 2, 10, 21
Topographic fields, 22–23
Topographic maps, 22–24
Topography, of landscape, 149
Transition zones, 114, 115
Translucent minerals, 108
Transparent minerals, 109
Transpiration, 66
Transported soil, 94
Transverse waves, 45
Trellis drainage, 157
Trellis patterns, 157
Trenches, 129, 131
Tropical air mass, 70
Tropical climates, 89
Tropic of Cancer, 32, 33
Tropic of Capricorn, 32, 33
Tropopause, 19
Troposphere, 19
  air temperature in, 65

Ultraviolet rays, 51
Unconformity, 143
Uniformitarianism, 134
United States Geological Survey, 118
Uplift, 118, 126, 143
  in landscape development, 152
Uranium-238, 147

Valley glaciers, landscape features of, 154
Valleys, 157
Vapor pressure, 64–65
  saturated, 64
Vectors, 22

Veins, in rocks, 135
Velocity, 22
  of streams, 96–97
  of transporting medium in deposition, 100
Ventifacts, 97, 98
Vernal equinox, 30, 49
Vertical rays, 32–33, 49
Vertical sorting, 100
Vibrating molecules, 42
Visible light, 45–46, 50, 53
Volcanic ash fall, 138
Volcanoes, 114, 120, 131, 132, 157
Volume
  equation for determining, 7
  mass and, 5

Warm fronts, 71, 73
Water
  changes of state of, 47
  climate and large bodies of, 89
  density-temperature plot for, 8
  distillation of, 84
  erosion by, 96–97
  filtration of, 84
  infiltration of, 79–81
  insolation absorption by, 50–51
  liquid state of, 46
  in oceans, 79
  specific heat of, 50
  for stream flow, 82–83
  surplus, 86
  temperature of, 84
  volume of, 8
Water budget, 85–86
Water cycle, 79–81
  groundwater zones, 79
  storage and movement of groundwater, 79–81
Water molecules, 46–47
Water table, 79
Water vapor, 19, 46–47, 83
  amount air can hold, 67

atmospheric pressure and, 57
dew-point temperature and, 60
energy loss in, 47
evaporation, 67
Wavelengths, 45
Weather, 57–58
  air temperature, 57
  atmospheric pressure, 57–58
  synoptic weather maps, 75–77
Weather fronts, 71
Weathering and soil, 93
Weather predictions, 77
Weather station, interpreting information shown at, 75–77
Weather station model, 76
Weather symbols, 76
Wegener, Alfred, 127
Wet-bulb depression, 61
Wet-bulb thermometer, 61
Wind, 58–60
  earth's rotation and, 29
  erosion by, 97–98
  planetary wind belts, 59–60
  in troposphere, 19
  velocity of, 22
Winter, length of day in, 38
Winter solstice, 30, 33, 49

Xenoliths, 136

Year, 28

Zenith
  of star, 27
  of sun, 32–33
Zero potential energy, 40
Zone of aeration, 79, 80
Zone of saturation, 79, 80
Zones of convergence, 73
Zones of crustal activity, 131
Zones of divergence, 71, 73
Zones of weakness, 156

Sample Examinations

EARTH SCIENCE
JANUARY 1997

Part I

Answer all 55 questions in this part.   [55]

Directions (1–55): For *each* statement or question, select the word or expression that, of those given, best completes the statement or answers the question. Record your answer on the separate answer sheet in accordance with the directions on the front page of this booklet.

1 The primary purpose of a classification system is to enable people to

  1 make measurements that are very accurate
  2 eliminate inaccurate inferences
  3 organize observations in a meaningful way
  4 extend their powers of observation

2 A quantity of water is frozen solid and then heated from 0°C to 10°C. Which statement best describes the properties of the water during this time?

  1 Mass and volume change.
  2 Volume and density change.
  3 Mass changes but volume remains constant.
  4 Volume changes but density remains constant.

3 A scientist who is studying a stream would have the most difficulty determining the stream's

  1 age in years
  2 velocity
  3 temperature
  4 transported sediment size

4 What is the diameter of the Earth? [Refer to the *Earth Science Reference Tables*.]

  (1) 6,370 km   (3) 12,740 km
  (2) 63,700 km   (4) 127,400 km

5 Which statement best describes the stratosphere? [Refer to the *Earth Science Reference Tables*.]

  1 It is warmer at the top than at the bottom.
  2 It is located 75 kilometers above sea level.
  3 It has greater pressure at the top than at the bottom.
  4 It absorbs large amounts of water vapor from the troposphere.

6 The data table below shows the stream discharge in April for a creek in the southern United States for a period of 8 days.

Day	Stream Discharge (ft³/sec)
1	20.0
2	6.0
3	269.0
4	280.0
5	48.0
6	21.0
7	14.0
8	5.0

Which graph most accurately shows stream discharge for the 8-day period?

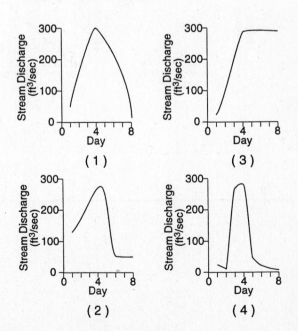

7 The world map below shows latitude and longitude. Letters *A*, *B*, *C*, and *D* represent locations on the map.

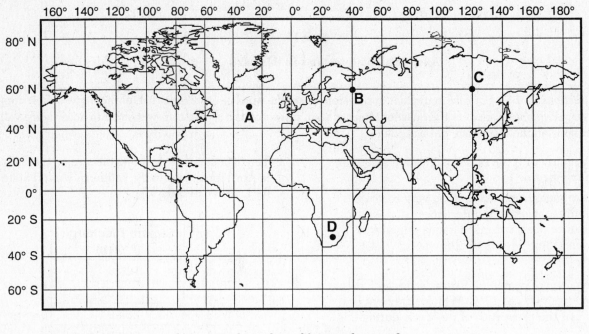

For which location are the correct latitude and longitude given?

(1) *A*: 45° S 30° W

(2) *B*: 40° N 60° W

(3) *C*: 60° N 120° E

(4) *D*: 30° S 30° W

---

8 Which graph best represents the altitude of Polaris observed at northern latitude positions on the Earth's surface?

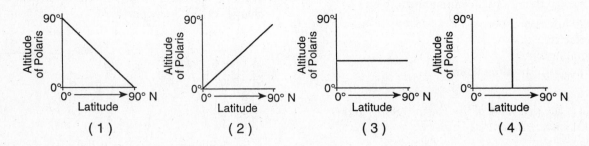

9 The period of time a planet takes to make one revolution around the Sun is most dependent on the planet's average

  1 rotation rate
  2 mass
  3 insolation from the Sun
  4 distance from the Sun

10 Which location on the Earth would the Sun's vertical rays strike on December 21?

  1 Tropic of Cancer ($23\frac{1}{2}°$ N)
  2 Equator ($0°$)
  3 Tropic of Capricorn ($23\frac{1}{2}°$ S)
  4 South Pole ($90°$ S)

11 The best evidence that the Earth rotates on its axis comes from observations of

  1 seasonal changes of constellations
  2 the apparent motion of a Foucault pendulum
  3 the changing altitude of the Sun at noon
  4 the changing altitude of Polaris

12 In our solar system, the orbits of the planets are best described as

  1 circular, with the planet at the center
  2 circular, with the Sun at the center
  3 elliptical, with the planet at one of the foci
  4 elliptical, with the Sun at one of the foci

13 By which process is heat energy transferred when molecules within a substance collide?

  1 conduction   3 radiation
  2 convection   4 sublimation

14 Water loses energy when it changes phase from

  1 gas to liquid   3 solid to gas
  2 solid to liquid   4 liquid to gas

15 When do maximum surface temperatures usually occur in the Northern Hemisphere?

  1 early June to mid-June
  2 mid-July to early August
  3 late August to mid-September
  4 mid-September to early October

16 Which graph best illustrates the relationship between the intensity of insolation and the angle of insolation?

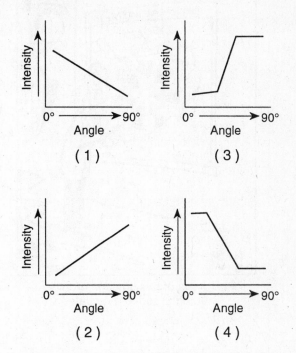

17 The diagram below represents energy being absorbed and reradiated by the Earth.

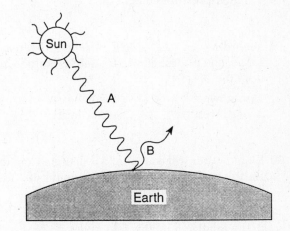

Which type of energy is represented by the radiation at *B*?

  1 insolation   3 ultraviolet rays
  2 visible light   4 infrared energy

18 In the cartoon below, the large arrows represent surface winds.

"Residents of this tiny community are being urged to evacuate."

What feature is found at the location to which the meteorologist is pointing?

1 an anticyclone
2 an area of divergence
3 a low-pressure center
4 a high-pressure center

19 According to the *Earth Science Reference Tables*, the prevailing winds at 45° S latitude are from the

1 southwest   3 southeast
2 northwest   4 northeast

20 Liquid water will continue to evaporate from the Earth's surface, increasing the amount of atmospheric water vapor, until

1 transpiration occurs
2 the relative humidity falls below 50%
3 the atmosphere becomes saturated
4 the temperature of the atmosphere becomes greater than the dewpoint temperature

21 Which weather station model indicates the highest relative humidity?

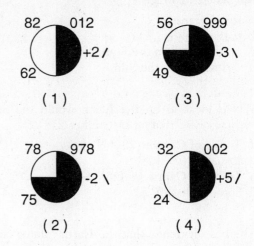

22 By which process are clouds, dew, and fog formed?

1 condensation   3 precipitation
2 evaporation   4 melting

23 Which graph best represents the chemical weathering rate of a limestone boulder as the boulder is broken into pebble-sized particles?

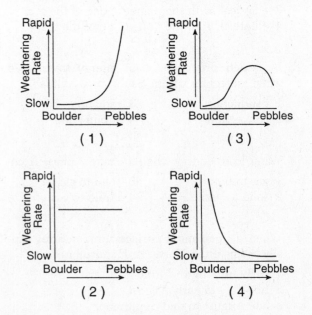

24 Which water budget condition exists when precipitation is less than potential evapotranspiration and storage is depleted?

1 moisture surplus   3 moisture usage
2 moisture recharge   4 moisture deficit

25 What is the source of most of the water vapor that enters the atmosphere?

1 lakes   3 soil
2 plants   4 oceans

26 Runoff is usually greater than infiltration when the

1 soil is porous   3 rainfall is low
2 slope is steep   4 temperature is high

27 The chief agent of erosion on Earth is

1 human beings   3 wind
2 running water   4 glaciers

28 Which graph best represents the relationship between the particle size and the capillarity of a sample of soil?

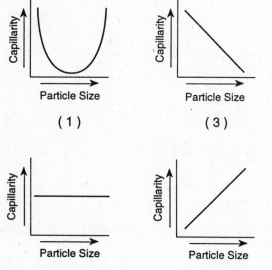

(1)   (3)

(2)   (4)

29 The diagrams below represent two containers, each filled with a sample of nonporous particles of uniform size.

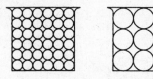

Compared to the sample of larger particles, the sample of smaller particles has

1 lower permeability   3 less porosity
2 higher permeability   4 more porosity

30 Most metamorphic rocks are formed when

1 sediments are cemented and compacted
2 magma cools slowly, deep underground
3 flows of lava cool rapidly
4 rocks are subjected to heat and pressure

31 The two pebbles shown below are dropped into a tank of water 1 meter deep.

Hematite   **Quartz**

Density = 6.5 g/cm^3 Density = 2.6 g/cm^3

Why does the hematite pebble settle faster than the quartz pebble?

1 Smaller objects settle faster than larger objects.
2 Flat objects settle faster than round objects.
3 Spherical objects have less gravitational attraction than flat objects.
4 Objects with higher density settle faster than objects with lower density.

32 In the diagram below of a straight-flowing stream, the lengths of the arrows represent differences in relative stream velocity on the stream's surface.

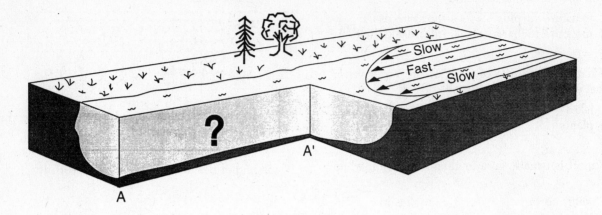

Which diagram best represents the relative stream velocity from the surface to the bottom of the stream for the cross section from A to A´?

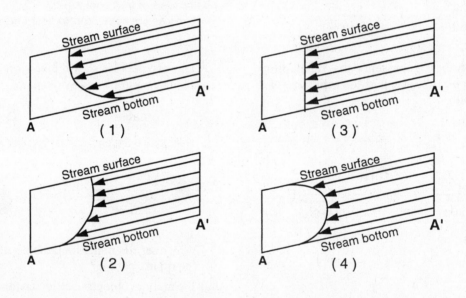

---

33 Igneous, sedimentary, and metamorphic rocks are usually composed of

1 intergrown crystals   3 minerals
2 fossils   4 sediments

34 Which feature is characteristic of sedimentary rocks?

1 layering   3 distorted structure
2 foliation   4 glassy texture

Base your answers to questions 35 and 36 on the table below, which shows some characteristics of a rock-forming mineral.

Mineral	Cleavage	Hardness	Density (g/cm^3)	Other Properties
Pyroxene (a complex family of minerals; augite is most common)	Two flat planes at nearly right angles	5–6	3.2–3.9	Found in igneous and metamorphic rocks; augite is dark green to black; other varieties are white to green

35 Which diagram best represents a sample of pyroxene?

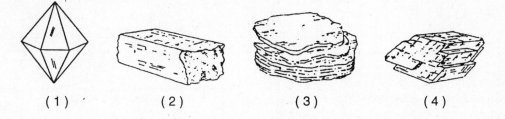

(1) (2) (3) (4)

36 According to the *Earth Science Reference Tables*, an igneous rock containing large, visible crystals of pyroxene is best described as

1 felsic and formed deep within the Earth's crust
2 felsic and formed near the Earth's surface
3 mafic and formed deep within the Earth's crust
4 mafic and formed near the Earth's surface

---

37 Most of the oceanic crust is composed of rock material similar to

1 basalt   3 sandstone
2 granite   4 limestone

38 Which statement best explains why the *P*-wave of an earthquake arrives at a seismic station before the *S*-wave?

1 The *S*-wave originates from the earthquake focus.
2 The *S*-wave decreases in velocity as it passes through a liquid.
3 The *P*-wave originates from the earthquake epicenter.
4 The *P*-wave has a greater velocity than the *S*-wave.

39 Evidence of crustal subsidence (sinking) is provided by

1 zones of igneous activity at mid-ocean ridges
2 heat-flow measurements on coastal plains
3 marine fossils on mountaintops
4 shallow-water fossils beneath the deep ocean

40 An earthquake *P*-wave arrived at a seismograph station at 01 hour 21 minutes 40 seconds. The distance from the station to the epicenter is 3,000 kilometers. The earthquake's origin time was

(1) 01 h 11 min 40 sec
(2) 01 h 16 min 00 sec
(3) 01 h 20 min 20 sec
(4) 01 h 27 min 20 sec

41 The map below shows the western part of the United States.

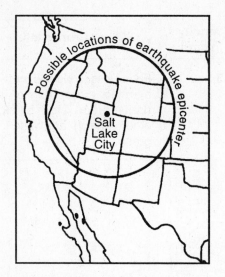

Which observation made at Salt Lake City would allow seismologists to determine that an earthquake had occurred somewhere along the circle shown on the map?

1 the relative strength of the *P*-waves and *S*-waves
2 the time interval between the arrival of the *P*-waves and *S*-waves
3 the difference in the direction of vibration of the *P*-waves and *S*-waves
4 the density of the subsurface bedrock through which the *P*-waves and *S*-waves travel

42 Which feature in the geologic cross section below was formed by erosion?

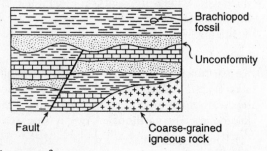

1 unconformity
2 fault
3 brachiopod fossil
4 coarse-grained igneous rock

43 Diagrams I and II show the same region of the Earth's surface at two different times in the geologic past.

Diagram I

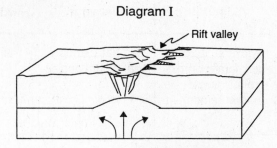

Diagram II

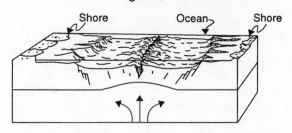

Which statement best explains the basic cause of the changes that occurred in this region?

1 Meteor impact on the crust caused widening of the valley.
2 Mantle convection currents caused crustal movement.
3 Climate changes caused flooding.
4 Temperature changes caused melting of polar ice caps.

44 When did dinosaurs become extinct?

1 before the earliest birds
2 before the earliest mammals
3 at the end of the Cretaceous Period
4 at the end of the Cambrian Period

45 Which locations are listed in order of the age of their surface bedrock, from oldest to youngest?

1 Syracuse, Watertown, Elmira, Old Forge
2 Elmira, Syracuse, Old Forge, Watertown
3 Old Forge, Watertown, Syracuse, Elmira
4 Syracuse, Elmira, Watertown, Old Forge

Base your answers to questions 46 and 47 on the table below, which shows the geologic ages of some index fossils.

GEOLOGIC TIME	INDEX FOSSILS			
MISSISSIPPIAN	Spirifer	Muensteroceras	Crinoid Stem	Pentremites
DEVONIAN	Mucrospirifer		Phacops	
SILURIAN	Eospirifer			
ORDOVICIAN	Michelinoceras		Flexicalymene	

46 According to the *Earth Science Reference Tables*, which index fossil might be found in rock layers that are approximately 387 million years old?

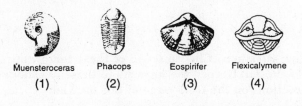

Muensteroceras	Phacops	Eospirifer	Flexicalymene
(1)	(2)	(3)	(4)

47 Which type of past environment is indicated by these index fossils?

1 equatorial rain forest   3 sandy desert
2 arctic tundra   4 ocean

---

48 Two rock units contain the same radioactive substance. Rock *A* is buried deep underground; rock *B* is at the Earth's surface. Which statement best describes the half-life of the radioactive substance?

1 The radioactive substance in rock *A* has a longer half-life.
2 The radioactive substance in rock *B* has a longer half-life.
3 The radioactive substance has the same half-life in rock *A* and in rock *B*.
4 The radioactive substance's half-life has increased with time in rocks *A* and *B*.

49 A marine fossil was found to contain one-half of its original quantity of carbon-14. According to the *Earth Science Reference Tables*, approximately how old is this fossil?

(1) 5,700 years   (3) 17,100 years
(2) 11,400 years   (4) 22,800 years

50 In New York State, the Susquehanna River and the Delaware River both flow over a region classified as a

1 lowland   3 coastal plain
2 plateau   4 mountain range

51 Which substance found in a soil sample collected in an arid region would most likely be absent in a soil sample collected in a humid region?

1 rock salt   3 obsidian
2 quartz   4 pyroxene

52 Features such as mountains, plains, and plateaus divide continents into

1 crustal activity zones
2 natural resource zones
3 landscape regions
4 erosional activity areas

53 According to the *Earth Science Reference Tables*, which New York State landscape surface is composed of gneisses, quartzites, marbles, and anorthositic bedrock?

1 Allegheny Plateau
2 Erie-Ontario Lowlands
3 the Catskills
4 Adirondack Mountains

54 Which New York State landscape region could have surface bedrock containing dinosaur fossils?

1 Adirondack Highlands
2 Erie-Ontario Lowlands
3 St. Lawrence Lowlands
4 Newark Lowlands

55 Which geologic cross section best represents the bedrock at Binghamton?

Key: Rock unit symbols are those found on the Generalized Bedrock Geology of New York State map. The symbol ∿∿∿ represents an unconformity.

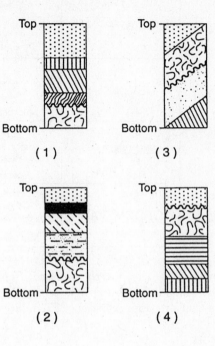

(1)   (3)

(2)   (4)

Part II

This part consists of ten groups, each containing five questions. Choose seven of these ten groups. Be sure that you answer all five questions in each group chosen. Record the answers to these questions on the separate answer sheet in accordance with the directions on the front page of this booklet. [35]

Group 1

If you choose this group, be sure to answer questions 56–60.

Base your answers to questions 56 through 60 on the *Earth Science Reference Tables*, the table and information below, and your knowledge of Earth science.

The Bay of Fundy, located on the east coast of Canada, has the highest ocean tides in the world. The St. John River enters the Bay of Fundy at the city of St. John, where the river actually reverses direction twice a day at high tides. Data for the famous Reversing Falls of the St. John River are given below for high and low tides on June 26 through 28, 1994.

Tidal Record for Reversing Falls, St. John River				
Date	Time of First High Tide	Time of First Low Tide	Time of Second High Tide	Time of Second Low Tide
June 26	2:25 a.m.	8:45 a.m.	2:55 p.m.	9:05 p.m.
June 27	3:15 a.m.	9:35 a.m.	3:45 p.m.	9:55 p.m.
June 28	4:05 a.m.	10:25 a.m.	4:35 p.m.	10:45 p.m.

56 Which graph best represents the tides recorded on June 28?

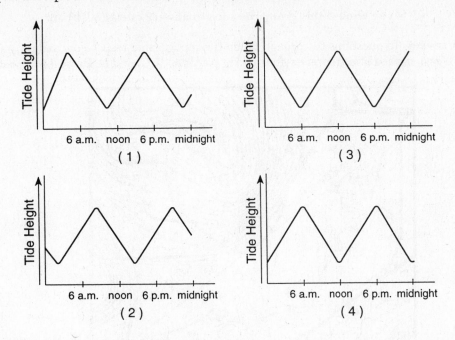

57 Which model of the Sun, Earth (*E*), and Moon (*M*) best represents a position that would cause the highest ocean tides in the Bay of Fundy? [Sizes and distances are not drawn to scale.]

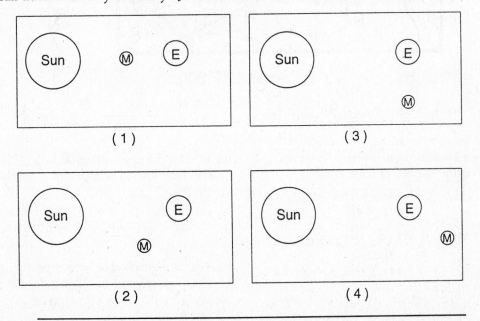

58 Compared to the first high tide on June 26, how much later in the day did the first high tide occur on June 27?

(1) 10 min   (3) 1 h 10 min
(2) 50 min   (4) 5 h 40 min

59 Tides in the Bay of Fundy are best described as

1 predictable and noncyclic
2 predictable and cyclic
3 unpredictable and noncyclic
4 unpredictable and cyclic

60 The Moon has a greater effect on the Earth's ocean tides than the Sun has because the

1 Sun has a higher density than the Moon
2 Sun has a higher temperature than the Moon
3 Moon has a greater mass than the Sun
4 Moon is closer to the Earth than the Sun is

Group 2

If you choose this group, be sure to answer questions 61–65.

Base your answers to questions 61 through 65 on the topographic map below and on your knowledge of Earth science. Heavy dashed lines represent four hiking paths, *A*, *B*, *C*, and *D*. Point *P* is a location on the map.

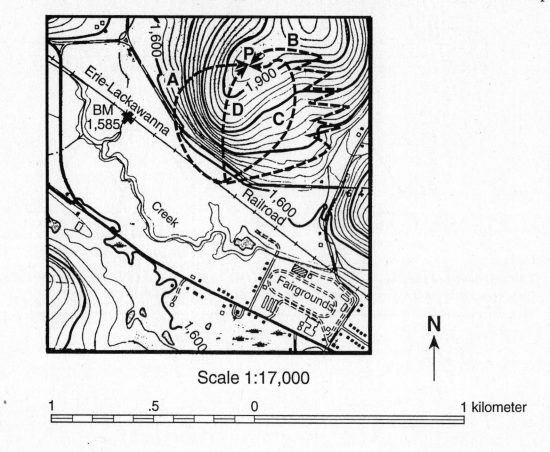

Scale 1:17,000

1   .5   0   1 kilometer

61 On this map, 1 centimeter represents how many centimeters on the surface of the Earth?

(1) 1,600   (3) 14,700
(2) 1,900   (4) 17,000

62 What is the contour interval for this map?

(1) 10 ft   (3) 25 ft
(2) 20 ft   (4) 100 ft

63 On what type of landscape are the fairgrounds located?

1 a cliff   3 a hilltop
2 a coastal plain   4 a floodplain

64 What is the approximate length of the portion of the Erie-Lackawanna railroad tracks shown on the map?

(1) 2.5 km   (3) 3.0 km
(2) 2.0 km   (4) 3.5 km

65 Which path climbs the steepest part of the hill from the railroad tracks to point *P*?

(1) *A*   (3) *C*
(2) *B*   (4) *D*

Group 3

If you choose this group, be sure to answer questions 66–70.

Base your answers to questions 66 through 70 on the *Earth Science Reference Tables*, the diagram below, and your knowledge of Earth science. The diagram represents a cross section of a portion of the Earth's crust. Points *A* through *D* represent locations in the bedrock. The rock layers have not been overturned.

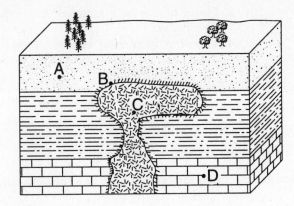

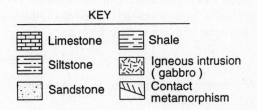

KEY

▦ Limestone   ▤ Shale

▤ Siltstone   ▨ Igneous intrusion (gabbro)

▨ Sandstone   ▨ Contact metamorphism

66 Which rock is *least* likely to contain fossils?

1 gabbro   3 limestone
2 shale   4 siltstone

67 Which rock formed most recently?

1 limestone   3 shale
2 siltstone   4 gabbro

68 Which rock formed as a result of heat and pressure at point *B*?

1 slate   3 marble
2 quartzite   4 anthracite coal

69 The limestone layer could have been formed primarily by

1 foliation of mica during faulting
2 chemical precipitation of calcite
3 deposition of quartz fragments
4 decomposition of plant remains

70 Which two minerals will probably be most abundant in the igneous intrusion?

1 quartz and calcite
2 halite and gypsum
3 potassium feldspar and biotite
4 plagioclase feldspar and pyroxene

Group 4

If you choose this group, be sure to answer questions 71–75.

Base your answers to questions 71 through 75 on the *Earth Science Reference Tables*, the graph below, and your knowledge of Earth science. The graph shows the amount of heat energy (calories) needed to raise the temperature of 1-gram samples of four different materials.

71 What is the total number of calories of heat needed to raise the temperature of the liquid water from 20°C to 30°C?

(1) 1 cal   (3) 20 cal
(2) 10 cal   (4) 30 cal

72 Which of these materials has the highest specific heat?

1 liquid water   3 basalt
2 dry air   4 iron

73 If all four materials were heated to 100°C and then allowed to cool, which material would show the most rapid drop in temperature?

1 basalt   3 dry air
2 iron   4 liquid water

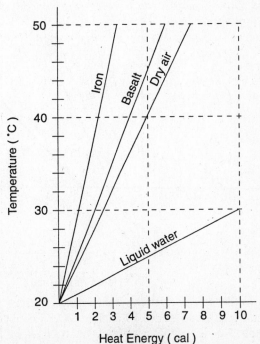

74 Which statement is best supported by the graph?

1 The same amount of heat energy is required to raise the temperature of each material by 10 Celsius degrees.

2 The temperature of a material with a high specific heat is raised faster than that of a material with a low specific heat.

3 Three of the four materials have the same specific heat.

4 The amount of heat energy needed to produce an equal temperature change varies with the materials heated.

---

75 Which graph below correctly shows where the line representing the temperature of a fifth material, lead, would be located?

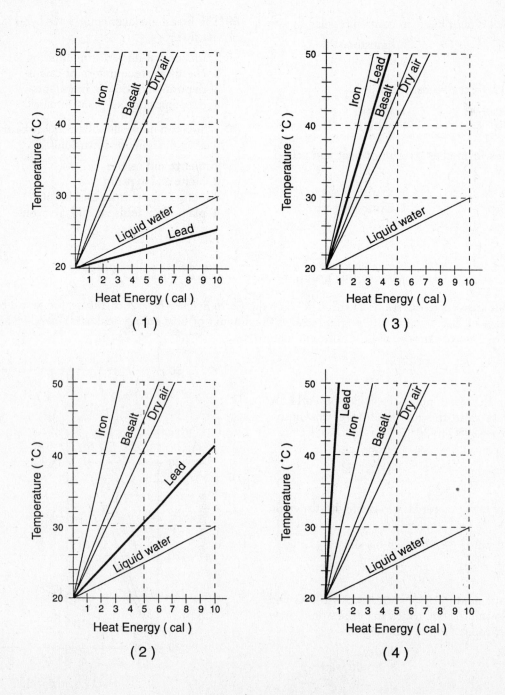

Group 5

If you choose this group, be sure to answer questions 76–80.

Base your answers to questions 76 through 80 on the *Earth Science Reference Tables*, the map below, and your knowledge of Earth science. The map represents a high-pressure air mass centered over New York State at 10 a.m. on June 16.

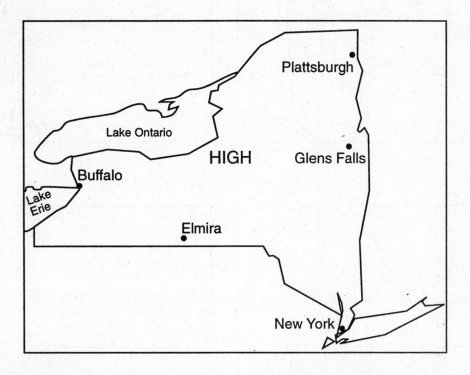

76 Which pattern represents the most likely surface wind direction of this high-pressure system?

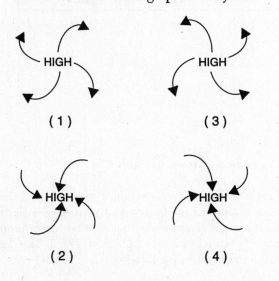

77 At Syracuse, the weather is most likely

   1 cold, with snow   3 clear and cool
   2 hot and humid   4 cloudy, with rain

78 Which type of air mass usually causes these high-pressure centers over New York State?

   1 continental tropical   3 maritime tropical
   2 continental polar   4 maritime polar

79 As this high-pressure center follows the usual air-mass track, it will travel toward

   1 Buffalo   3 Lake Ontario
   2 Elmira   4 Glens Falls

80 Which map shows the most likely pattern of isobars associated with this weather system?

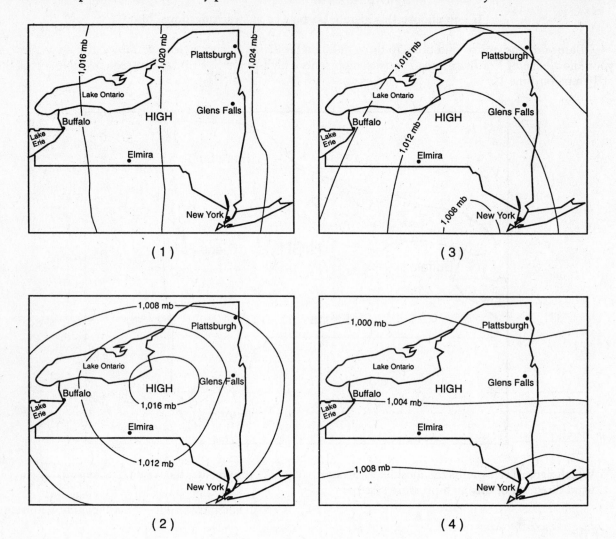

(1) (3)

(2) (4)

Group 6

If you choose this group, be sure to answer questions 81–85.

Base your answers to questions 81 through 85 on the *Earth Science Reference Tables*, the map and data table below, and your knowledge of Earth science. The map represents an imaginary continent on the Earth. Letters *B* through *G* are locations on the map for which climate ratios are given. The climate ratio is determined by dividing the average yearly precipitation by the average yearly potential evapotranspiration (P/E_p). The data table shows the monthly precipitation and potential evapotranspiration values for location *A*.

Imaginary Continent

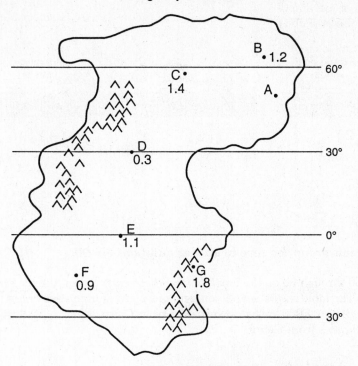

Climate Ratio (Yearly P/E_p)	Climate Type
Less than 0.4	Arid
0.4 – 0.8	Semiarid
0.8 – 1.2	Subhumid
Greater than 1.2	Humid

Water Budget Data for Location A (mm)

	Jan.	Feb.	Mar.	Apr.	May	June	July	Aug.	Sept.	Oct.	Nov.	Dec.	Totals
Precipitation (P)	68	76	89	96	81	68	75	71	67	65	70	63	889
Potential Evapotranspiration (E_p)	5	10	35	60	85	155	170	159	82	60	34	10	865

81 At location *A*, the value of the yearly P/E_p ratio is 1089 mm/865 mm. What is the type of climate at location *A*?

1 arid
2 semiarid
3 subhumid
4 humid

82 Which graph best shows the monthly precipitation and potential evapotranspiration values for location *A*?

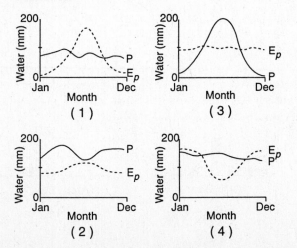

83 The potential evapotranspiration (E_p) recorded at these locations depends primarily on the

1 soil composition in the area
2 height of the water table
3 level of water in the streams
4 amount of solar radiation absorbed

84 Which climate condition is characteristic of both location *C* and location *D*?

1 a large amount of yearly precipitation
2 a large yearly temperature range
3 the same yearly potential evapotranspiration
4 the same number of months of moisture surplus

85 Location *G* has a cold, humid climate. Which profile best represents the position of location *G* with respect to the mountains and the prevailing winds?

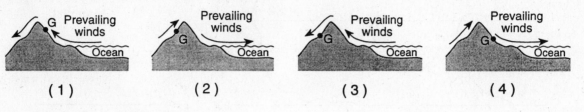

(1)　　　　　　(2)　　　　　　(3)　　　　　　(4)

Group 7

If you choose this group, be sure to answer questions 86–90.

Base your answers to questions 86 through 90 on the *Earth Science Reference Tables*, the data table below, and your knowledge of Earth science. The table shows the percentages of different grain sizes deposited as sediment in the Mississippi River 100 miles to 1,000 miles downstream from Cairo, Illinois. The river's mouth empties into the Gulf of Mexico 1,000 miles from Cairo.

Grain Size Percentages

Grain Size	Miles Downstream from Cairo					
	100 mi	300 mi	500 mi	700 mi	900 mi	1,000 mi
Small Pebbles	29%	8%	14%	5%	none	none
Coarse Sand	30%	22%	9%	8%	1%	none
Medium Sand	32%	50%	46%	44%	26%	9%
Fine Sand	8%	19%	28%	41%	70%	69%
Silt	trace	trace	2%	1%	2%	10%
Clay	trace	trace	1%	trace	1%	10%

86 Which graph best shows the percentage of each grain size found at a location 300 miles downstream from Cairo?

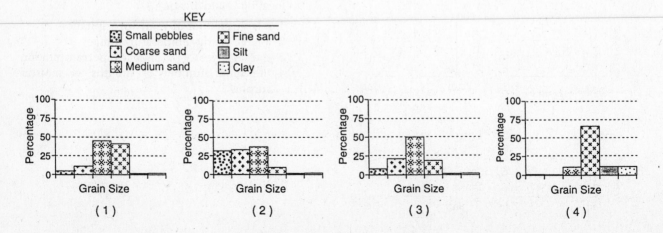

KEY

🔲 Small pebbles　　🔲 Fine sand
🔲 Coarse sand　　🔲 Silt
🔲 Medium sand　　🔲 Clay

(1)　　　　　　(2)　　　　　　(3)　　　　　　(4)

87 At the river's mouth, 1,000 miles downstream from Cairo, small pebbles and coarse sand are *not* being deposited because these particles are

1 dissolved in the river water
2 deposited before reaching this location
3 being carried in suspension
4 being rolled along the stream bottom

88 What was the *minimum* water velocity needed to transport the sediments deposited 900 miles downstream from Cairo?

(1) 20 cm/sec   (3) 170 cm/sec
(2) 50 cm/sec   (4) 200 cm/sec

89 As a pebble travels downstream from Cairo toward the Gulf of Mexico, it most likely becomes more

1 dense   3 flattened
2 angular   4 rounded

90 Which statement best describes the changes in the velocity of the stream and the particle sizes carried by the stream between 500 and 900 miles below Cairo?

1 Velocity decreased and particle size decreased.
2 Velocity decreased and particle size increased.
3 Velocity increased and particle size decreased.
4 Velocity increased and particle size increased.

Group 8

If you choose this group, be sure to answer questions 91–95.

Base your answers to questions 91 through 95 on the *Earth Science Reference Tables*, the world map below, and your knowledge of Earth science. The small dots on the map represent earthquake epicenters. The letters on the map represent locations.

Earthquake Epicenters

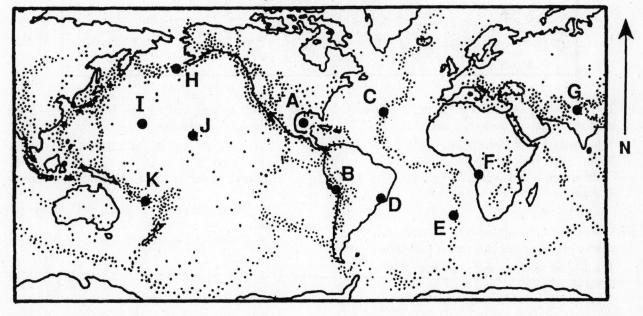

91 Where do most of these earthquakes occur?

1 in the centers of the continents
2 in specific belts within the crust
3 randomly throughout the mantle
4 along the core-mantle interface

92 Locations *H* and *K* are found at tectonic plate boundaries referred to as

1 divergent zones   3 ridges
2 rift zones   4 trenches

93 At which location do rocks, minerals, and fossils most closely match those at location *D*?

   (1) *H*   (3) *E*
   (2) *B*   (4) *F*

94 At which location did earthquakes occur as a result of the Nazca plate sliding under the South American plate?

   (1) *A*   (3) *C*
   (2) *B*   (4) *D*

95 Which processes normally occur in association with the plotted earthquakes?

   1 glaciation and erosion
   2 deposition and sedimentation
   3 volcanism and mountain building
   4 fossilization and evolution

Group 9

If you choose this group, be sure to answer questions 96–100.

Base your answers to questions 96 through 100 on the *Earth Science Reference Tables*, the diagram below, and your knowledge of Earth science. The diagram shows a cross section of a landscape and a nearby sea. Letters *A* and *B* indicate locations on the landscape surface. The geologic age of three of the rock types is shown.

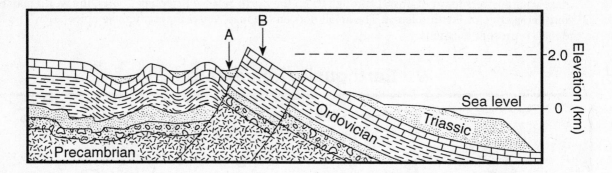

96 The landscape near locations *A* and *B* is considered mountainous because it contains

   1 horizontal rock layers of low relief
   2 horizontal rock layers of high relief
   3 deformed rock layers of low relief
   4 deformed rock layers of high relief

97 Which particle size and type of fossil would be characteristic of the Ordovician rock layer?

   1 silt-sized particles and shark fossils
   2 silt-sized particles and coral fossils
   3 clay-sized particles and shark fossils
   4 clay-sized particles and coral fossils

98 The structural feature shown in the bedrock between locations *A* and *B* is a

   1 volcano   3 glacial moraine
   2 fault   4 plateau

99 Which activity caused the limestone bedrock layer to become folded?

   1 slow movement of volcanic rock as it was deposited
   2 crustal movement that occurred after deposition
   3 deposition of sediments with different densities
   4 deposition of loose fragments in angular beds

100 Which change would occur at location *B* when uplifting forces dominate leveling forces?

   1 Streams would decrease in velocity.
   2 Erosion and deposition would decrease.
   3 Hillslopes would increase in steepness.
   4 Topographic features would become smoother.

Group 10

If you choose this group, be sure to answer questions 101–105.

Base your answers to questions 101 through 105 on the *Earth Science Reference Tables* and on your knowledge of Earth science.

101 Which graph best represents the percentage by volume of the elements making up the Earth's hydrosphere?

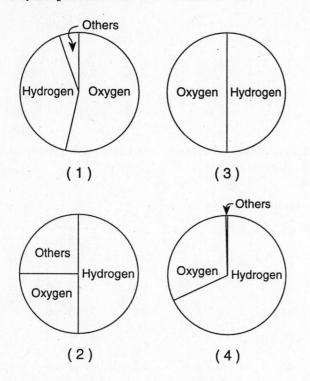

(1)   (3)

(2)   (4)

102 At which temperature would an object radiate the most electromagnetic energy?
  (1) 50°C
  (2) 80°C
  (3) 310 K
  (4) 140°F

103 Which information in the *Earth Science Reference Tables* is an inference rather than an observation?
  1 Temperature decreases as elevation in the troposphere increases.
  2 Saturn's period of rotation is 10 hours 14 minutes.
  3 A *P*-wave travels 5,600 kilometers in 9 minutes.
  4 The Earth's outer core is made of iron.

104 An observer incorrectly measured the mass of a rock as 428.7 grams. The actual mass was 450.0 grams. What was the observer's approximate percentage of error?
  (1) 5.0%
  (2) 2.1%
  (3) 4.3%
  (4) 4.7%

105 When the height of the mercury in a barometer is 29.92 inches, the barometric pressure is
  (1) 1,000.0 mb
  (2) 1,005.5 mb
  (3) 1,013.2 mb
  (4) 1,020.4 mb

EARTH SCIENCE
JANUARY 1997

_____

ANSWER SHEET

Student . . . .

Teacher . . . . School . . . .

Grade (circle one)   8   9   10   11   12

Record all of your answers on this answer sheet in accordance with the instructions on the front cover of the test booklet.

Part I (55 credits)

1	1 2 3 4	**16**	1 2 3 4	**31**	1 2 3 4	**46**	1 2 3 4
2	1 2 3 4	**17**	1 2 3 4	**32**	1 2 3 4	**47**	1 2 3 4
3	1 2 3 4	**18**	1 2 3 4	**33**	1 2 3 4	**48**	1 2 3 4
4	1 2 3 4	**19**	1 2 3 4	**34**	1 2 3 4	**49**	1 2 3 4
5	1 2 3 4	**20**	1 2 3 4	**35**	1 2 3 4	**50**	1 2 3 4
6	1 2 3 4	**21**	1 2 3 4	**36**	1 2 3 4	**51**	1 2 3 4
7	1 2 3 4	**22**	1 2 3 4	**37**	1 2 3 4	**52**	1 2 3 4
8	1 2 3 4	**23**	1 2 3 4	**38**	1 2 3 4	**53**	1 2 3 4
9	1 2 3 4	**24**	1 2 3 4	**39**	1 2 3 4	**54**	1 2 3 4
10	1 2 3 4	**25**	1 2 3 4	**40**	1 2 3 4	**55**	1 2 3 4
11	1 2 3 4	**26**	1 2 3 4	**41**	1 2 3 4		
12	1 2 3 4	**27**	1 2 3 4	**42**	1 2 3 4		
13	1 2 3 4	**28**	1 2 3 4	**43**	1 2 3 4		
14	1 2 3 4	**29**	1 2 3 4	**44**	1 2 3 4		
15	1 2 3 4	**30**	1 2 3 4	**45**	1 2 3 4		

Part II (35 credits)

Answer the questions in only seven of the ten groups in this part. Be sure to mark the answers to the groups of questions you choose in accordance with the instructions on the front cover of the test booklet. Leave blank the three groups of questions you do not choose to answer.

	Group 1			
56	1	2	3	4
57	1	2	3	4
58	1	2	3	4
59	1	2	3	4
60	1	2	3	4

	Group 2			
61	1	2	3	4
62	1	2	3	4
63	1	2	3	4
64	1	2	3	4
65	1	2	3	4

	Group 3			
66	1	2	3	4
67	1	2	3	4
68	1	2	3	4
69	1	2	3	4
70	1	2	3	4

	Group 4			
71	1	2	3	4
72	1	2	3	4
73	1	2	3	4
74	1	2	3	4
75	1	2	3	4

	Group 5			
76	1	2	3	4
77	1	2	3	4
78	1	2	3	4
79	1	2	3	4
80	1	2	3	4

	Group 6			
81	1	2	3	4
82	1	2	3	4
83	1	2	3	4
84	1	2	3	4
85	1	2	3	4

	Group 7			
86	1	2	3	4
87	1	2	3	4
88	1	2	3	4
89	1	2	3	4
90	1	2	3	4

	Group 8			
91	1	2	3	4
92	1	2	3	4
93	1	2	3	4
94	1	2	3	4
95	1	2	3	4

	Group 9			
96	1	2	3	4
97	1	2	3	4
98	1	2	3	4
99	1	2	3	4
100	1	2	3	4

	Group 10			
101	1	2	3	4
102	1	2	3	4
103	1	2	3	4
104	1	2	3	4
105	1	2	3	4

EARTH SCIENCE
JUNE 1997

Part I

Answer all 55 questions in this part. [55]

Directions (1–55): For *each* statement or question, select the word or expression that, of those given, best completes the statement or answers the question. Record your answer on the separate answer sheet in accordance with the directions on the front page of this booklet. Some questions may require the use of the *Earth Science Reference Tables*.

1 The circumference of the Earth is about 4.0×10^4 kilometers. This value is equal to

(1) 400 km   (3) 40,000 km
(2) 4,000 km   (4) 400,000 km

2 The diagram below shows a process of weathering called frost wedging.

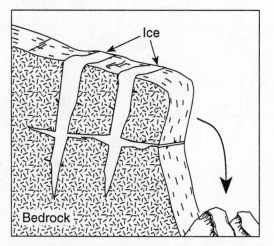

Frost wedging breaks rocks because as water freezes it increases in

1 mass   3 density
2 volume   4 specific heat

3 A student calculates the period of Saturn's revolution to be 31.33 years. What is the student's approximate deviation from the accepted value?

(1) 1.9%   (3) 6.3%
(2) 5.9%   (4) 19%

4 Which object best represents a true scale model of the shape of the Earth?

1 a Ping-Pong ball   3 an egg
2 a football   4 a pear

5 Which graph best represents the most common relationship between the amount of air pollution and the distance from an industrial city?

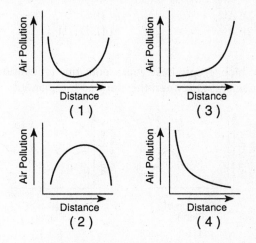

6 Isolines on the topographic map below show elevations above sea level, measured in meters.

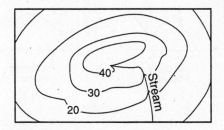

What could be the highest possible elevation represented on this map?

(1) 39 m   (3) 45 m
(2) 41 m   (4) 49 m

7 Oxygen is the most abundant element by volume in the Earth's

1 inner core   3 hydrosphere
2 crust   4 troposphere

Base your answers to questions 8 and 9 on the diagram below and on your knowledge of Earth science. The diagram represents the path of a planet orbiting a star. Points *A*, *B*, *C*, and *D* indicate four orbital positions of the planet.

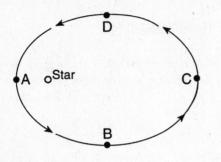

8 When viewed by an observer on the planet, the star has the largest apparent diameter at position

(1) *A*   (3) *C*
(2) *B*   (4) *D*

9 Which graph best represents the gravitational attraction between the star and the planet?

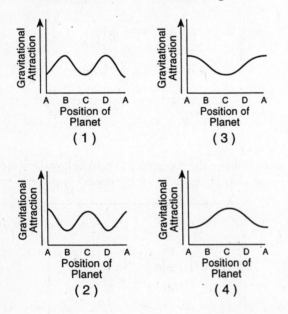

10 Which statement best explains why different phases of the Moon can be observed from the Earth?

1 The size of the Earth's shadow falling on the Moon changes.
2 The Moon moves into different parts of the Earth's shadow.
3 Differing amounts of the Moon's sunlit surface are seen because the Moon revolves around the Sun.
4 Differing amounts of the Moon's sunlit surface are seen because the Moon revolves around the Earth.

11 The diagram below represents an activity in which an eye dropper was used to place a drop of water on a spinning globe. Instead of flowing due south toward the target point, the drop followed a curved path and missed the target.

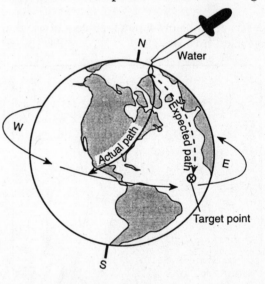

The actual path results from

1 the tilt of the globe's axis
2 the Coriolis effect
3 the globe's revolution
4 dynamic equilibrium

Base your answers to questions 12 and 13 on the diagrams below, which show laboratory equipment setups *A* and *B* being used to study energy transfer in a classroom laboratory.

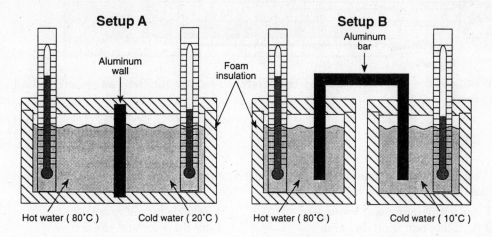

12 In both *A* and *B*, most of the heat energy transferred from the hot water to the cold water is transferred by

1 convection 3 radiation

2 conduction 4 gravity

13 Which laboratory setup is more efficient at transferring heat energy from the hot water to the cold water?

(1) *A*, because less energy is lost to the surrounding environment

(2) *A*, because the hot water has a higher temperature

(3) *B*, because the aluminum bar is bigger than the aluminum wall

(4) *B*, because the cold water has a lower temperature

14 Which diagram best shows how air inside a greenhouse warms as a result of insolation from the Sun?

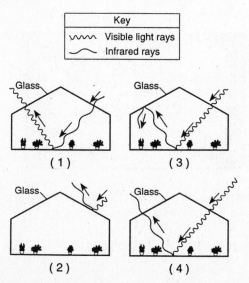

15 Why do the locations of sunrise and sunset vary in a cyclical pattern throughout the year?

1 The Earth's orbit around the Sun is an ellipse.

2 The Sun's orbit around the Earth is an ellipse.

3 The Sun rotates on an inclined axis while revolving around the Earth.

4 The Earth rotates on an inclined axis while revolving around the Sun.

16 On a clear April morning near Rochester, New York, which surface will absorb the most insolation per square meter?

1 a calm lake

2 a snowdrift

3 a white-sand beach

4 a freshly plowed farm field

Base your answers to questions 17 and 18 on the weather instrument shown in the diagram below.

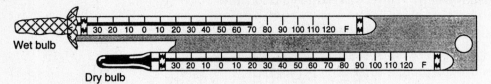

17 What are the equivalent Celsius temperature readings for the Fahrenheit readings shown?

   1 wet 21°C, dry 27°C   3 wet 70°C, dry 80°C
   2 wet 26°C, dry 37°C   4 wet 158°C, dry 176°C

18 Which weather variables are most easily determined by using this weather instrument and the *Earth Science Reference Tables*?

   1 air temperature and windspeed   3 relative humidity and dewpoint
   2 visibility and wind direction   4 air pressure and cloud type

---

19 All of the containers shown below contain the same volume of water and are at room temperature. In a two-day period, from which container will the *least* amount of water evaporate?

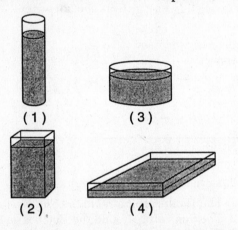

20 Which statement best explains why precipitation occurs at the frontal surfaces between air masses?

   1 Warm, moist air sinks when it meets cold, dry air.
   2 Warm, moist air rises when it meets cold, dry air.
   3 Cold fronts move faster than warm fronts.
   4 Cold fronts move slower than warm fronts.

21 By which process does water vapor leave the atmosphere and form dew?

   1 condensation   3 convection
   2 transpiration   4 precipitation

22 The diagram below represents a section of a weather map showing high- and low-pressure systems. The lines represent isobars.

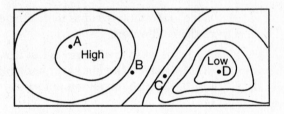

At which point is the windspeed greatest?

   (1) A   (3) C
   (2) B   (4) D

23 A low-pressure system is shown on the weather map below.

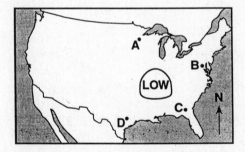

Toward which point will the low-pressure system move if it follows a typical storm track?

   (1) A   (3) C
   (2) B   (4) D

24 The diagram below shows equal volumes of loosely packed sand, clay, and small pebbles placed in identical funnels. The soils are dry, and the beakers are empty.

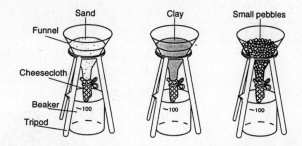

A 100-milliliter sample of water is poured into each funnel at the same time and allowed to seep through for 15 minutes. Which diagram best shows the amount of water that passes through each funnel into the beakers?

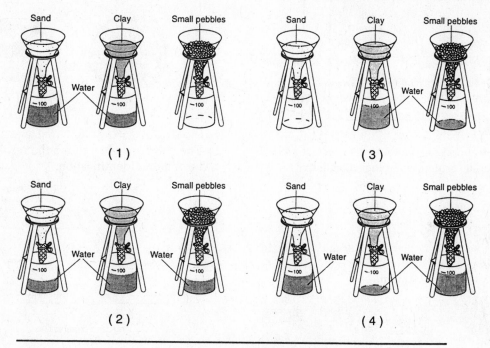

(1)   (3)

(2)   (4)

25 The upward movement of water through tiny spaces in soil or rock is called

1 water retention   3 porosity
2 capillary action   4 permeability

26 A deposit of rock particles that are angular, scratched, and unsorted has most likely been transported and deposited by

1 ocean waves   3 a glacier
2 running water   4 wind

27 When the soil is saturated in a gently sloping area, any additional rainfall in the area will most likely

1 become ground water
2 become surface runoff
3 cause a moisture deficit
4 cause a higher potential evapotranspiration

28 Which graph best represents conditions in an area with a moisture deficit?

[Key: E_p = potential evapotranspiration; P = precipitation; St = storage]

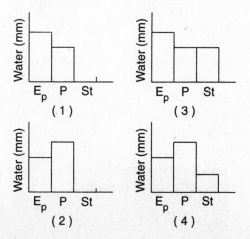

29 The diagram below shows a residual soil profile formed in an area of granite bedrock. Four different soil horizons, A, B, C, and D, are shown.

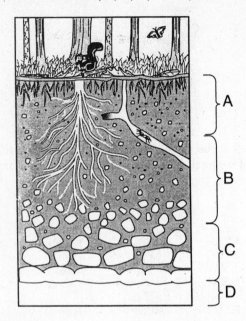

Which soil horizon contains the greatest amount of material formed by biological activity?

(1) A　　　　　　(3) C
(2) B　　　　　　(4) D

Base your answers to questions 30 and 31 on the diagram below. The diagram shows points A, B, C, and D on a meandering stream.

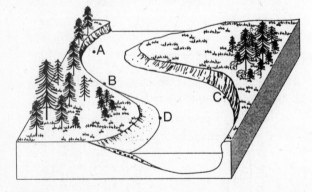

30 Which material is most likely to be transported in suspension during periods of slowest stream velocity?

1 gravel　　　　3 silt
2 sand　　　　　4 clay

31 At which point is the amount of deposition more than the amount of erosion?

(1) A　　　　　　(3) C
(2) B　　　　　　(4) D

32 Which rock is usually composed of several different minerals?

1 gneiss　　　　　3 rock gypsum
2 quartzite　　　　4 chemical limestone

33 Which granite sample most likely formed from magma that cooled and solidified at the slowest rate?

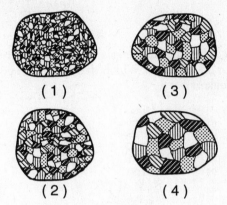

34 The diagram below shows the results of one test for mineral identification.

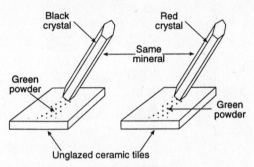

Which mineral property is being tested?

1 density　　　　　3 streak
2 fracture　　　　　4 luster

35 Which statement about the formation of a rock is best supported by geologic evidence?

1 Magma must be weathered before it can change to metamorphic rock.
2 Sediment must be compacted and cemented before it can change to sedimentary rock.
3 Sedimentary rock must melt before it can change to metamorphic rock.
4 Metamorphic rock must melt before it can change to sedimentary rock.

36 The scale below shows the age of the sea-floor crust in relation to its distance from the Mid-Atlantic Ridge.

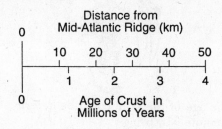

Distance from
Mid-Atlantic Ridge (km)

Age of Crust in
Millions of Years

Crust that originally formed at the Mid-Atlantic Ridge is now 37 kilometers from the ridge. Approximately how long ago did this crust form?

(1) 1.8 million years ago
(2) 2.0 million years ago
(3) 3.0 million years ago
(4) 4.5 million years ago

37 A conglomerate contains pebbles of shale, sandstone, and granite. Based on this information, which inference about the pebbles in the conglomerate is most accurate?

1 They were eroded by slow-moving water.
2 They came from other conglomerates.
3 They are all the same age.
4 They had various origins.

38 The diagrams below show demonstrations that represent the behavior of two seismic waves, A and B.

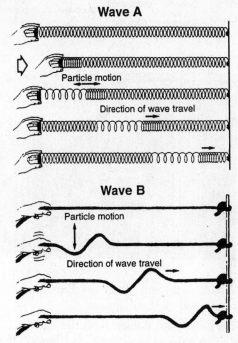

Wave A

Particle motion

Direction of wave travel

Wave B

Particle motion

Direction of wave travel

Which statement concerning the demonstrated waves is correct?

1 Wave A represents a compressional wave, and wave B represents a shear wave.
2 Wave A represents a shear wave, and wave B represents a compressional wave.
3 Wave A represents compressional waves in the crust, and wave B represents compressional waves in the mantle.
4 Wave A represents shear waves in the crust, and wave B represents shear waves in the mantle.

39 The cartoon below presents a humorous view of Earth science.

PEANUTS   BY CHARLES M. SCHULZ

© 1991 United Feature Syndicate, Inc.

..AND A THOUSAND YEARS FROM NOW PEOPLE WILL LOOK AT WHAT WE HAVE BUILT HERE TODAY, AND BE TOTALLY AMAZED...

The cartoon character on the right realizes that the sand castle will eventually be

1 preserved as fossil evidence
2 deformed during metamorphic change
3 removed by agents of erosion
4 compacted into solid bedrock

40 The diagram below represents a cross section of a portion of the Earth's lithosphere.

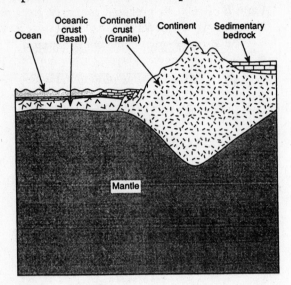

Which statement about the Earth's crust is best supported by the diagram?

1 The crust is thicker than the mantle.
2 The continental crust is thicker than the oceanic crust.
3 The crust is composed primarily of sedimentary rock.
4 The crust is composed of denser rock than the mantle.

41 The epicenter of an earthquake is 6,000 kilometers from an observation point. What is the difference in travel time for the *P*-waves and *S*-waves?

(1) 7 min 35 sec   (3) 13 min 10 sec
(2) 9 min 20 sec   (4) 17 min 00 sec

42 At a depth of 2,000 kilometers, the temperature of the stiffer mantle is inferred to be

(1) 6,500°C   (3) 3,500°C
(2) 4,200°C   (4) 1,500°C

43 Hot springs on the ocean floor near the mid-ocean ridges provide evidence that

1 climate change has melted huge glaciers
2 marine fossils have been uplifted to high elevations
3 meteor craters are found beneath the oceans
4 convection currents exist in the asthenosphere

44 The diagram below represents the skull of a saber-toothed tiger that died 30,000 years ago.

The age of the skull could be determined most accurately by using

1 uranium-238   3 potassium-40
2 rubidium-87   4 carbon-14

45 A geologist collected the fossils shown below from locations in New York State.

Which sequence correctly shows the fossils from oldest to youngest?

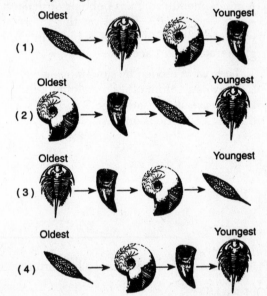

46 Present-day corals live in warm, tropical ocean water. Which inference is best supported by the discovery of Ordovician-age corals in the surface bedrock of western New York State?

1 Western New York State was covered by a warm, shallow sea during Ordovician time.
2 Ordovician-age corals lived in the forests of western New York State.
3 Ordovician-age corals were transported to western New York State by cold, freshwater streams.
4 Western New York State was covered by a continental ice sheet that created coral fossils of Ordovician time.

47 The diagram below represents the radioactive decay of uranium-238.

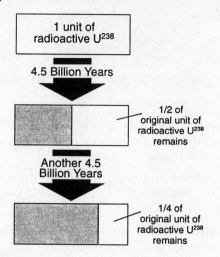

1 unit of radioactive U²³⁸

4.5 Billion Years

1/2 of original unit of radioactive U²³⁸ remains

Another 4.5 Billion Years

1/4 of original unit of radioactive U²³⁸ remains

According to the *Earth Science Reference Tables*, shaded areas on the diagram represent the amount of

1 undecayed radioactive rubidium-87 (Rb^{87})
2 undecayed radioactive uranium-238 (U^{238})
3 stable lead-206 (Pb^{206})
4 stable carbon-14 (C^{14})

48 In which way are index fossils and volcanic ash deposits similar?

1 Both can usually be dated with radiocarbon.
2 Both normally occur in nonsedimentary rocks.
3 Both strongly resist chemical weathering.
4 Both often serve as geologic time markers.

49 The block diagrams below show a landscape region before and after uplift and erosion.

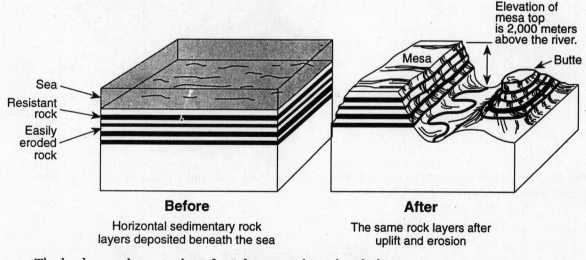

Sea
Resistant rock
Easily eroded rock

Before
Horizontal sedimentary rock layers deposited beneath the sea

Elevation of mesa top is 2,000 meters above the river.
Mesa
Butte

After
The same rock layers after uplift and erosion

The landscape shown in the "after" diagram is best classified as a

1 folded mountain
2 plateau region

3 plains region
4 volcanic dome

50 Which statement correctly describes an age relationship in the geologic cross section below?

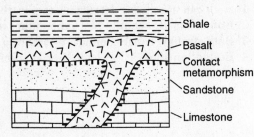

— Shale
— Basalt
— Contact metamorphism
— Sandstone
— Limestone

1 The sandstone is younger than the basalt.
2 The shale is younger than the basalt.
3 The limestone is younger than the shale.
4 The limestone is younger than the sandstone.

51 The landscape around Old Forge, New York, consists of

1 flat, low-lying volcanic rock
2 hills of horizontal sedimentary rock layers
3 mountains of metamorphic rock
4 eroded, tilted sedimentary rock

52 The diagrams below represent geologic cross sections from two widely separated regions.

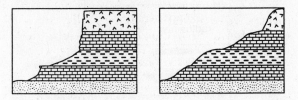

The layers of rock appear very similar, but the hillslopes and shapes are different. These differences are most likely the result of

1 volcanic eruptions   3 soil formation
2 earthquake activity   4 climate variations

53 Which bedrock characteristics most influence landscape development?

1 composition and structure
2 structure and age
3 age and color
4 color and composition

---

54 The map below shows the location of an ancient sea, which evaporated to form the Silurian-age deposits of rock salt and rock gypsum now found in some New York State bedrock.

Within which two landscape regions are these large rock salt and rock gypsum deposits found?

1 Hudson Highlands and Taconic Mountains
2 Tug Hill Plateau and Adirondack Mountains
3 Erie-Ontario Lowlands and Allegheny Plateau
4 Catskills and Hudson-Mohawk Lowlands

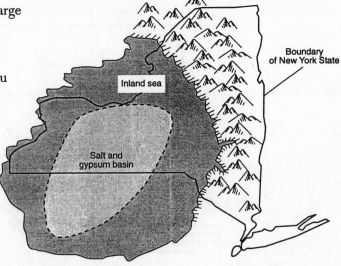

Boundary of New York State

Inland sea

Salt and gypsum basin

55 The diagram below represents a cross section of the bedrock and land surface in part of Tennessee. The dotted lines indicate missing rock layers.

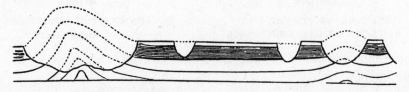

Which statement is best supported by the diagram?

1 Rocks are weathered and eroded evenly.
2 Folded rocks are more easily weathered and eroded.
3 Deposits of sediments provide evidence of erosion.
4 Climate differences affect the amount of erosion.

Part II

This part consists of ten groups, each containing five questions. Choose seven of these ten groups. Be sure that you answer all five questions in each group chosen. Record the answers to these questions on the separate answer sheet in accordance with the directions on the front page of this booklet.   [35]

Group 1

If you choose this group, be sure to answer questions 56–60.

Base your answers to questions 56 through 60 on the table below and on your knowledge of Earth science. The table shows data for a student's collection of rock samples A through I, which are classified into groups X, Y, and Z. For each rock sample, the student recorded mass, volume, density, and a brief description. The density for rock D has been left blank.

Rock Collection

Group	Rock	Mass (g)	Volume (cm³)	Density (g/cm³)	Description
X	A	82.9	34.4	2.41	Grey, smooth, rounded
	B	114.2	42.6	2.68	Brown, smooth, rounded
	C	144.7	63.2	2.29	Black, smooth, rounded
Y	D	159.4	59.7		Black and grey crystals, angular
	E	87.7	33.1	2.65	Clear and pink crystals, angular
	F	59.6	21.0	2.84	White, grey, and black crystals; angular
Z	G	201.1	68.4	2.94	Grey, shiny, flat
	H	85.1	39.8	2.14	Brown, sandy feel, flat
	I	110.2	47.3	2.33	Dark grey, flaky, flat

56 The student's classification system is based on

1 density
2 shape
3 color
4 mass

57 The approximate density of rock sample D is

(1) 2.67 g/cm³
(2) 2.75 g/cm³
(3) 3.32 g/cm³
(4) 3.75 g/cm³

58 Which statement is an inference rather than an observation?

1 Rock H is flat.
2 Rock B has been rounded by stream action.
3 Rock E has a volume of 33.1 cm³.
4 Rock G is the same color as rock I.

59 To obtain the data recorded in the column labeled "Description," the student used

1 a triple-beam balance
2 an overflow can
3 a calculator
4 her senses

Note that question 60 has only three choices.

60 The student broke rock G into two pieces. Compared to the density of the original rock, the density of one piece would most likely be

1 less
2 greater
3 the same

Group 2

If you choose this group, be sure to answer questions 61–65.

Base your answers to questions 61 through 65 on the topographic map below and on your knowledge of Earth science. Points *A*, *B*, *C*, *D*, *E*, *F*, *X*, and *Y* are locations on the map. Elevation is measured in feet.

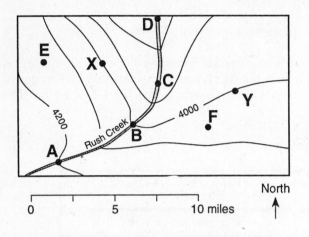

North

0   5   10 miles

61 What is the contour interval used on this map?

(1) 20 ft   (3) 100 ft
(2) 50 ft   (4) 200 ft

62 Which locations have the greatest difference in elevation?

(1) *A* and *D*   (3) *C* and *F*
(2) *B* and *X*   (4) *E* and *Y*

63 Between points *C* and *D*, Rush Creek flows toward the

1 north   3 east
2 south   4 west

64 The gradient between points *A* and *B* is closest to

(1) 20 ft/mi   (3) 80 ft/mi
(2) 40 ft/mi   (4) 200 ft/mi

65 Which diagram best represents the profile along a straight line between points *X* and *Y*?

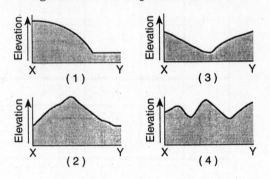

Group 3

If you choose this group, be sure to answer questions 66–70.

Base your answers to questions 66 through 70 on the *Earth Science Reference Tables*, the map below, and your knowledge of Earth science. The map represents a view of the Earth looking down from above the North Pole (N.P.), showing the Earth's 24 standard time zones. The Sun's rays are striking the Earth from the right. Points *A*, *B*, *C*, and *D* are locations on the Earth's surface.

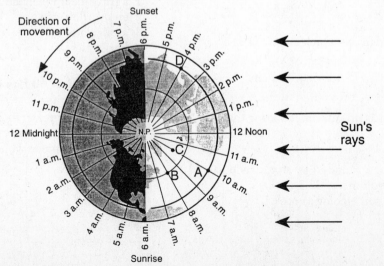

Sun's rays

66 The timekeeping system shown in the diagram is based on the

1 Sun's revolution   3 Earth's revolution
2 Sun's rotation   4 Earth's rotation

67 Which date could this diagram represent?

1 January 21   3 June 21
2 March 21   4 August 21

68 Which two points have the same longitude?

(1) A and C   (3) A and D
(2) B and C   (4) B and D

69 Areas within a time zone generally keep the same standard clock time. In degrees of longitude, approximately how wide is one standard time zone?

(1) $7\frac{1}{2}°$ (3) $23\frac{1}{2}°$
(2) 15°   (4) 30°

70 At which position would the altitude of the North Star (Polaris) be greatest?

(1) A   (3) C
(2) B   (4) D

Group 4

If you choose this group, be sure to answer questions 71–75.

Base your answers to questions 71 through 75 on the *Earth Science Reference Tables*, the weather map below, and your knowledge of Earth science. The map shows a low-pressure system over the eastern part of the United States. Weather data is given for cities *A* through *I*. The temperature at city *E* has been left blank.

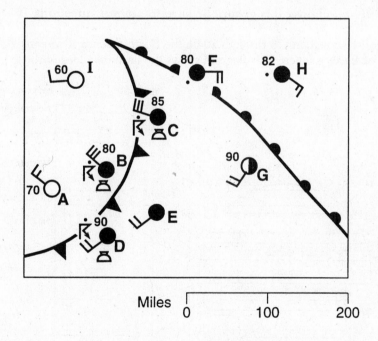

Miles 0   100   200

71 Which map correctly shows the locations of the cP and mT air-mass labels?

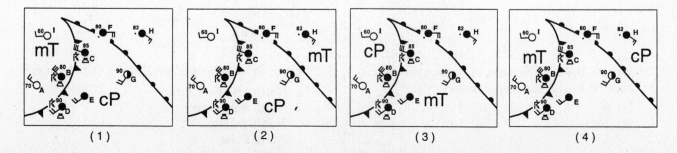

     (1)   (2)   (3)   (4)

72 The symbol ⌂ represents a cumulonimbus cloud. What is the most probable explanation for the absence of this cloud symbol at city A?

1 City A's atmosphere lacks the necessary moisture.
2 City A is located ahead of the cold front.
3 Cumulonimbus clouds form only at temperatures higher than 70°F.
4 Cumulonimbus clouds form only when a location has southwesterly winds.

73 What is the most probable temperature for city E?

(1) 60°F   (3) 75°F
(2) 70°F   (4) 88°F

74 Which city is *least* likely to have precipitation in the next few hours?

(1) A   (3) C
(2) F   (4) H

75 Which map correctly shows arrows indicating the surface wind pattern?

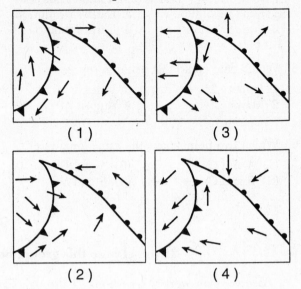

(1)   (3)

(2)   (4)

Group 5

If you choose this group, be sure to answer questions 76–80.

Base your answers to questions 76 through 80 on the *Earth Science Reference Tables*, the diagram below, and your knowledge of Earth science. The diagram shows the latitude zones of the Earth.

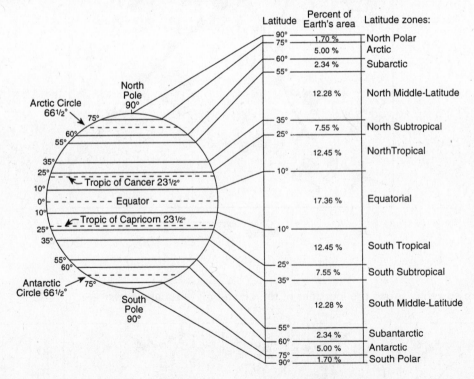

Latitude	Percent of Earth's area	Latitude zones:
90°	1.70 %	North Polar
75°	5.00 %	Arctic
60°	2.34 %	Subarctic
55°		
	12.28 %	North Middle-Latitude
35°		
25°	7.55 %	North Subtropical
	12.45 %	North Tropical
10°		
	17.36 %	Equatorial
10°		
	12.45 %	South Tropical
25°		
35°	7.55 %	South Subtropical
	12.28 %	South Middle-Latitude
55°		
60°	2.34 %	Subantarctic
75°	5.00 %	Antarctic
90°	1.70 %	South Polar

76 What is the total number of degrees of latitude covered by the Equatorial zone?

(1) 0°   (3) 17°
(2) 10°   (4) 20°

77 In which latitude zone is New York State located?

1 North Middle-Latitude
2 North Subtropical
3 North Tropical
4 North Polar

78 Which graph best represents the relationship between average yearly temperatures and latitude?

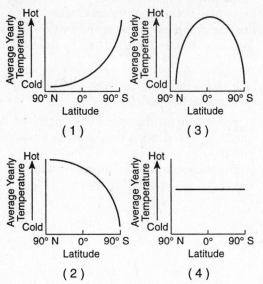

(1) (3)

(2) (4)

79 Which zone receives the greatest intensity of sunlight on June 21?

1 North Tropical 3 South Tropical
2 Equatorial 4 North Polar

80 The locations of the Tropic of Cancer and the Tropic of Capricorn are set at $23\frac{1}{2}°$ from the Equator because the

1 Earth is slightly bulged at the equatorial region
2 direct rays of the Sun move between these latitudes
3 Arctic Circle and the Antarctic Circle are $23\frac{1}{2}°$ from the poles
4 center of the Earth's gravitational field is located $23\frac{1}{2}°$ from the Equator

Group 6

If you choose this group, be sure to answer questions 81–85.

Base your answers to questions 81 through 85 on the *Earth Science Reference Tables*, the maps and cross section below, and your knowledge of Earth science. The maps show the stages in the growth of a stream delta. Point *X* represents a location in the stream channel. The side view of a stream shows rock particles transported in the stream at a point close to its source.

Maps: Stages in Growth of a Stream Delta

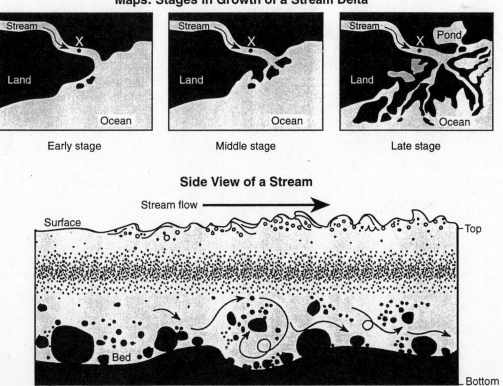

Early stage Middle stage Late stage

Side View of a Stream

81 The rock materials transported in the stream are most likely transported by which methods?

  1 in solution, only
  2 in suspension, only
  3 in solution and in suspension, only
  4 in solution, in suspension, and by rolling

82 The velocity of the stream at location X is controlled primarily by the

  1 amount of sediment carried at location X
  2 distance from location X to the stream source
  3 slope of the stream at location X
  4 temperature of the stream at location X

83 Which graph best illustrates the effect that changes in stream discharge have on stream velocity at location X?

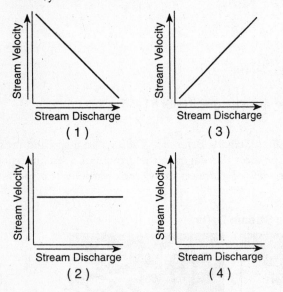

84 A decrease in the velocity of the stream at location X will usually cause an increase in

  1 downcutting by the stream
  2 deposition within the stream channel
  3 the size of the particles carried by the stream
  4 the amount of material carried by the stream

85 Which characteristics are most likely shown by the sediments in the delta?

  1 jagged fragments deposited in elongated hills
  2 unsorted mixed sizes deposited in scattered piles
  3 large cobbles deposited in parallel lines
  4 round grains deposited in layers

Group 7

If you choose this group, be sure to answer questions 86–90.

Base your answers to questions 86 through 90 on the *Earth Science Reference Tables*, the information below, and your knowledge of Earth science. The map shows surface geology of a portion of the Schoharie Valley in New York State. Patterns and letters are used to indicate bedrock of different ages. The Schoharie Valley contains mostly horizontal rock structure in which overturning has not occurred. The table provides information about the rocks shown on the map.

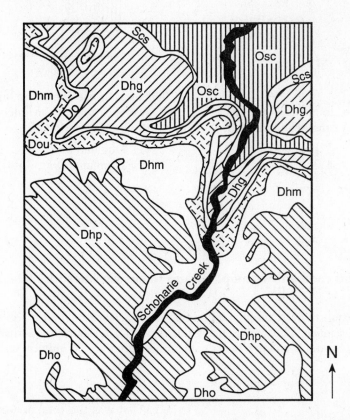

Age of the Rock	Symbol	Composition of the Rock
Middle Devonian	Dho	Shale, sandstone
	Dhp	Shale, siltstone, sandstone
	Dhm	Shale, sandstone, limestone
Early Devonian	Dou	Limestone, shale, siltstone
	Do	Sandstone, limestone
	Dhg	Limestone, dolostone
Late Silurian	Scs	Limestone, shale, dolostone
Middle–Late Ordovician	Osc	Sandstone, siltstone, shale

86 What is the age of the surface bedrock in this portion of the Schoharie Valley?

(1) 320–374 million years
(2) 374–478 million years
(3) 478–505 million years
(4) 505–540 million years

87 The surface bedrock of this portion of the Schoharie Valley is composed mainly of

1 metamorphic rock
2 sedimentary rock
3 extrusive igneous rock
4 intrusive igneous rock

88 Which fossil could be found in the surface bedrock of this portion of the Schoharie Valley?

1 figlike leaf   3 brachiopod
2 mastodont   4 coelophysis

89 Which cross section represents a possible arrangement of rock units in a cliff along this portion of Schoharie Creek?

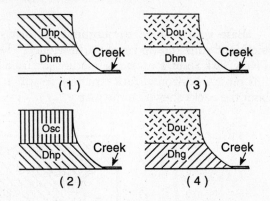

90 Based on the age of the bedrock, between which two rock units is an unconformity representing the longest period of time located?

(1) Dhg and Scs   (3) Do and Dhg
(2) Dhm and Dou   (4) Scs and Osc

Group 8

If you choose this group, be sure to answer questions 91–95.

Base your answers to questions 91 through 95 on the *Earth Science Reference Tables*, the graph below, and your knowledge of Earth science. The graph shows the results of a laboratory activity in which a 200-gram sample of ice at –50°C was heated in an open beaker at a uniform rate for 70 minutes and was stirred continually.

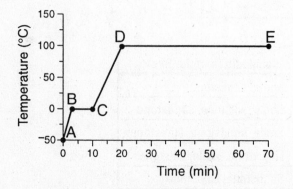

91 What was the temperature of the water 17 minutes after the heating began?

(1) 0°C   (3) 75°C
(2) 12°C   (4) 100°C

92 Which change occurred between point *A* and point *B*?

1 Ice melted.   3 Water froze.
2 Ice warmed.   4 Water condensed.

93 What was the total amount of energy absorbed by the sample during the time between points *B* and *C* on the graph?

(1) 200 calories   (3) 10,800 calories
(2) 800 calories   (4) 16,000 calories

94 During which time interval was the greatest amount of energy added to the water?

(1) *A* to *B*   (3) *C* to *D*
(2) *B* to *C*   (4) *D* to *E*

95 Which change could shorten the time needed to melt the ice completely?

1 using colder ice
2 stirring the sample more slowly
3 reducing the initial sample to 100 grams of ice
4 reducing the number of temperature readings taken

Group 9

If you choose this group, be sure to answer questions 96–100.

Base your answers to questions 96 through 100 on the *Earth Science Reference Tables*, the map below, and your knowledge of Earth science. The map shows many of the major faults and fractures in the surface bedrock of New York State.

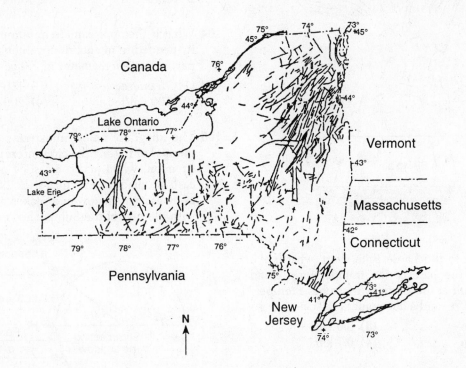

96 In which landscape region do the faults and fractures appear most concentrated?

1 Adirondack Mountains
2 the Catskills
3 Atlantic Coastal Plain
4 St. Lawrence Lowlands

97 Most of the faults found along the New York–New Jersey border lie in which direction?

1 north to south
2 east to west
3 northwest to southwest
4 northeast to southwest

98 The faults and fractures in the bedrock have the greatest effect on the locations and patterns of

1 streams   3 precipitation
2 residual soils   4 temperature zones

99 The surface of Long Island shows no visible faults and fractures because the surface is

1 a flat plain
2 old bedrock
3 primarily composed of unconsolidated sediments
4 extensively eroded by ocean waves

100 A large earthquake associated with one of these faults occurred at 45° N 75° W on September 5, 1994. Which location in New York State was closest to the epicenter of the earthquake?

1 Buffalo   3 Albany
2 Massena   4 New York City

Group 10

If you choose this group, be sure to answer questions 101–105.

101 The diagram below shows air rising from the Earth's surface to form a thunderstorm cloud.

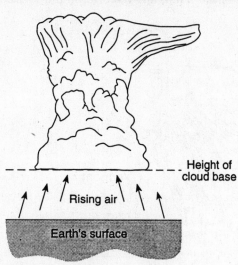

According to the Lapse Rate chart, what is the height of the base of the thunderstorm cloud when the air at the Earth's surface has a temperature of 30°C and a dewpoint of 22°C?

(1) 1.0 km   (3) 3.0 km
(2) 1.5 km   (4) 0.7 km

102 Which list shows atmospheric layers in the correct order upward from the Earth's surface?

1 thermosphere, mesosphere, stratosphere, troposphere
2 troposphere, stratosphere, mesosphere, thermosphere
3 stratosphere, mesosphere, troposphere, thermosphere
4 thermosphere, troposphere, mesosphere, stratosphere

103 Which planet takes longer for one spin on its axis than for one orbit around the Sun?

1 Mercury   3 Earth
2 Venus   4 Mars

104 What is the approximate minimum water velocity needed to maintain movement of a sediment particle with a diameter of 5.0 centimeters?

(1) 75 cm/sec   (3) 150 cm/sec
(2) 100 cm/sec   (4) 200 cm/sec

105 The diagram below illustrates Eratosthenes' method of finding the circumference of a planet. At noon, when a vertical stick at the Equator casts no shadow, a vertical stick 2,500 kilometers away casts a shadow and makes an angle of 40° with the rays of the Sun as shown.

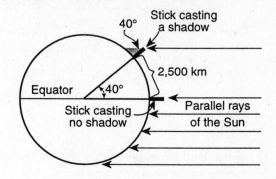

(Not drawn to scale)

What is the circumference of this planet?

(1) 2,500 km   (3) 22,500 km
(2) 20,000 km   (4) 45,000 km

EARTH SCIENCE
JUNE 1997

Part I Credits . . . .

Part II Credits . . . .

Performance Test Credits. . ...

Total (Official Regents)
Examination Mark . . . .

Reviewer's Initials: _____

ANSWER SHEET

Student . . . .

Teacher . . . . School . . . .

Grade (circle one)   8   9   10   11   12

Record all of your answers on this answer sheet in accordance with the instructions on the front cover of the test booklet.

Part I (55 credits)

1	1 2 3 4		16	1 2 3 4		31	1 2 3 4		46	1 2 3 4
2	1 2 3 4		17	1 2 3 4		32	1 2 3 4		47	1 2 3 4
3	1 2 3 4		18	1 2 3 4		33	1 2 3 4		48	1 2 3 4
4	1 2 3 4		19	1 2 3 4		34	1 2 3 4		49	1 2 3 4
5	1 2 3 4		20	1 2 3 4		35	1 2 3 4		50	1 2 3 4
6	1 2 3 4		21	1 2 3 4		36	1 2 3 4		51	1 2 3 4
7	1 2 3 4		22	1 2 3 4		37	1 2 3 4		52	1 2 3 4
8	1 2 3 4		23	1 2 3 4		38	1 2 3 4		53	1 2 3 4
9	1 2 3 4		24	1 2 3 4		39	1 2 3 4		54	1 2 3 4
10	1 2 3 4		25	1 2 3 4		40	1 2 3 4		55	1 2 3 4
11	1 2 3 4		26	1 2 3 4		41	1 2 3 4			
12	1 2 3 4		27	1 2 3 4		42	1 2 3 4			
13	1 2 3 4		28	1 2 3 4		43	1 2 3 4			
14	1 2 3 4		29	1 2 3 4		44	1 2 3 4			
15	1 2 3 4		30	1 2 3 4		45	1 2 3 4			

Part II (35 credits)

Answer the questions in only seven of the ten groups in this part. Be sure to mark the answers to the groups of questions you choose in accordance with the instructions on the front cover of the test booklet. Leave blank the three groups of questions you do not choose to answer.

Group 1				
56	1	2	3	4
57	1	2	3	4
58	1	2	3	4
59	1	2	3	4
60	1	2	3	

Group 2				
61	1	2	3	4
62	1	2	3	4
63	1	2	3	4
64	1	2	3	4
65	1	2	3	4

Group 3				
66	1	2	3	4
67	1	2	3	4
68	1	2	3	4
69	1	2	3	4
70	1	2	3	4

Group 4				
71	1	2	3	4
72	1	2	3	4
73	1	2	3	4
74	1	2	3	4
75	1	2	3	4

Group 5				
76	1	2	3	4
77	1	2	3	4
78	1	2	3	4
79	1	2	3	4
80	1	2	3	4

Group 6				
81	1	2	3	4
82	1	2	3	4
83	1	2	3	4
84	1	2	3	4
85	1	2	3	4

Group 7				
86	1	2	3	4
87	1	2	3	4
88	1	2	3	4
89	1	2	3	4
90	1	2	3	4

Group 8				
91	1	2	3	4
92	1	2	3	4
93	1	2	3	4
94	1	2	3	4
95	1	2	3	4

Group 9				
96	1	2	3	4
97	1	2	3	4
98	1	2	3	4
99	1	2	3	4
100	1	2	3	4

Group 10				
101	1	2	3	4
102	1	2	3	4
103	1	2	3	4
104	1	2	3	4
105	1	2	3	4

Part I

Answer all 55 questions in this part. [55]

Directions (1–55): For *each* statement or question, select the word or expression that, of those given, best completes the statement or answers the question. Record your answer on the separate answer sheet in accordance with the directions on the front page of this booklet.

1 The diagram below is a cross section of an ice-covered lake in New York State during the month of January. Points *A*, *B*, *C*, and *D* are locations at various levels in the lake. The temperature of the water at location *D* is 4°C.

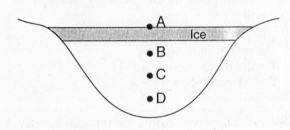

Which graph best represents the relationship between location and density of the ice or water?

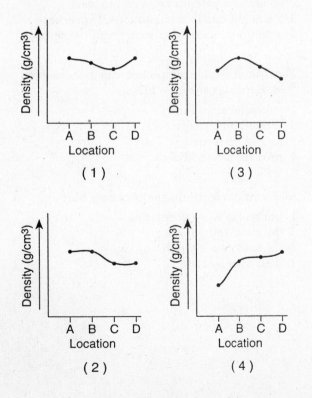

Base your answers to questions 2 and 3 on the graph below, which shows the average daily precipitation for Paris, France, during an 8-year period.

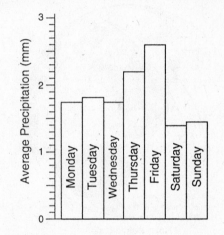

2 Which days showed the greatest difference in average precipitation during this 8-year period?

1 Mondays and Tuesdays
2 Wednesdays and Thursdays
3 Thursdays and Fridays
4 Fridays and Saturdays

3 The average weekly precipitation total for Paris, France, during the 8-year period was approximately

(1) 13 mm/week
(2) 2 mm/week
(3) 30 mm/week
(4) 91 mm/week

4 For an observer in New York State, the altitude of Polaris is 43° above the northern horizon. This observer's latitude is closest to the latitude of

1 New York City   3 Plattsburgh
2 Utica   4 Jamestown

5 Compared to the weight of a person at the North Pole, the weight of the same person at the Equator would be

1 slightly less, because the person is farther from the center of Earth
2 slightly less, because the person is closer to the center of Earth
3 slightly more, because the person is farther from the center of Earth
4 slightly more, because the person is closer to the center of Earth

6 The diagram below represents the approximate distances covered by one degree of longitude on Earth's surface at various latitudes.

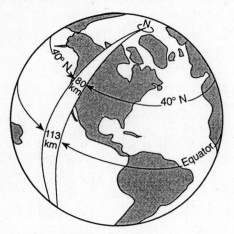

(Not drawn to scale)

What is the distance represented by one degree of longitude at Massena, New York?

(1) 78 km   (3) 90 km
(2) 85 km   (4) 113 km

7 Most of the water vapor in the atmosphere is found in the

1 mesosphere
2 thermosphere
3 troposphere
4 stratosphere

8 Which planet has the most eccentric orbit?

1 Mercury
2 Venus
3 Neptune
4 Pluto

9 The planetary winds on Earth are indicated by the curving arrows in the diagram below.

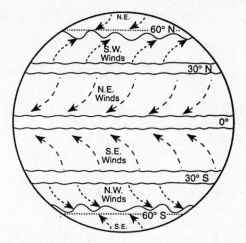

The curved paths of the planetary winds are a result of

1 changes in humidity
2 changes in temperature
3 Earth's rotation on its axis
4 Earth's gravitational force

10 The Sun's apparent daily path through the daytime sky is best described by an observer in New York State as

1 a circle around the North Star
2 an arc that extends from east to west
3 a straight line that passes directly overhead
4 a random motion that varies with the seasons

11 The Moon's cycle of phases can be observed from Earth because the Moon

1 is smaller than Earth
2 is tilted on its axis
3 rotates on its axis
4 revolves around Earth

12 All forms of electromagnetic energy have

1 transverse wave properties
2 the same temperature
3 the same wavelength
4 their own half-life

13 The diagram below shows a solid iron bar that is being heated in a flame.

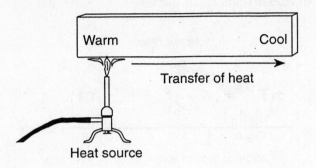

The primary method of heat transfer in the solid iron bar is

1 convection
2 conduction
3 absorption
4 advection

14 An object that is a good absorber of electromagnetic energy is most likely a good

1 convector
2 reflector
3 radiator
4 refractor

15 The hottest climates on Earth are located near the Equator because this region

1 is usually closest to the Sun
2 reflects the greatest amount of insolation
3 receives the most hours of daylight
4 receives the most nearly perpendicular insolation

16 In which geographic region are air masses most often warm with a high moisture content?

1 Central Canada
2 Central Mexico
3 Gulf of Mexico
4 North Pacific Ocean

17 The diagrams below represent Earth's tilt on its axis on four different dates. The shaded portion represents the nighttime side of Earth. Which diagram best represents the day on which the longest duration of insolation occurs in New York State?

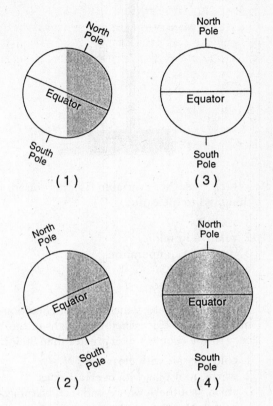

18 If Earth's tilt were to increase from $23\frac{1}{2}°$ to $33\frac{1}{2}°$, the result would be

1 shorter days and longer nights at the Equator
2 less difference between winter and summer temperatures in New York State
3 colder winters and warmer summers in the Northern Hemisphere
4 an increase in the amount of solar radiation received by Earth

Base your answers to questions 19 and 20 on the diagram below of a weather instrument.

Base your answers to questions 23 and 24 on the diagram below, which shows the frontal boundary between mT and cP air masses.

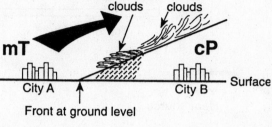

19 Which weather variable is this instrument designed to measure?

1 visibility
2 relative humidity
3 dewpoint temperature
4 air pressure

20 In New York State, which weather conditions are most likely to exist when the height of the mercury in the tube is much greater than 30 inches?

1 cold, dry air with clear skies
2 warm, moist air with overcast skies
3 strong southerly winds with hail warnings
4 a violent storm associated with the autumn season

21 Surface ocean currents resulting from the prevailing winds over the oceans illustrate a transfer of energy from

1 lithosphere to atmosphere
2 hydrosphere to lithosphere
3 atmosphere to hydrosphere
4 stratosphere to troposphere

22 A low-pressure system near Utica, New York, causes heavy precipitation. If this system followed the usual track, which city most likely had the same weather conditions a few hours earlier?

1 Syracuse   3 Albany
2 Kingston   4 Plattsburgh

23 If the front at ground level is moving toward city B, which type of weather front is shown?

1 cold front   3 occluded front
2 warm front   4 stationary front

24 Why do clouds and precipitation usually occur along the frontal surface?

1 The warm air rises, expands, and cools.
2 The warm air sinks, expands, and warms.
3 The cool air rises, compresses, and cools.
4 The cool air sinks, compresses, and warms.

25 What is the name of the warm ocean current that flows along the east coast of the United States?

1 California Current
2 Florida Current
3 Labrador Current
4 North Pacific Current

26 Why would a stream in New York State have a lower stream discharge in late summer than in spring?

1 Potential evapotranspiration is less in late summer than in spring.
2 Plants carry on more transpiration in spring than in late summer.
3 The local water budget shows a surplus in late summer.
4 The local water budget shows a deficit in late summer.

27 The lines on the map below represent the average yearly amount of precipitation in inches.

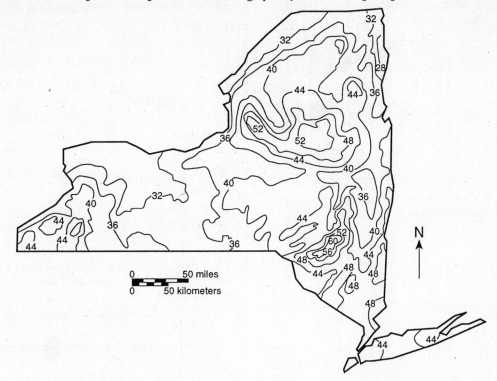

Which statement best explains the difference in yearly precipitation between Watertown and Plattsburgh?

1 Watertown receives more precipitation because it is farther from the Atlantic Ocean.
2 Plattsburgh receives more precipitation because it is closer to the Atlantic Ocean.
3 Watertown receives more precipitation because of the effects of change in elevation and prevailing winds.
4 Plattsburgh receives more precipitation because of the effects of change in elevation and prevailing winds.

---

28 Soil with the greatest porosity has particles that are

1 poorly sorted and densely packed
2 poorly sorted and loosely packed
3 well sorted and densely packed
4 well sorted and loosely packed

29 Which factor has the most influence on the development of soil?

1 climate
2 longitude
3 amount of rounded sediment
4 slope of the landscape

30 Which diagram best represents a cross section of the sediment deposited directly by a glacier in New York State?

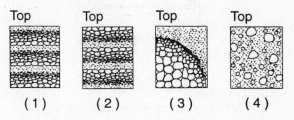

(1) (2) (3) (4)

31 The diagram below shows a meandering stream. Measurements of stream velocity were taken along straight line *AB*.

Which graph best shows the relative stream velocities across the stream from *A* to *B*?

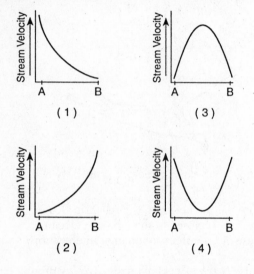

32 The diagram below shows cobbles used in the construction of the walls of a cobblestone building.

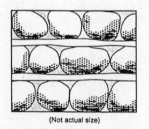

(Not actual size)

The shape and size of the cobbles suggest that they were collected from

1 the channel of a fast-flowing stream
2 volcanic ash deposits
3 a desert sand dune
4 the base of a cliff from which they had weathered

33 Which mineral property is illustrated by the peeling of muscovite mica into thin, flat sheets?

1 luster
2 streak
3 hardness
4 cleavage

34 Which sedimentary rock may form as a result of biologic processes?

1 shale
2 siltstone
3 fossil limestone
4 breccia

35 Which rock type is most likely to be mono-mineralic?

1 rock salt
2 rhyolite
3 basalt
4 conglomerate

36 The diagram below shows actual sizes and shapes of particles removed from a clastic sedimentary rock.

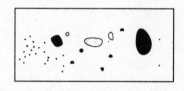

The sediments are from

1 chemical limestone
2 conglomerate
3 granite
4 sandstone

37 Which rock forms by the recrystallization of unmelted rock material under conditions of high temperature and pressure?

1 granite
2 gneiss
3 rock gypsum
4 bituminous coal

38 Seafloor spreading is occurring at the boundary between the

1 African plate and Antarctic plate
2 Nazca plate and South American plate
3 China plate and Philippine plate
4 Australian plate and Eurasian plate

39 In which area of Earth's interior is the pressure most likely to be 2.5 million atmospheres?

1 asthenosphere
2 stiffer mantle
3 inner core
4 outer core

Base your answers to questions 40 and 41 on the map below. The map shows point *X*, which is the location of an earthquake epicenter, and point *A*, which is the location of a seismic station.

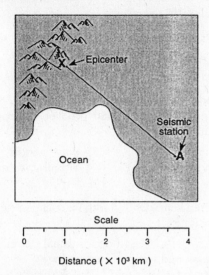

Scale

Distance (× 10³ km)

40 Approximately how long did the earthquake's *P*-wave take to arrive at the seismic station?

(1) 3 min 40 sec   (3) 6 min 20 sec
(2) 5 min 10 sec   (4) 11 min 5 sec

41 Which statement best describes the arrival of the initial *S*-wave at the seismic station?

1 It arrived later than the *P*-wave because *S*-waves travel more slowly.
2 It arrived earlier than the *P*-wave because *S*-waves travel faster.
3 It arrived at the same time as the *P*-wave because *S*-waves and *P*-waves have the same velocity on Earth's surface.
4 It never reached location *A* because *S*-waves can travel only through a liquid medium.

42 Which statement best describes Earth's crust and mantle?

1 The crust is thicker and less dense than the mantle.
2 The crust is thicker and more dense than the mantle.
3 The crust is thinner and less dense than the mantle.
4 The crust is thinner and more dense than the mantle.

43 The map below shows continental and oceanic crustal plates along the west coast of North America.

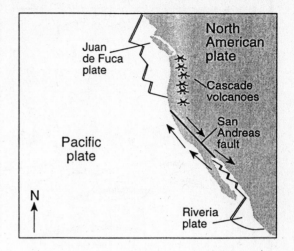

Which conclusion is best supported by the map?

1 The boundary of the Pacific plate has very few faults.
2 The Pacific plate has stopped moving.
3 The west coast of North America is composed of the oldest rocks on the continent.
4 The west coast of North America is a zone of frequent crustal movement.

44 Which feature of a sandstone rock layer usually is the youngest?

1 sand grains that make up the rock
2 cement that binds the sand grains together
3 fossils found in the rock
4 faults that have broken the rock

45 Which bedrock would be most likely to contain fossils?

1 Precambrian granite
2 Cambrian shale
3 Pleistocene basalt
4 Middle-Proterozoic quartzite

46 Which life-forms existed on Earth during the same time period?

1 trilobites and mastodonts
2 ammonoids and Naples trees
3 armored fish and flowering plants
4 dinosaurs and early humans

47 The cartoon below is a humorous interpretation of the results of an invention.

50,000 B.C.: Gak invents the first and last silent mammoth whistle.

The dominant life-forms existing on Earth at the time represented by the cartoon are classified as

1 mammals   3 amphibians
2 reptiles   4 invertebrates

48 What is the age of most of the surface bedrock found in New York State at a latitude of 45°?

1 Precambrian Middle Proterozoic
2 Triassic and Jurassic
3 Silurian and Devonian
4 Cambrian and Ordovician

49 Radioactive carbon-14 dating has determined that a fossil is 5.7×10^3 years old. What is the total amount of the original C^{14} still present in the fossil?

(1) 0%   (3) 50%
(2) 25%   (4) 75%

50 Using radioactive dating methods and mathematical inferences, scientists have estimated the date of Earth's formation to be approximately

(1) 1.1×10^6 years ago
(2) 2.4×10^6 years ago
(3) 3.3×10^9 years ago
(4) 4.6×10^9 years ago

51 A landscape region that has broad, U-shaped valleys with polished and grooved bedrock was most likely formed by

1 glaciers   3 wave action
2 wind   4 running water

52 Continents are divided into landscape regions on the basis of

1 bedrock fossils and depositional patterns
2 rainfall and temperature changes
3 surface features and bedrock structure
4 boundaries of the drainage basins of major rivers

53 In which New York State landscape region is Albany located?

1 Catskills
2 Taconic Mountains
3 Hudson-Mohawk Lowlands
4 Champlain Lowlands

54 Bedrock in the area of Binghamton, New York, consists of

1 plutonic igneous rock
2 sedimentary rock layers
3 faulted and tilted volcanic rock
4 folded metamorphic rock

55 Which New York State landscape region is composed primarily of metamorphic bedrock at its surface?

1 Manhattan Prong
2 Allegheny Plateau
3 St. Lawrence Lowlands
4 Erie-Ontario Lowlands

Part II

This part consists of ten groups, each containing five questions. Choose seven of these ten groups. Be sure that you answer all five questions in each group chosen. Record the answers to these questions on the separate answer sheet in accordance with the directions on the front page of this booklet.   [35]

Group 1

If you choose this group, be sure to answer questions 56–60.

Base your answers to questions 56 through 60 on the *Earth Science Reference Tables*, the diagrams below, and your knowledge of Earth science. The diagrams represent four different mineral samples with different shapes and masses. Diagrams are not drawn to scale.

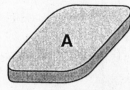

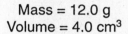

| Mass = 12.0 g | Mass = 16.0 g | Mass = 20.0 g | Mass = 24.0 g |
| Volume = 4.0 cm³ | Volume = 4.0 cm³ | Volume = 4.0 cm³ | Volume = 4.0 cm³ |

56 Which instrument was most likely used to find the volume of each sample?

1 graduated cylinder   3 thermometer
2 balance   4 psychrometer

57 A second sample of mineral *A* has a mass of 48 grams. What is the volume of this sample?

(1) 24.0 cm³   (3) 12.0 cm³
(2) 16.0 cm³   (4) 4.0 cm³

58 A student finds the mass of sample *B* to be 17.5 grams. What is the student's approximate percent deviation (percentage of error)?

(1) 1.5%   (3) 8.8%
(2) 6.7%   (4) 9.4%

59 Which sample would most likely be the slowest to settle in a quiet body of water?

(1) *A*   (3) *C*
(2) *B*   (4) *D*

60 Which graph best represents the density of each sample?

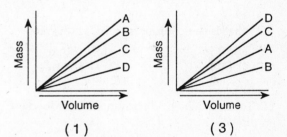

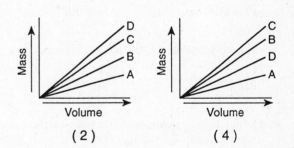

Group 2

If you choose this group, be sure to answer questions 61–65.

Base your answers to questions 61 through 65 on the topographic map below and on your knowledge of Earth science. Letters *A* through *F* represent locations on the map.

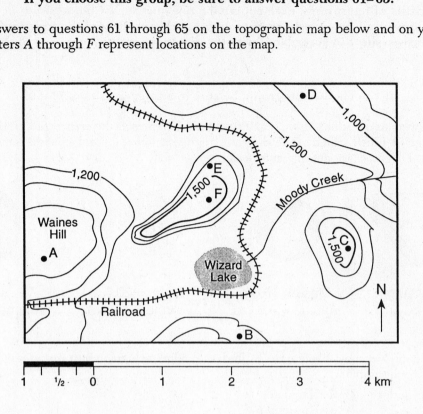

61 What is the contour interval of this map?

   (1) 10 m   (3) 100 m
   (2) 50 m   (4) 150 m

62 Toward which direction does Moody Creek flow?

   1 southwest   3 northeast
   2 northwest   4 southeast

63 Which location has the lowest elevation?

   (1) *A*   (3) *C*
   (2) *E*   (4) *D*

64 What is the approximate length of the railroad tracks shown on the map?

   (1) 15 km   (3) 8 km
   (2) 12 km   (4) 4 km

65 Which diagram best represents the profile along a straight line from point *D* to point *C*?

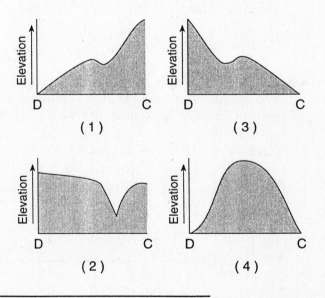

Group 3

If you choose this group, be sure to answer questions 66–70.

Base your answers to questions 66 through 70 on the graph below and on your knowledge of Earth science. The graph shows temperature data taken at four different depths in the soil at one location on Long Island, New York, for one year.

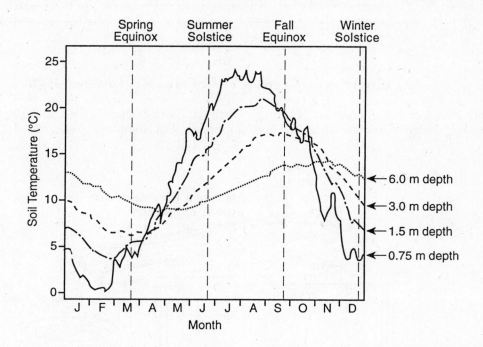

66 Which graph best represents the relationship between soil temperature and depth in the soil on June 21?

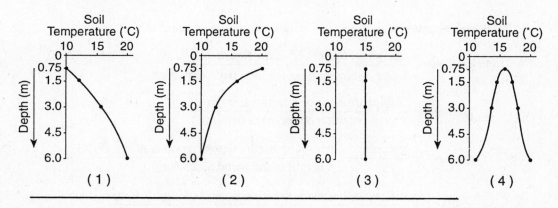

67 When did maximum soil temperature occur at depths in the soil of less than 5 meters?

1 at the spring equinox
2 between the spring equinox and the summer solstice
3 at the summer solstice
4 between the summer solstice and the fall equinox

68 On what date was the temperature at the 3-meter depth greater than the temperature at any of the other three depths?

1 July 11   3 November 1
2 August 31   4 December 21

69 The general yearly pattern shown in the diagram of temperature changes at each depth in the soil is best described as

1 a one-way change
2 a random change
3 an unpredictable change
4 a cyclic change

Note that question 70 has only three choices.

70 The graph shows that as depth increases, the annual temperature range

1 decreases
2 increases
3 remains the same

Group 4

If you choose this group, be sure to answer questions 71–75.

Base your answers to questions 71 through 75 on the *Earth Science Reference Tables*, the diagram below, and your knowledge of Earth science. The diagram represents a laboratory stream table.

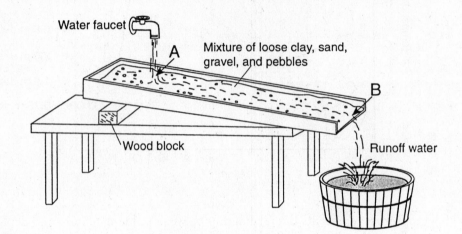

71 Which equation should be used to determine the gradient of the stream?

1 $\text{gradient} = \dfrac{\text{height of faucet above the floor (cm)}}{\text{water discharge from the tube (m}^3\text{/sec)}}$

2 $\text{gradient} = \dfrac{\text{falling distance of runoff water (cm)}}{\text{volume of water collected in pan (mL)}}$

3 $\text{gradient} = \dfrac{\text{volume of water in the stream between points } A \text{ and } B \text{ (mL)}}{\text{height of the wood block (cm)}}$

4 $\text{gradient} = \dfrac{\text{difference in elevation between points } A \text{ and } B \text{ (cm)}}{\text{distance between points } A \text{ and } B \text{ (m)}}$

---

72 Which particles are transported most easily by the water in this stream?

1 clay
2 sand
3 silt
4 pebbles

Note that question 73 has only three choices.

73 When stream volume increases after the faucet is opened, stream velocity will

1 decrease
2 increase
3 remain the same

74 Water flowing in the stream can move sediments along the stream channel because of an exchange of energy from the

1 channel to the water
2 water to the sediment
3 sediment to the channel
4 channel to the sediment

75 How do streams transport sediments?

1 in suspension, only
2 by rolling, only
3 in suspension and by rolling, only
4 in solution, in suspension, and by rolling

Group 5

If you choose this group, be sure to answer questions 76–80.

Base your answers to questions 76 through 80 on the *Earth Science Reference Tables*, the diagram below, and your knowledge of Earth science. The diagram represents a cross section of the shoreline of Lake Erie.

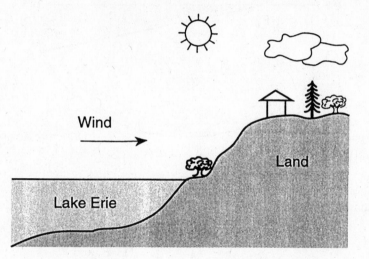

76 From 9 a.m. to 1 p.m. each day, the land surface temperature will usually

1 rise, then fall   3 rise steadily
2 fall, then rise   4 fall steadily

77 Which characteristics of the land surface have the greatest effect on the amount of insolation the land surface absorbs?

1 hardness and age
2 density and hardness
3 age and roughness
4 roughness and color

78 Most water vapor enters the atmosphere by the processes of

1 conduction and convection
2 radiation and condensation
3 absorption and infiltration
4 evaporation and transpiration

79 Compared with the change in temperature of the water surface, the change in temperature of the land surface will be

1 faster, because the land has a lower specific heat
2 faster, because the land has a higher specific heat
3 slower, because the land has a lower specific heat
4 slower, because the land has a higher specific heat

80 The direction of the wind shown in this diagram is probably due to air moving from areas of

1 low air pressure to areas of high air pressure
2 high air pressure to areas of low air pressure
3 low air humidity to areas of high air humidity
4 high air humidity to areas of low air humidity

Group 6

If you choose this group, be sure to answer questions 81–85.

Base your answers to questions 81 through 85 on the *Earth Science Reference Tables,* the diagram below, and your knowledge of Earth science. The diagram represents a planet, P, in an elliptical orbit around a star located at F_1. The foci of the elliptical orbit are F_1 and F_2. Orbital locations are represented by P_1 through P_6.

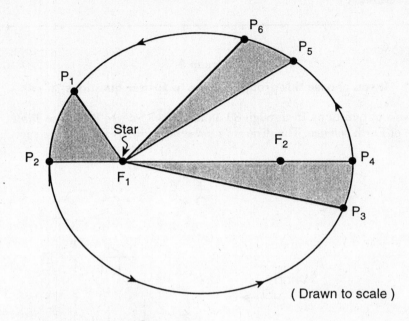

(Drawn to scale)

81 The gravitational attraction between planet P and the star is greatest when the planet is located at position

(1) P_1 (3) P_3

(2) P_2 (4) P_4

82 When observed from the planet, the star would have its greatest apparent angular diameter when the planet is located at position

(1) P_1 (3) P_3

(2) P_2 (4) P_4

83 What is the approximate eccentricity of planet P's orbit?

(1) 0.52   (3) 2.11

(2) 0.83   (4) 4.47

84 If the shaded portions of the orbital plane are equal in area, the time period between P_1 and P_2 will be equal to the time period between

(1) P_2 and P_3 (3) P_4 and P_5

(2) P_3 and P_4 (4) P_6 and P_1

85 If the mass of planet P were tripled, the gravitational force between the star and planet P would

1 remain the same
2 be two times greater
3 be three times greater
4 be nine times greater

Group 7

If you choose this group, be sure to answer questions 86–90.

Base your answers to questions 86 through 90 on the *Earth Science Reference Tables* and on the diagrams below. The diagrams represent 500-milliliter containers that are open at the top and the bottom and filled with well-sorted, loosely packed particles of uniform size. A piece of screening placed at the bottom of each container prevents the particles from falling out.

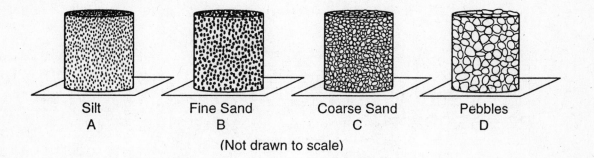

| Silt | Fine Sand | Coarse Sand | Pebbles |
| A | B | C | D |

(Not drawn to scale)

86 Container *A* is filled with particles that could have a diameter of

(1) 0.0001 cm   (3) 0.01 cm
(2) 0.001 cm   (4) 0.1 cm

87 The sample in which container would have the greatest capillarity when placed in water?

(1) *A*   (3) *C*
(2) *B*   (4) *D*

88 Assume that the samples in each container were taken from surface soil in different locations. Which location would produce the *least* amount of runoff during a heavy rainfall?

(1) *A*   (3) *C*
(2) *B*   (4) *D*

89 The sample in which container would retain the most water on the particles after 500 milliliters of water is poured through the sample?

(1) *A*   (3) *C*
(2) *B*   (4) *D*

90 Which graph best represents the rate of permeability of the samples?

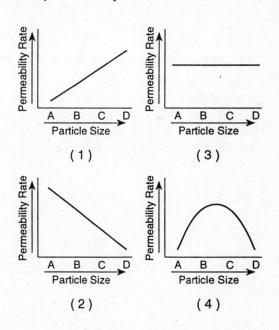

Group 8

If you choose this group, be sure to answer questions 91–95.

Base your answers to questions 91 through 95 on the *Earth Science Reference Tables*, the cross section below, and your knowledge of Earth science. Letters *A* through *J* represent rock units. An unconformity is shown at letter *X*. A fault is shown at letter *Y*.

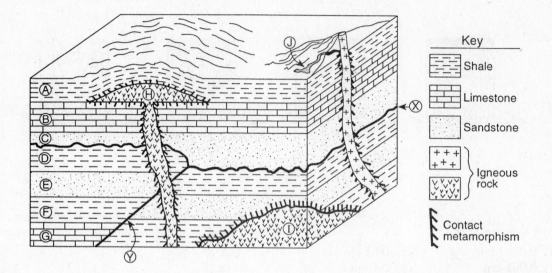

Key

- Shale
- Limestone
- Sandstone
- Igneous rock (+ + + / v v v)
- Contact metamorphism

91 Rock units *A* through *H* all contain

1 intergrown crystals   3 fossils
2 sediments   4 minerals

92 If rock layer *B* was deposited during the Carboniferous Period, igneous intrusion *H* could have occurred during the

1 Cambrian Period   3 Permian Period
2 Devonian Period   4 Silurian Period

93 Rock *I* was formed deep underground and is composed of 70% pyroxene, 15% plagioclase, 10% olivine, and 5% hornblende. Rock *I* is classified as

1 granite   3 rhyolite
2 gabbro   4 basalt

94 Which process occurred most recently?

1 formation of fault *Y*
2 development of unconformity *X*
3 formation of intrusion *H*
4 deposition of rock layers *D*, *E*, and *F*

95 Rock *J* in the diagram represents a lava flow that has cooled rapidly at the surface of Earth. Which diagram and description best represents rock *J*?

Bands of alternating light and dark minerals

(1)

Glassy black rock that breaks with a shell-shape fracture

(3)

Easily split layers of 0.0001-cm-diameter particles cemented together

(2)

Interlocking 0.5-cm-diameter crystals of various colors

(4)

Group 9

If you choose this group, be sure to answer questions 96–100.

Base your answers to questions 96 through 100 on the *Earth Science Reference Tables*, the diagram below, and your knowledge of Earth science. The diagram shows a cross section of the bedrock where the Niagara River flows over Niagara Falls.

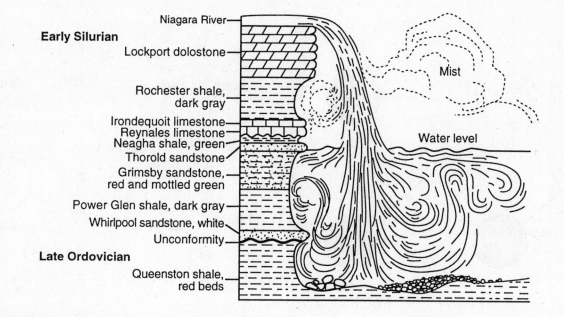

96 The Rochester shale and the Queenston shale are similar in that both

   1 contain the same index fossils
   2 have the same color
   3 are the same age
   4 contain the same size sediment

97 What is the most probable age of the Irondequoit limestone?

   1 Silurian   3 Devonian
   2 Cambrian   4 Permian

98 The unconformity above the Queenston shale was most likely caused by

   1 faulting   3 erosion
   2 folding   4 volcanism

99 The sediment carried by the Niagara River will have its greatest potential energy at the level of the

   1 Lockport dolostone
   2 Rochester shale
   3 Thorold sandstone
   4 Queenston shale

100 Which kind of rock in this formation appears to be *least* resistant to weathering?

   1 dolomite   3 limestone
   2 shale   4 sandstone

Group 10

If you choose this group, be sure to answer questions 101–105.

101 Which station model correctly shows the weather conditions of a thunderstorm with heavy rain?

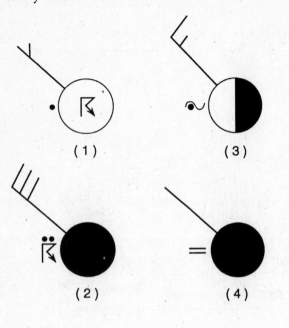

104 Which diagram most accurately represents the diameter of the Moon and the diameter of Earth?

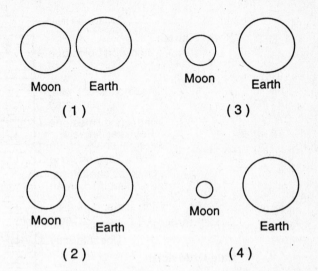

102 Which type of radiation has the shortest wavelength?

1 radar 3 ultraviolet
2 visible light 4 infrared

103 What is the dewpoint temperature when the dry-bulb temperature is 12°C and the wet-bulb temperature is 7°C?

(1) 1°C (3) 6°C
(2) –5°C (4) 4°C

105 The end product of the weathering of gabbro or basalt rocks is a solution of dissolved material that most likely would contain high amounts of

1 iron and magnesium
2 magnesium and potassium
3 aluminum and iron
4 aluminum and potassium

EARTH SCIENCE
JANUARY 1998

Part I Credits . . . .

Part II Credits . . . .

Performance Test Credits. .   ...

Total (Official Regents)
Examination Mark . . . .

Reviewer's Initials: _____

ANSWER SHEET

Student ....

Teacher .... School ....

Grade   (circle one)   8   9   10   11   12

Record all of your answers on this answer sheet in accordance with the instructions on the front cover of the test booklet.

Part I (55 credits)

1 1 2 3 4	16 1 2 3 4	31 1 2 3 4	46 1 2 3 4
2 1 2 3 4	17 1 2 3 4	32 1 2 3 4	47 1 2 3 4
3 1 2 3 4	18 1 2 3 4	33 1 2 3 4	48 1 2 3 4
4 1 2 3 4	19 1 2 3 4	34 1 2 3 4	49 1 2 3 4
5 1 2 3 4	20 1 2 3 4	35 1 2 3 4	50 1 2 3 4
6 1 2 3 4	21 1 2 3 4	36 1 2 3 4	51 1 2 3 4
7 1 2 3 4	22 1 2 3 4	37 1 2 3 4	52 1 2 3 4
8 1 2 3 4	23 1 2 3 4	38 1 2 3 4	53 1 2 3 4
9 1 2 3 4	24 1 2 3 4	39 1 2 3 4	54 1 2 3 4
10 1 2 3 4	25 1 2 3 4	40 1 2 3 4	55 1 2 3 4
11 1 2 3 4	26 1 2 3 4	41 1 2 3 4	
12 1 2 3 4	27 1 2 3 4	42 1 2 3 4	
13 1 2 3 4	28 1 2 3 4	43 1 2 3 4	
14 1 2 3 4	29 1 2 3 4	44 1 2 3 4	
15 1 2 3 4	30 1 2 3 4	45 1 2 3 4	

Record your answers for Part II on the back of this sheet.

Part II (35 credits)

Answer the questions in only seven of the ten groups in this part. Be sure to mark the answers to the groups of questions you choose in accordance with the instructions on the front cover of the test booklet. Leave blank the three groups of questions you do not choose to answer.

Group 1				
56	1	2	3	4
57	1	2	3	4
58	1	2	3	4
59	1	2	3	4
60	1	2	3	4

Group 2				
61	1	2	3	4
62	1	2	3	4
63	1	2	3	4
64	1	2	3	4
65	1	2	3	4

Group 3				
66	1	2	3	4
67	1	2	3	4
68	1	2	3	4
69	1	2	3	4
70	1	2	3	

Group 4				
71	1	2	3	4
72	1	2	3	4
73	1	2	3	
74	1	2	3	4
75	1	2	3	4

Group 5				
76	1	2	3	4
77	1	2	3	4
78	1	2	3	4
79	1	2	3	4
80	1	2	3	4

Group 6				
81	1	2	3	4
82	1	2	3	4
83	1	2	3	4
84	1	2	3	4
85	1	2	3	4

Group 7				
86	1	2	3	4
87	1	2	3	4
88	1	2	3	4
89	1	2	3	4
90	1	2	3	4

Group 8				
91	1	2	3	4
92	1	2	3	4
93	1	2	3	4
94	1	2	3	4
95	1	2	3	4

Group 9				
96	1	2	3	4
97	1	2	3	4
98	1	2	3	4
99	1	2	3	4
100	1	2	3	4

Group 10				
101	1	2	3	4
102	1	2	3	4
103	1	2	3	4
104	1	2	3	4
105	1	2	3	4

EARTH SCIENCE
JUNE 1998

Part I

Answer all 55 questions in this part. [55]

Directions (1–55): For *each* statement or question, select the word or expression that, of those given, best completes the statement or answers the question. Record your answer on the separate answer sheet in accordance with the directions on the front page of this booklet. Some questions may require the use of the *Earth Science Reference Tables*.

1 A student examined a patch of mud and recorded several statements about footprints in the mud. Which statement is most likely an inference?

  1 There are five footprints in the mud.
  2 The depth of the deepest footprint is 3 centimeters.
  3 The footprints were made by a dog.
  4 The footprints are oriented in an east-west direction.

2 Which statement best explains why water in a glass becomes colder when ice cubes are added?

  1 The water changes into ice.
  2 Heat flows from the water to the ice cubes.
  3 Water is less dense than ice.
  4 Ice has a higher specific heat than water.

3 The diagram below represents the route of a ship traveling from New York City to Miami, Florida. Each night, a passenger on the ship observes Polaris.

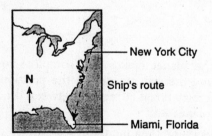

Which statement best describes the observed changes in the altitude of Polaris made by the passenger during the voyage?

  1 Each night the altitude decreases in the northern sky.
  2 Each night the altitude decreases in the southern sky.
  3 Each night the altitude increases in the northern sky.
  4 Each night the altitude increases in the southern sky.

4 The diagrams below represent photographs of a large sailboat taken through a telescope over time as the boat sailed away from shore out to sea. Each diagram shows the magnification of the lenses and the time of day.

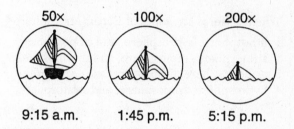

Which statement best explains the apparent sinking of this sailboat?

  1 The sailboat is moving around the curved surface of Earth.
  2 The sailboat appears smaller as it moves farther away.
  3 The change in density of the atmosphere is causing refraction of light rays.
  4 The tide is causing an increase in the depth of the ocean.

5 Which observation is a direct result of the $23\frac{1}{2}°$ tilt of Earth's axis as Earth orbits the Sun?

  1 Locations on Earth's Equator receive 12 hours of daylight every day.
  2 The apparent diameter of the Sun shows predictable changes in size.
  3 A Foucault pendulum shows predictable shifts in its direction of swing.
  4 Winter occurs in the Southern Hemisphere at the same time that summer occurs in the Northern Hemisphere.

6 The diagram below shows spheres associated with Earth.

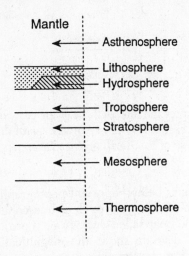

(Not drawn to scale)

Which spheres are zones of Earth's atmosphere?

1 lithosphere, hydrosphere, and troposphere
2 stratosphere, mesosphere, and thermosphere
3 asthenosphere, lithosphere, and hydrosphere
4 hydrosphere, troposphere, and stratosphere

7 An observer on Earth measured the apparent diameter of the Sun over a period of 2 years. Which graph best represents the Sun's apparent diameter during the 2 years?

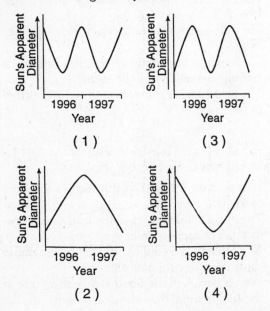

8 Which diagram best represents a portion of the heliocentric model of the solar system? [S = Sun, E = Earth, and M = Moon]

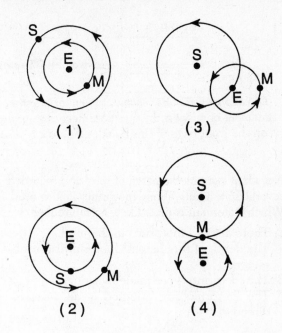

9 The diagram below represents a planet revolving in an elliptical orbit around a star.

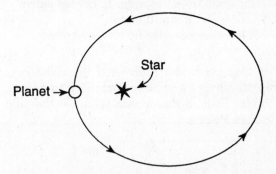

As the planet makes one complete revolution around the star, starting at the position shown, the gravitational attraction between the star and the planet will

1 decrease, then increase
2 increase, then decrease
3 continually decrease
4 remain the same

10 The diagrams below represent four series of events over the passage of time.

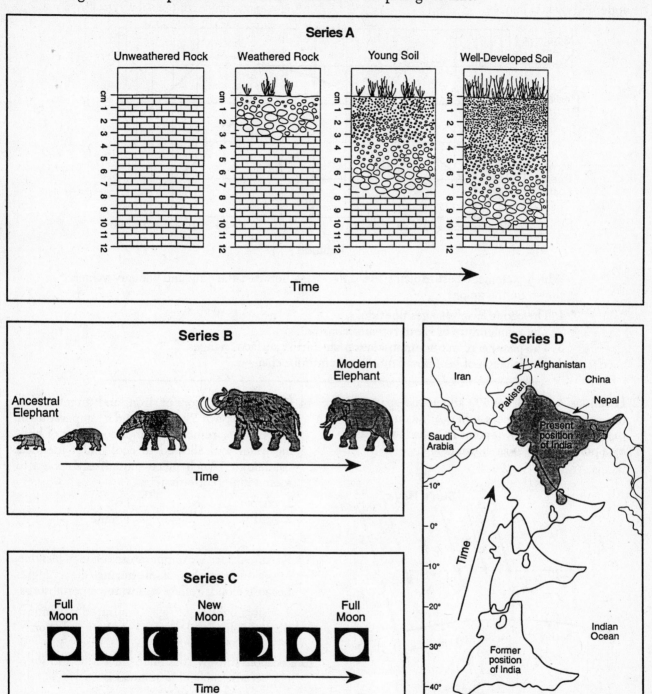

Which series of events took the *least* amount of time to complete?

(1) *A*   (3) *C*
(2) *B*   (4) *D*

11 The graph below shows the relative amount of radiation energy gained and lost by Earth's surface at all latitudes in July and January.

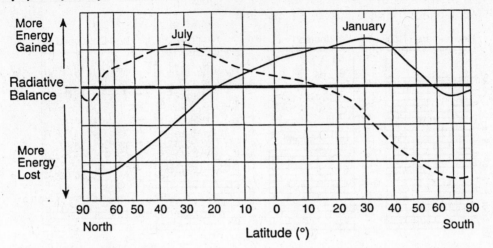

Which statement best explains the differences between the July and January values shown on the graph?

1 The ozone layer changes position.
2 The temperature of Earth remains constant.
3 The position of maximum insolation on Earth's surface changes.
4 The location of heat flow from Earth's interior changes.

---

12 Locations A and B are 600 kilometers apart on the equator of a planet's spherical moon. When the Sun is directly over point B, a shadow is cast by a pole at point A as shown below.

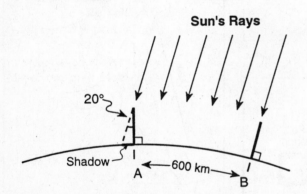

According to Eratosthenes' method, the circumference of the moon would be calculated as

(1) 2,400 km   (3) 5,400 km
(2) 3,300 km   (4) 10,800 km

13 Friction occurring at an interface always produces a

1 transformation of energy
2 form of pollution
3 chemical change
4 phase change

14 Pieces of lead, copper, iron, and granite, each having a mass of 1 kilogram and a temperature of 100°C, were removed from a container of boiling water and allowed to cool under identical conditions. Which piece most likely cooled to room temperature first?

1 copper   3 iron
2 lead   4 granite

15 Earth's surface air temperatures change less during cloudy nights than during clear nights because clouds reflect and water vapor absorbs

1 visible light   3 infrared radiation
2 ultraviolet light   4 gamma radiation

16 Locations in New York State are warmest in summer because sunlight in summer is

1 least intense and of shortest duration
2 least intense and of longest duration
3 most intense and of shortest duration
4 most intense and of longest duration

17 A parcel of air has a dry-bulb temperature of 16°C and a wet-bulb temperature of 10°C. What are the dewpoint and relative humidity of the air?

(1) –5°C dewpoint and 33% relative humidity
(2) –5°C dewpoint and 45% relative humidity
(3) 4°C dewpoint and 33% relative humidity
(4) 4°C dewpoint and 45% relative humidity

18 Winds are blowing from high-pressure to low-pressure systems over identical ocean surfaces. Which diagram represents the area of greatest windspeed? [Arrows indicate wind direction.]

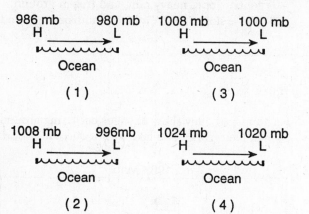

(1)   (3)

(2)   (4)

19 Under which set of atmospheric conditions does water usually evaporate at the fastest rate?

1 warm temperatures, calm winds, and high humidity
2 warm temperatures, high winds, and low humidity
3 cold temperatures, calm winds, and low humidity
4 cold temperatures, high winds, and high humidity

20 A storm system centered over Elmira, New York, will most often track toward

1 Albany
2 Jamestown
3 Rochester
4 New York City

21 A weather station model for a location in New York State is shown below.

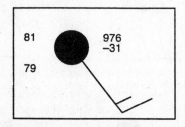

The air mass over this location is best described as

1 cold with low humidity and high air pressure
2 cold with high humidity and low air pressure
3 warm with high humidity and low air pressure
4 warm with low humidity and high air pressure

22 The diagram below shows a cross section of a cumulus cloud. Line AB indicates the base of the cloud.

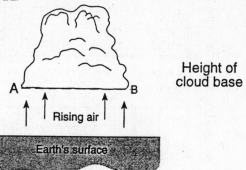

Height of cloud base

Which graph best represents the temperature measured along line AB?

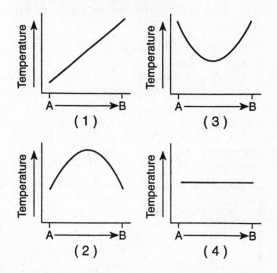

(1)   (3)

(2)   (4)

23 The diagram below is a cross-sectional view of rain falling on a farm field and then moving to the water table.

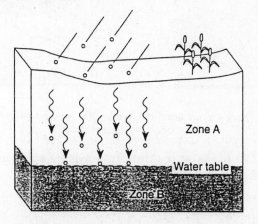

Which word best describes the movement of the rainwater through zone A?

1 runoff
2 saturation
3 infiltration
4 precipitation

24 The graph below shows the discharge rate of a stream during a 1-year period.

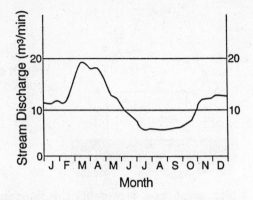

During which time span did a water deficit most likely exist in the water budget for the surrounding area?

1 January and February
2 May and June
3 August and September
4 November and December

25 The cartoon below presents a humorous look at wave action.

"Here comes another big one, Roy, and here—we—gooooooowheeeeeeeeoooo!"

The ocean waves that are providing enjoyment for Roy's companion are the result of the

1 interaction of the hydrosphere with the moving atmosphere
2 interaction of the lithosphere with the moving troposphere
3 absorption of short-wave radiation in the stratosphere
4 absorption of energy in the asthenosphere

26 Which conditions produce the most surface water runoff?

1 steep slope, heavy rain, and frozen ground
2 steep slope, gentle rain, and unfrozen ground
3 gentle slope, heavy rain, and frozen ground
4 gentle slope, gentle rain, and unfrozen ground

27 The maps below show changes occurring around a small New York State lake over a 30-year period.

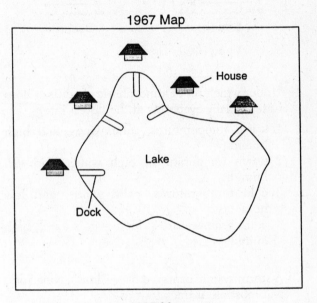

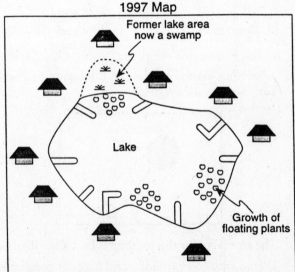

(Continued on next page.)

Which graph best shows the probable changes in the quality of ground water and lake water in this region as the changes indicated in the maps took place from 1967 to 1997?

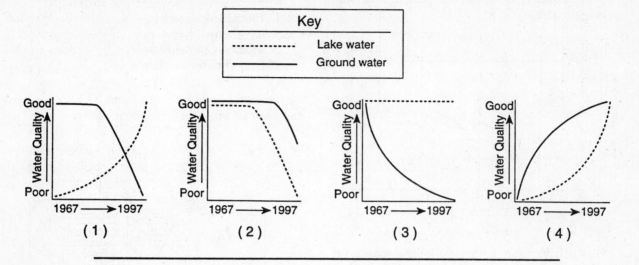

28 The diagram below is a map view of a stream flowing through an area of loose sediments. Arrows show the location of the strongest current.

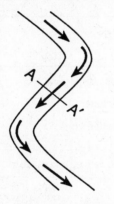

Which stream profile best represents the cross section from *A* to *A'*?

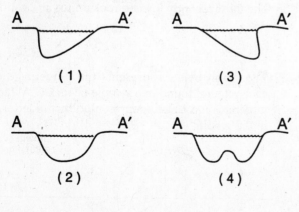

29 What occurs when a rock is crushed into a pile of fragments?

1 The total surface area decreases and chemical composition changes.
2 The total surface area decreases and chemical composition remains the same.
3 The total surface area increases and chemical composition changes.
4 The total surface area increases and chemical composition remains the same.

30 In which group do the rocks usually have the mineral quartz as part of their composition?

1 granite, rhyolite, sandstone, hornfels
2 shale, scoria, gneiss, metaconglomerate
3 conglomerate, gabbro, rock salt, schist
4 breccia, fossil limestone, bituminous coal, siltstone

31 The diagram below shows a hand-sized rock sample with parallel sets of grooves. This rock sample was found in a gravel bank in central New York State.

The grooves were most likely caused by

1 stream erosion
2 wind erosion
3 a landslide
4 glacial erosion

32 The graph below shows the general pattern of erosion and deposition for a small tributary stream. Points A, B, C, and D represent locations along the stream.

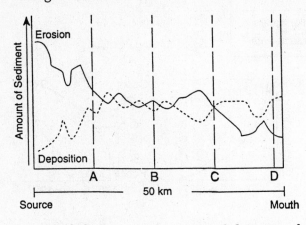

At which location is the erosional-depositional system of the stream in dynamic equilibrium?

(1) A   (2) B   (3) C   (4) D

33 Which kind of sedimentary rock may be formed both chemically and organically?

1 limestone   3 rock salt
2 rock gypsum   4 bituminous coal

34 The cross section below represents the transport of sediments by a glacier.

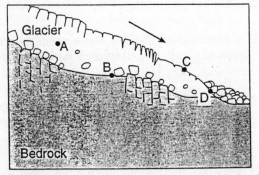

At which location is deposition most likely the dominant process?

(1) A   (2) B   (3) C   (4) D

35 The diagrams below represent fractured samples of four minerals.

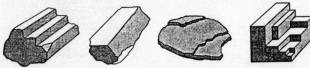

Which mineral property is best illustrated by the samples?

1 hardness   3 cleavage
2 streak   4 density

36 Which New York State landscape region is composed mainly of metamorphosed surface bedrock?

1 Taconic Mountains
2 Allegheny Plateau
3 Atlantic Coastal Plain
4 Erie-Ontario Lowlands

Base your answers to questions 37 through 39 on the geologic cross section shown below.

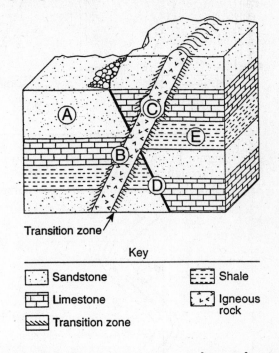

Key

Sandstone   Shale
Limestone   Igneous rock
Transition zone

37 At which location is metamorphic rock most likely to be found?

(1) A   (3) C
(2) B   (4) D

38 The most recently formed rock unit is at location

(1) A   (3) C
(2) E   (4) D

39 The graph below represents the percentage of each mineral found in a sample of rock C. Which mineral is most likely represented by the letter X in the graph?

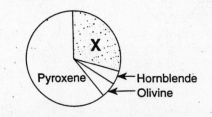

1 potassium feldspar   3 quartz
2 plagioclase feldspar   4 biotite

40 The photograph below represents a mountainous area in the Pacific Northwest.

Scientists believe that sedimentary rocks like these represent evidence of crustal change because these rocks were

1 formed by igneous intrusion
2 faulted during deposition
3 originally deposited in horizontal layers
4 changed from metamorphic rocks

41 How far from an earthquake epicenter is a city where the difference between the *P*-wave and *S*-wave arrival times is 6 minutes and 20 seconds?

(1) 1.7×10^3 km   (3) 3.5×10^3 km
(2) 9.9×10^3 km   (4) 4.7×10^3 km

42 The photograph below shows a large crater located in the southwestern United States.

Some fragments taken from the site have a nickel-iron composition. This evidence indicates that the crater probably was formed by

1 the impact of a meteorite from space
2 the collapse of a cavern roof
3 an eruption of a volcano
4 an underwater explosion of steam

43 Which map best represents the general pattern of magnetism in the oceanic bedrock near the mid-Atlantic Ridge?

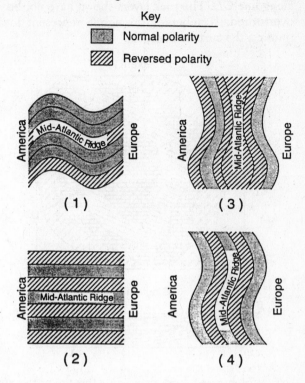

44 Which features are commonly formed at the plate boundaries where continental crust converges with oceanic crust?

1 large volcanic mountain ranges parallel to the coast at the center of the continents
2 a deep ocean trench and a continental volcanic mountain range near the coast
3 an underwater volcanic mountain range and rift valley on the ocean ridge near the coast
4 long chains of mid-ocean volcanic islands perpendicular to the coast

Base your answers to questions 45 and 46 on the diagrams below. Diagram I shows part of a geologic map. Diagram II shows a geologic cross section taken along line *CD*. The rock layers shown have not been overturned. Numbers 1 through 5 represent locations on the surface bedrock.

Diagram I

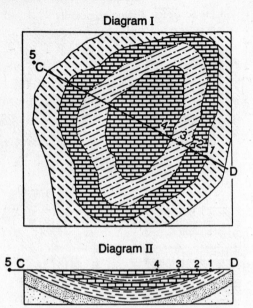

Diagram II

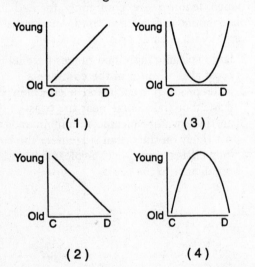

45 Which graph best represents the age of the surface bedrock along line *CD*?

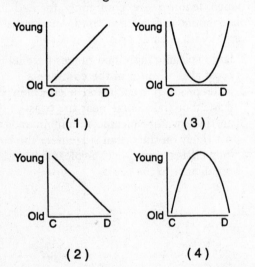

(1)   (3)

(2)   (4)

46 Which type of surface bedrock would most likely be found at location 5?

1 shale   3 chemical limestone
2 sandstone   4 siltstone

47 Which column best represents the relative duration of the major intervals of geologic history?

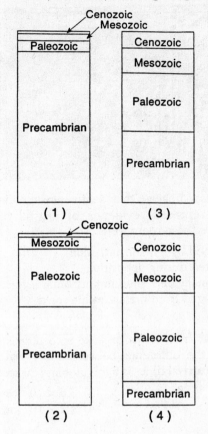

(1)   (3)

(2)   (4)

48 The diagram below represents a landscape area.

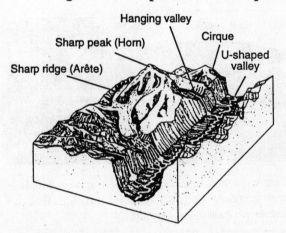

The labeled surface features of this landscape area resulted mainly from

1 wind erosion   3 stream erosion
2 wave erosion   4 glacial erosion

Base your answers to questions 49 through 51 on the map below, which shows an area of the northwestern United States affected by a major volcanic eruption at Crater Lake during the Holocene Epoch.

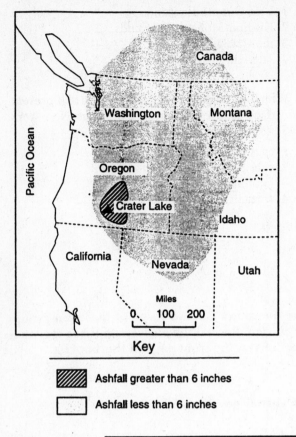

Key

Ashfall greater than 6 inches

Ashfall less than 6 inches

49 The pattern of distribution of the ash from the volcano was most likely caused by the direction of the

1 magnetic field
2 force of the volcanic eruption
3 flow of surface water
4 atmospheric air movements

50 The age of this volcanic eruption was most accurately determined to be Holocene by measuring the radioactive

1 potassium in the fine-grained volcanic rock
2 carbon in trees buried by the ash
3 uranium in the volcanic ash
4 rubidium in the igneous glass

51 This volcanic eruption is most useful to scientists today as a relative time marker in the geologic record of this map region because the

1 lava cooled quickly at the surface
2 lava contained radioactive rubidium-87
3 volcanic ash spread quickly over a large area
4 volcanic ash fell to Earth more quickly near the volcano than far from the volcano

52 The diagrams below represent the rock layers and fossils found at four widely separated rock outcrops.

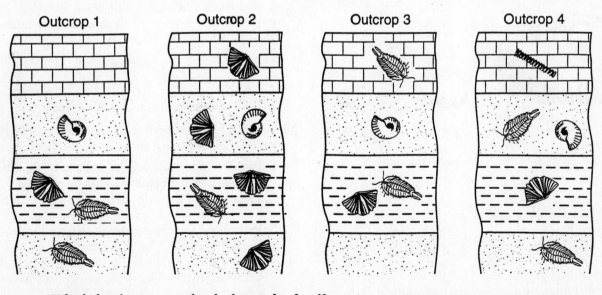

Which fossil appears to be the best index fossil?

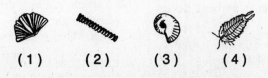

(1)   (2)   (3)   (4)

53 The diagram below represents a landscape region and its underlying bedrock structure.

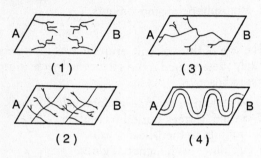

Which stream pattern is most likely present in this area?

(1)   (3)

(2)   (4)

54 Which New York State landscape region is located at 42° N, 75° W?

1 Erie-Ontario Lowlands
2 Hudson-Mohawk Lowlands
3 the Catskills
4 Tug Hill Plateau

55 Which geologic processes produced the present surface landscape features of most New York State landscapes?

1 crustal movement and erosion
2 subsidence and metamorphism
3 faulting and folding
4 volcanism and igneous activity

Part II

This part consists of ten groups, each containing five questions. Choose seven of these ten groups. Be sure that you answer all five questions in each group chosen. Record the answers to these questions on the separate answer sheet in accordance with the directions on the front page of this booklet. [35]

Group 1

If you choose this group, be sure to answer questions 56–60.

Base your answers to questions 56 through 60 on the *Earth Science Reference Tables*, the diagrams below, and your knowledge of Earth science. The diagrams represent particles of the same type of sedimentary rock material collected from a streambed. The diagrams are drawn actual size.

Particle A   Particle B   Particle C

(Actual size)

56 Particle C is classified as

1 sand   3 a boulder
2 a cobble   4 a pebble

57 A student finds the mass of particle B to be 2.8 grams. The actual mass of the particle is 2.6 grams. What is the student's percent deviation (percent error)?

(1) 7.1%   (3) 7.7%
(2) 2.0%   (4) 8.0%

58 Equal masses of each of the three particles are placed in a container of weak acid and shaken. Which particle size will weather most rapidly?

(1) A
(2) B
(3) C
(4) All samples will weather at the same rate.

59 Which inference about the density of particle A and particle B is most accurate?

1 Particle A and particle B have the same density because they are made of the same material.
2 Particle A has a greater density than particle B because particle A has a greater volume.
3 Particle A has a greater density than particle B because particle A has a greater mass.
4 Particle B has a greater density than particle A because particle B has been worn to a smaller size.

60 Particle A has a density of 2.7 grams per cubic centimeter and a volume of 15.0 cubic centimeters. What is the mass of this particle?

(1) 5.5 g   2) 15.0 g   (3) 40.5 g   (4) 109.3 g

Group 2

If you choose this group, be sure to answer questions 61–65.

Base your answers to questions 61 through 65 on the *Earth Science Reference Tables*, the contour map below, and your knowledge of Earth science. Points *A, B, C, D, X,* and *Y* are locations on the map. Elevations are expressed in feet. The maximum elevation of Basket Dome is indicated at point *X*.

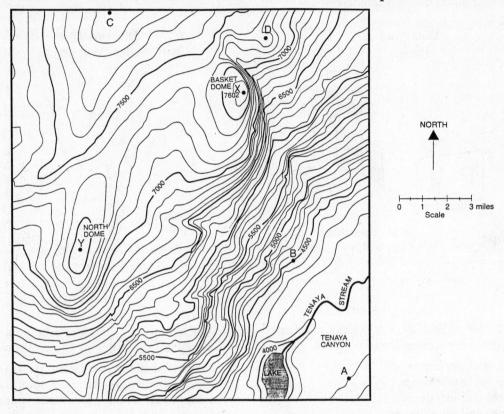

61 In which general direction does Tenaya Stream flow?

  1 southeast to northwest
  2 northwest to southeast
  3 southwest to northeast
  4 northeast to southwest

62 Which graph best represents the profile along a line between point *B* and point *A*?

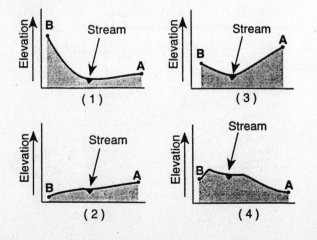

63 The highest elevation on the map is at point

  (1) *X*   (3) *C*
  (2) *Y*   (4) *D*

64 The highest elevation of Basket Dome 40 years ago was measured at 7,600 feet. What is the rate of change in elevation for this area?

  (1) 0.6 in/yr   (3) 24 in/yr
  (2) 1.7 in/yr   (4) 40 in/yr

65 Fossils of trilobites and eurypterids found in the rock near the top of Basket Dome provide evidence that this map area has most likely undergone

  1 metamorphism from crustal plate collision
  2 uplift from crustal plate movement
  3 recent flooding from changes in worldwide sea level
  4 volcanism from seafloor spreading

Group 3

If you choose this group, be sure to answer questions 66–70.

Base your answers to questions 66 through 70 on the *Earth Science Reference Tables*, the diagrams below, and your knowledge of Earth science. Diagram I shows a house located in New York State. Diagram II shows a solar collector that the homeowner is using to help heat the house.

Diagram I
House

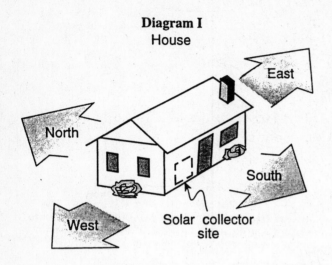

Diagram II
Solar Collector

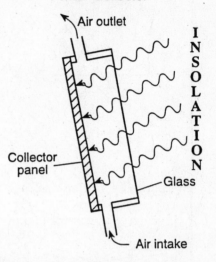

66 Air leaves the outlet of the solar collector because the air within the solar collector becomes

1 cooler and less dense
2 cooler and more dense
3 warmer and less dense
4 warmer and more dense

67 The homeowner decides to install carpet on the floor in the room that receives the most sunlight. A carpet with which characteristics would absorb the most insolation?

1 smooth texture and light color
2 smooth texture and dark color
3 rough texture and light color
4 rough texture and dark color

68 Which sequence best describes the pattern of energy transfer affecting the solar collector?

1 Sun (radiation) → collector panel (conduction and radiation) → air in collector (convection)
2 Sun (convection) → collector panel (convection and radiation) → air in collector (radiation)
3 Sun (conduction) → collector panel (conduction and convection) → air in collector (conduction)
4 Sun (conduction and convection) → collector panel (radiation) → air in collector (radiation)

69 For the angle of the Sun's rays shown, which side view best represents the correct placement of the solar collector to absorb the maximum amount of insolation?

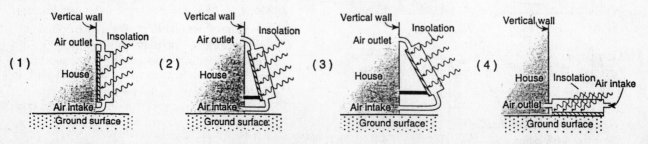

70 Which diagram best represents the apparent path of the Sun on June 21 for this location?

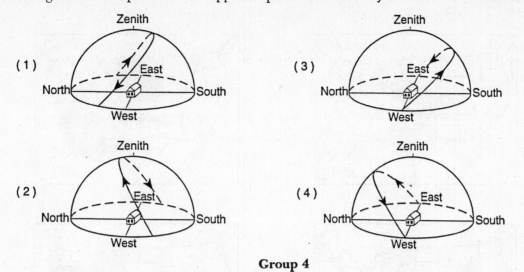

(1)   (3)

(2)   (4)

Group 4

If you choose this group, be sure to answer questions 71–75.

Base your answers to questions 71 through 75 on the *Earth Science Reference Tables*, the weather map below, and your knowledge of Earth science. The map shows a weather system that is affecting part of the United States.

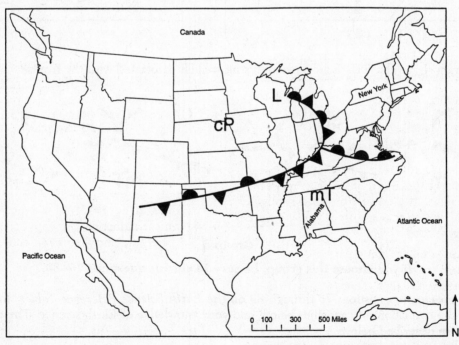

71 What is the total number of different kinds of weather fronts shown on this weather map?

(1) 1   (3) 3
(2) 2   (4) 4

72 Compared to the air over most of the map region, the air mass centered over Alabama is

1 warmer and more humid
2 warmer and drier
3 colder and more humid
4 colder and drier

73 Which sequence of events forms the clouds associated with this weather system?

1 Moist air rises and becomes saturated in clean air.
2 Moist air rises, becomes saturated, and condenses on microscopic particles.
3 Moist air falls and reaches the dewpoint in clean air.
4 Moist air falls, reaches the dewpoint, and condenses on microscopic particles.

74 Which map best shows the areas in which precipitation is most likely occurring? [Darkened areas represent precipitation.]

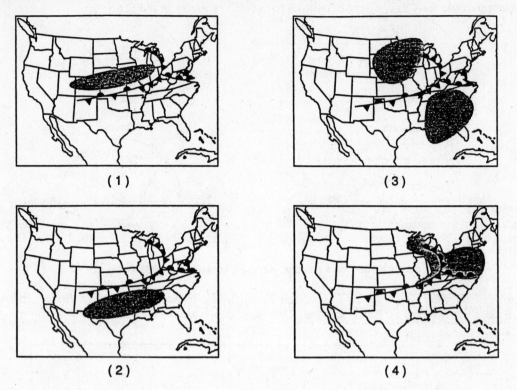

(1)

(3)

(2)

(4)

75 Which diagram shows the surface air movements most likely associated with the fronts?

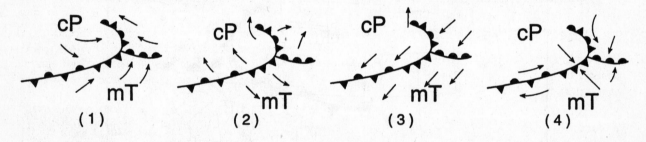

(1)

(2)

(3)

(4)

Group 5

If you choose this group, be sure to answer questions 76–80.

Base your answers to questions 76 through 80 on the *Earth Science Reference Tables*, the diagrams and descriptions of the two laboratory activities below, and your knowledge of Earth science. The particles used in these activities are described below.

Particles Used in Activities

Particle	Diameter	Density
	15 mm Al (aluminum)	2.7 g/cm³
	10 mm Al (aluminum)	2.7 g/cm³
	5 mm Al (aluminum)	2.7 g/cm³

Particle	Diameter	Density
	15 mm Fe (iron)	7.9 g/cm³
	15 mm Pb (lead)	11.4 g/cm³

Activity 1

Three aluminum particles of different sizes were released in a plastic tube filled with water. The length of time each particle took to drop from point A to point B is shown in data table 1.

Data Table 1

Particle Size	Time of Settling
15 mm Al	3.2 sec
10 mm Al	5.4 sec
5 mm Al	7.2 sec

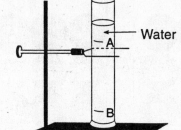

Water

A

B

Activity 2

Different combinations of particles were placed in a tube filled with a thick liquid and allowed to fall to the bottom. The tube was then stoppered and quickly turned upside down, allowing the particles to settle. The different combinations of particles are shown in data table 2. The diagram of the particle sorting in data table 2 has been omitted intentionally.

Data Table 2

Combination	Particles Mixed	Diagram of Sorting
A	15 mm Al 10 mm Al 5 mm Al	
B	15 mm Al 15 mm Fe 15 mm Pb	

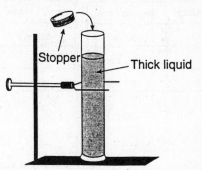

Stopper

Thick liquid

Note that question 76 has only three choices.

76 During Activity 1, as the 10-millimeter aluminum particle drops from A to B, the potential energy of the particle

1 decreases
2 increases
3 remains the same

77 In Activity 1, the three sizes of aluminum particles are placed in a stream with a velocity that will carry them all to a lake. Which cross section shows how the three sizes of particles are sorted when the stream slows as it empties into the lake?

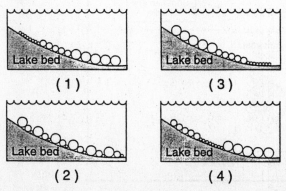

Lake bed

(1)

Lake bed

(3)

Lake bed

(2)

Lake bed

(4)

78 In Activity 2, when the tube is turned upside down, the aluminum particles, labeled "Combination A," are allowed to settle. Which diagram represents the sorting that is most likely to occur?

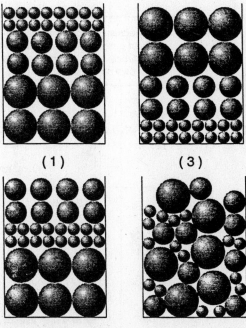

(1)

(3)

(2)

(4)

79 In Activity 2, when the tube is turned upside down, the particles of three different metals, labeled "Combination *B*," are allowed to settle. Which diagram represents the sorting that is most likely to occur?

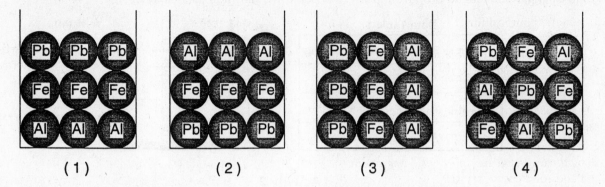

(1)　　　　　　　(2)　　　　　　　(3)　　　　　　　(4)

80 A third activity, similar in setup to Activity 1, was done using flat, oval, and round aluminum particles with identical masses. Which table shows the most likely results of this third activity?

Particle Shape	Settling Time
Round	5.1 sec
Oval	5.1 sec
Flat	5.1 sec

(1)

Particle Shape	Settling Time
Round	5.1 sec
Oval	3.2 sec
Flat	6.7 sec

(2)

Particle Shape	Settling Time
Round	6.7 sec
Oval	5.1 sec
Flat	3.2 sec

(3)

Particle Shape	Settling Time
Round	3.2 sec
Oval	5.1 sec
Flat	6.7 sec

(4)

Group 6

If you choose this group, be sure to answer questions 81–85.

Base your answers to questions 81 through 85 on the *Earth Science Reference Tables*, the diagram below, and your knowledge of Earth science. The diagram shows the structure of a student-developed chart for identifying some rock samples. The circles labeled choice 1 through choice 4 represent decisionmaking steps leading either to path (*a*) or path (*b*). Choice 5 has not been completed.

Student Chart

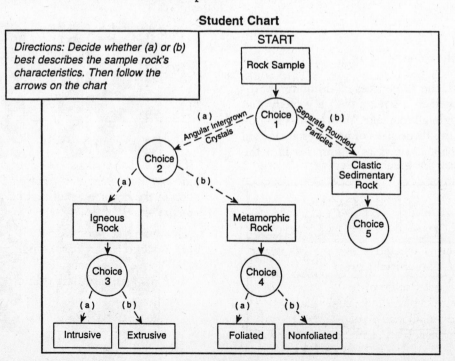

81 Before the student can select either path (*a*) or path (*b*) at choice 1, the student must make a decision about

1 mineral composition
2 crystal size
3 the temperature at which rocks form
4 the appearance of the rock grains

82 At choice 2, the student should generally select path (*a*) if the student observes

1 a random arrangement of mineral crystals
2 distorted structure and crystal alignment
3 bands of mineral crystals
4 layers of same-sized crystals

83 Which rock specimen should lead the student to choice 4, path (*a*)?

1 peridotite   3 gneiss
2 quartzite   4 dolostone

84 Which characteristic should be used at choice 5 to further identify the types of clastic sedimentary rocks?

1 grain size   3 mineral color
2 mineral cement   4 horizontal layering

85 The chart is best described as

1 a rock cycle diagram
2 a classification system
3 an erosional-depositional system
4 a mineral identification diagram

Group 7

If you choose this group, be sure to answer questions 86–90.

Base your answers to questions 86 through 90 on the *Earth Science Reference Tables*, the map below, and your knowledge of Earth science. The map shows a portion of California along the San Andreas Fault zone. The map shows the probability (percentage chance) that an earthquake strong enough to damage buildings and other structures will occur between now and the year 2024.

Earthquake Damage Probability

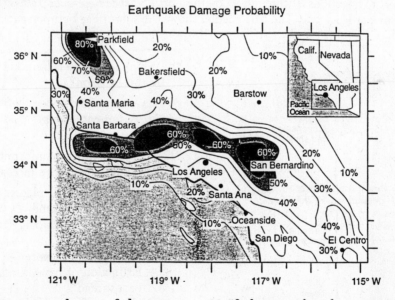

86 Which city has the greatest danger of damage from an earthquake?

1 Barstow   3 Oceanside
2 Parkfield   4 San Bernardino

87 This fault zone is located along the boundary between which two crustal plates?

1 Cocos plate and Pacific plate
2 North American plate and Pacific plate
3 Nazca plate and Cocos plate
4 North American plate and South American plate

88 If a large earthquake were to occur at San Diego, the earliest indication at another California location of the occurrence of that earthquake would be the arrival of the

(1) *S*-waves at Oceanside
(2) *S*-waves at San Bernardino
(3) *P*-waves at Oceanside
(4) *P*-waves at San Bernardino

89 Which diagram best represents the relative movements of the crustal plates along the San Andreas Fault in the map area?

Key

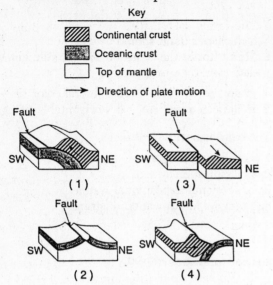

90 Which map best represents the location of the primary San Andreas Fault line?

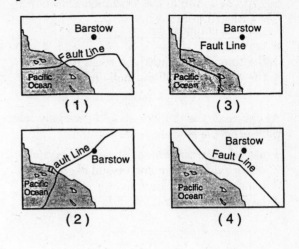

Group 8

If you choose this group, be sure to answer questions 91–95.

Base your answers to questions 91 through 95 on the *Earth Science Reference Tables*, the core section below, and your knowledge of Earth science. The core section shows the subsurface bedrock geology for a location north of Buffalo, New York.

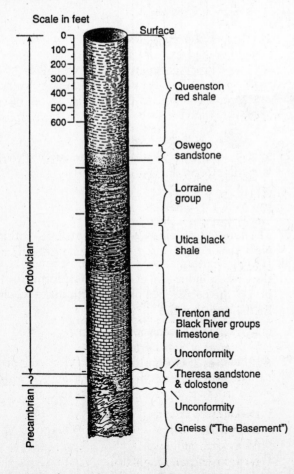

91 Which rock type is found at a depth of 1,800 feet at this location?

1 Oswego sandstone
2 "Basement" gneiss
3 Trenton limestone
4 Theresa sandstone

92 What do the unconformities shown near the base of the drill core indicate?

1 The continental plates were separated for a long period of time.
2 Part of the geologic rock record has been destroyed.
3 This area was covered by a warm, shallow sea.
4 Extinction of many kinds of living things was widespread.

93 Which "Important Fossils of New York" are most likely to be found in the Utica black shale or the Black River limestone?

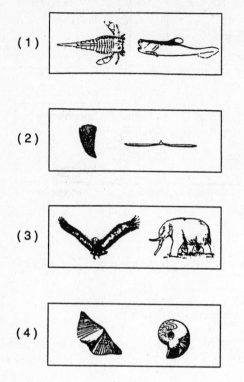

(1)

(2)

(3)

(4)

94 Which statement best explains why more fossils are found in outcrops of Black River rocks than in outcrops of Utica shales?

1 Life-forms lacked hard parts at the time of Black River deposition.

2 Many fossils of the Utica shales were destroyed by metamorphism.

3 The Black River group was deposited in an environment that supported more life-forms.

4 The Utica shales were deposited over a wider geographic area.

95 Based on studies of fossils found in the Trenton group, scientists have estimated that the climate of New York State during this part of the Ordovician Period was much warmer than the present climate. Which statement best explains this change in climate?

1 The North American Continent was nearer to the Equator during the Ordovician Period.

2 The Sun emitted less sunlight during the Ordovician Period.

3 Earth was farther from the Sun during the Ordovician Period.

4 Many huge volcanic eruptions occurred during the Ordovician Period.

Group 9

If you choose this group, be sure to answer questions 96–100.

Base your answers to questions 96 through 100 on the *Earth Science Reference Tables*, the map below, and your knowledge of Earth science. The map shows the Generalized Landscape Regions of New York State as they appear in the *Earth Science Reference Tables*. Letters *A* through *K* represent the different landscape regions. Letters *P* and *Q* indicate viewpoints for interpreting landscape cross sections. Letters *X* and *Y* are two points along the New York–New Jersey border.

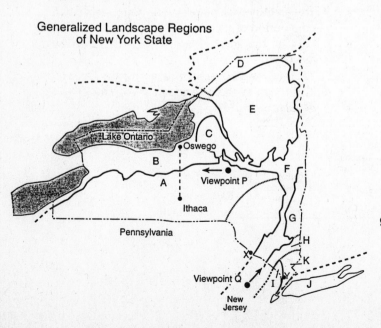

Generalized Landscape Regions of New York State

96 Which letter represents the Manhattan Prong landscape region?

(1) *H*   (3) *J*
(2) *I*   (4) *K*

97 The location of these landscape regions within New York State is mostly determined by differences in regional

1 human population densities

2 climate characteristics

3 bedrock structure and composition

4 rock age and stream-drainage patterns

98 Which features within these landscape regions have developed primarily because the underlying rock is resistant to weathering and erosion?

1 lowlands and plains

2 hilltops and plains

3 valleys and hilltops

4 escarpments and highlands

99 As seen from viewpoint P, which bedrock cross section best illustrates the geologic changes that occur between Ithaca in landscape region A and Oswego in landscape region B? [Cross sections are not drawn to scale.]

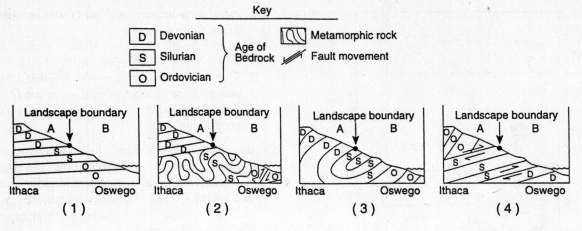

100 Which cross section best illustrates the surface landscape and the underlying bedrock across line XY as seen from viewpoint Q?

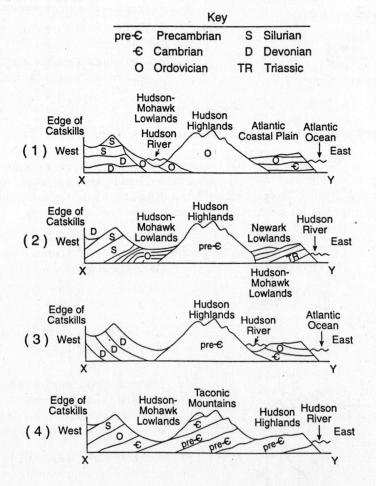

Group 10

If you choose this group, be sure to answer questions 101–105.

Base your answers to questions 101 through 105 on the *Earth Science Reference Tables* and on your knowledge of Earth science.

101 Which model of a planet's orbit best represents the actual eccentricity of the orbit of Mars? [Models are drawn to scale.]

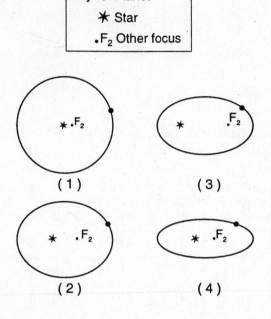

Key: ● Planet
    ✳ Star
    .F₂ Other focus

(1) (3)

(2) (4)

102 What is the total number of calories required to melt 100 grams of ice at 0°C to liquid water at 0°C?

(1) 5,400 cal   (3) 54,000 cal
(2) 8,000 cal   (4) 80,000 cal

103 Which member of the solar system has an equatorial diameter of 3.48×10^3 kilometers?

1 Moon   3 Sun
2 Earth   4 Pluto

104 What is the approximate age of an igneous rock that contains only one-fourth of its original potassium-40 content due to radioactive decay?

(1) 1.3×10^9 years   (3) 3.9×10^9 years
(2) 2.6×10^9 years   (4) 5.2×10^9 years

105 The diagram below shows a cross section of some Devonian-age rocks along the western side of the mid-Hudson River Valley.

Hudson
River
Valley

East   West

Which two mountain-building episodes could have been responsible for deforming these rock layers?

1 Grenville and Taconian orogenies
2 Taconian and Acadian orogenies
3 Acadian and Appalachian orogenies
4 Appalachian and Grenville orogenies

EARTH SCIENCE
JUNE 1998

ANSWER SHEET

Student . . . .

Teacher . . . . School . . . .

Grade   (circle one)   8   9   10   11   12

Record all of your answers on this answer sheet in accordance with the instructions on the front cover of the test booklet.

Part I (55 credits)

1 1 2 3 4	16 1 2 3 4	31 1 2 3 4	46 1 2 3 4
2 1 2 3 4	17 1 2 3 4	32 1 2 3 4	47 1 2 3 4
3 1 2 3 4	18 1 2 3 4	33 1 2 3 4	48 1 2 3 4
4 1 2 3 4	19 1 2 3 4	34 1 2 3 4	49 1 2 3 4
5 1 2 3 4	20 1 2 3 4	35 1 2 3 4	50 1 2 3 4
6 1 2 3 4	21 1 2 3 4	36 1 2 3 4	51 1 2 3 4
7 1 2 3 4	22 1 2 3 4	37 1 2 3 4	52 1 2 3 4
8 1 2 3 4	23 1 2 3 4	38 1 2 3 4	53 1 2 3 4
9 1 2 3 4	24 1 2 3 4	39 1 2 3 4	54 1 2 3 4
10 1 2 3 4	25 1 2 3 4	40 1 2 3 4	55 1 2 3 4
11 1 2 3 4	26 1 2 3 4	41 1 2 3 4	
12 1 2 3 4	27 1 2 3 4	42 1 2 3 4	
13 1 2 3 4	28 1 2 3 4	43 1 2 3 4	
14 1 2 3 4	29 1 2 3 4	44 1 2 3 4	
15 1 2 3 4	30 1 2 3 4	45 1 2 3 4	

Part II (35 credits)

Answer the questions in only seven of the ten groups in this part. Be sure to mark the answers to the groups of questions you choose in accordance with the instructions on the front cover of the test booklet. Leave blank the three groups of questions you do not choose to answer.

Group 1				
56	1	2	3	4
57	1	2	3	4
58	1	2	3	4
59	1	2	3	4
60	1	2	3	4

Group 2				
61	1	2	3	4
62	1	2	3	4
63	1	2	3	4
64	1	2	3	4
65	1	2	3	4

Group 3				
66	1	2	3	4
67	1	2	3	4
68	1	2	3	4
69	1	2	3	4
70	1	2	3	4

Group 4				
71	1	2	3	4
72	1	2	3	4
73	1	2	3	4
74	1	2	3	4
75	1	2	3	4

Group 5				
76	1	2	3	
77	1	2	3	4
78	1	2	3	4
79	1	2	3	4
80	1	2	3	4

Group 6				
81	1	2	3	4
82	1	2	3	4
83	1	2	3	4
84	1	2	3	4
85	1	2	3	4

Group 7				
86	1	2	3	4
87	1	2	3	4
88	1	2	3	4
89	1	2	3	4
90	1	2	3	4

Group 8				
91	1	2	3	4
92	1	2	3	4
93	1	2	3	4
94	1	2	3	4
95	1	2	3	4

Group 9				
96	1	2	3	4
97	1	2	3	4
98	1	2	3	4
99	1	2	3	4
100	1	2	3	4

Group 10				
101	1	2	3	4
102	1	2	3	4
103	1	2	3	4
104	1	2	3	4
105	1	2	3	4